MY KIDNEY & ME
A half century journey overcoming kidney failure

Professor
ANDREW DEMAINE

ISBN: 978 - 1 - 8384919 - 0 - 1
First published: November 2021

Jacket design:
Jon Puckey, A2Z Sign and Print, Liskeard, Cornwall.
jonpuckey@yahoo.com

Paperback and eBook design, formatting and typesetting
David Siddall Multimedia, Dartmouth, UK
www.davidsiddall.com

Printed by Amazon
Also available as a Kindle eBook

This book is dedicated to
Ann, Lucy. Olly and in memory of Tom.

Contents

Foreword

It is my pleasure to introduce Professor Andrew Demaine's memoirs entitled My Kidney and Me: A half-century overcoming kidney failure'. As a transplant surgeon I have devoted much of my professional lifetime to relieving the effects of kidney disease, but here is a patient who has spent most of his lifetime with kidney disease who has described the benefits of the treatments he has received and experienced over such a long time. Both of us are participants in the remarkable advances in medical science that have occurred in our lifetimes.

I can thoroughly recommend his book. It is a remarkable story of courage and resilience. It is unique as he has used his own medical records over half a century to provide a first-hand account into the remarkable advances in medical science from an intelligent patient and highly regarded scientist in molecular immunogenetics. It will be of great interest to clinical community, kidney patients, their carers as well those afflicted by chronic disease.

Professor Sir Roy Calne
Cambridge
November 2021

Prologue

It's late Christmas morning and I've just finished unwrapping presents. I'm thinking about starting to prepare the Christmas turkey when my hospital bleep goes off, loud and shrill, jolting me into action. I am on-call for tissue typing so I have to phone Guy's Hospital switchboard straight away. The operator puts me through to the on-call transplant surgeon, Mr Mick Bewick. 'Andy, we've got two kidneys. I'm on my way to Guy's now to drop them off.'

He only has time to give me a few details. The kidneys are from a young adult who was pronounced brain dead a few hours ago. I must get to the hospital as soon as possible to start the process of deciding which patient on the kidney transplant list will be offered 'the gift of life'. At least some good will come out of this tragedy.

The hospital is half an hour away and I know I'm going to be out of the house for hours, so I switch off the preheated oven. Tossing a few mince pies and sausage rolls into a holdall, I put on my crash helmet, start up my motorbike and head for the hospital. It's bitterly cold. Between occasional rays of weak winter sun, flurries of snow are settling on the road. The festive lights decorating the almost empty London streets are twinkling as I speed towards the hospital. I screech to a halt and park close to the entrance, racing for the lifts, which will take me up to the tissue typing laboratory.

As I pass the reception desk, the porter shouts, 'Hey, Andy, I've got something for you.' Two large cardboard boxes are there waiting, bearing the words 'Human Kidneys for Transplant' written in red. I pick up the boxes and wish the porter a 'Merry Christmas'. Carrying the valuable boxes, I arrive on the eighteenth floor which looks out over St Paul's Cathedral and the London skyline.

I open the laboratory door and the darkness looks foreboding until I switch on the lights. I can hear the familiar buzzing of the fridges and freezers containing blood samples from kidney patients. The lab has been locked up for a few days and it smells different – a mixture of organic chemicals, plastic and disinfectant.

I quickly open the boxes. Do they contain enough ice to keep the kidneys viable? I put my hand in to check, removing part of the donor's spleen and lymph nodes, which will be needed for tissue typing. Then I top up the ice and reseal the boxes with their valuable contents. The next time they are opened, the transplant surgeon will be in the operating theatre, taking out a donor kidney for a patient.

I start getting the materials I need from various fridges to begin finding out the tissue type of the donor. Slade's *Merry Christmas Everybody* is playing on the radio, then it's Bing Crosby's *White Christmas*. Most people will be putting a tray of roast potatoes in the oven by now, along with their turkey.

In the quiet lab, I use a needle and syringe to tease out the valuable white cells contained in the lymph node and place them in a test tube. Then I pop the tube into a small centrifuge to ensure the white cells can be purified. These white cells will reveal the tissue type of the donor. It's impossible to hear the radio now, with the whirring of the centrifuge. Everything's in order and there's time for a quick coffee and a sausage roll.

Just as the coffee is made, the telephone rings. It's Mick Bewick. He wants to go through the list of potential recipients who might be lucky enough to get a new kidney tonight. He has decided to use both kidneys at Guy's, rather than offer one to another hospital. We go through a list of half a dozen names, and I make notes. The donor has a common blood group and I tell Mick I should have the donor tissue type identified in about two hours.

Now I can start to put together samples from the potential recipients to ensure that they have no antibodies to the donor's white cells. If they do, they cannot have a kidney. At this point, the patients on my list have no idea that one of them may soon be getting a phone call, offering them a kidney. Maybe they have had their Christmas lunch, but without any salt or gravy and hardly any turkey. They must be strict because they are on kidney dialysis. Their life depends on sticking to the rules. Perhaps they are wondering what the coming year will bring for them, tied to a kidney machine. Will they even survive long enough to get a transplant?

The centrifuge finally stops, and I can see the lovely band of the donor's white cells. I carefully take them out, wash them and place some of them on a microscope slide. It's hard to believe that these white cells were circulating in the donor's bloodstream just twenty hours ago. Looking down the microscope, I see that they look good so I can dispense them into the wells of plastic plates to do the tissue typing.

More coffee and mince pies are called for, as there is another lengthy wait before I can peer down the microscope again and mark the wells that contain dead white cells and those that do not.

I now know the tissue type of the donor. I go through my list of possible recipients again and have to cross off one of the names. This individual has antibodies to the donor tissue which would cause rejection of the kidney, resulting in a medical emergency that would require its immediate removal.

It's now time to do the cross-match for the remaining patients. The phone rings and it's Mick Bewick again. I tell him the tissue type of the donor and the names of those I have set up for the cross-match. I tell him about the patient we must rule out, and he tells me she's a mother with young children. She's not coping very well on dialysis and desperately needs a kidney. She will never know that she missed this chance of a normal life. She will have to wait for another opportunity – if she lives long enough.

Mick tells me he's going to phone the remaining five candidates to ask them to prepare themselves for possible hospital admission. Who will be the lucky ones? 'Get the switchboard to bleep me as soon as the cross-match is through,' he says. Now he must get the hospital theatres mobilised, ready to carry out the life-saving operations.

The alarm buzzes on my laboratory bench telling me the cross-match is ready to read. I take the small plastic plates, add the blue dye and peer down the microscope again. It is eerily quiet in the laboratory, just John Lennon's 'Imagine' playing in the background. I am totally focused now, quiet, apprehensive. What I see in the plastic plates will determine who gets the transplant and who does not.

My heart sinks as not all the wells in the plates are clear. That means another one of the recipients cannot receive a kidney tonight. I phone the switchboard, get put through to Mick and read out the names of the remaining four possible recipients. I also tell him about the fifth who can't have one of the kidneys because the cross-match is positive.

Mick tells me there is a young male at the top of the list. He's seventeen years old and desperate for a kidney because he's running out of vascular access sites for dialysis. The conversation ends. Mick thanks me and we wish each other 'Merry Christmas'. It's time to tidy everything away, switch off the lights in the laboratory and take the boxes containing the donor kidneys down to reception, where they will wait for the transplant surgeon.

It's evening now and festive lights are shining brightly outside. The seventeen-year-old boy and one other person will be getting the best possible Christmas present. The others on the list will have to wait their turn. Meanwhile, somewhere else, a family is grieving the loss of their loved one. That family's generous decision to donate their relative's kidneys is giving two other people the chance of a new life, in which they will no longer be tied to a kidney machine. And the machines they used will be available for two other patients to receive dialysis.

I leave the boxes with their precious cargo with the porter and wish him good night and a safe journey home, before heading out. I am still carrying the smells and emotions of the laboratory with me as I ride home carefully. Sitting down later that evening to eat a hearty Christmas dinner, I think about a seventeen-year-old boy who, at that very moment, is being wheeled into a hospital theatre for a life-changing operation. He will always be grateful for the 'gift of life' he received on Christmas Day and the gracious decision made by the donor's relatives.

This is the story of how such a gift saved my life – and how I was eventually able to help save others.

Chapter 1: Landing on the Moon

Monday 7th July 1969 is a date engraved in my memory. The day started well. Aged 12, I was looking forward to representing my school in a local Swimming Gala and that afternoon I was taking part in swimming practice at the old swimming baths at the Marine Spa, Torquay.

I did a few practice lengths, but then I started to feel ill and took myself off to the toilets where I started to vomit. I never finished the practice as my swimming teacher, who also taught me chemistry, took me home. Over the next few hours, my condition worsened and later that evening the GP was called out to see me. By then I had become feverish and started to develop a purpuric (bruise-like) rash. My urine had turned an alarming red colour (haematuria) and my face and eyes had become puffy (peri-orbital oedema). This was clearly not a run-of-the-mill childhood illness and must have been worrying for my parents, as I had always been pretty healthy.

The GP came again the next morning and, after one swift look, immediately phoned for an ambulance to take me to Torbay Hospital. For the first few days I was quite excited by all the attention I was receiving. I had only ever visited a hospital once before, to see my mum after a back operation at the Princess Elizabeth Orthopaedic hospital in Exeter. I can still remember a visitor bringing me a bottle of Lucozade at Torbay. Our family always had to be careful with money and never had drinks like Lucozade at home. I was very disappointed when it was quickly removed before I had a chance to taste it.

Over the following week my clinical situation quickly deteriorated and on Monday 15th July I was transferred by ambulance to the children's ward (Bowring) of the old Royal Devon and Exeter (RDE) Hospital, close to Exeter Cathedral. The last days at Torbay Hospital and my first at the RDE are ones I have never been able to recall. My admission notes at the RDE show that an initial diagnosis of Henoch-Schönlein purpura was made, then crossed out and replaced with thrombotic thrombocytopenia purpura, before that too was crossed out and at the third attempt I was labelled with haemolytic uraemic syndrome (HUS), although this became (and still is) a contentious point.

Over that week I had lost over 4kg in weight and was still vomiting, while the purpuric rash, jaundice, abdominal pain and haematuria persisted. There was also a problem with my blood platelets, which were abnormally low at under 100,000 per microlitre of blood (the normal range is 150,000–450,000). Platelets are essential for clotting and the repair of damaged tissues.

By now my kidneys had failed and I urgently needed dialysis. Consequently, at 11.30am the next day, Tuesday 16th July, peritoneal dialysis was started, with a machine that was very different from today's sophisticated peritoneal dialysis machines with all their bells and whistles. The one I had in 1969 consisted of a plastic tubing catheter with an input/output valve that had been inserted through my abdominal wall into the peritoneum. More tubing ran from the catheter to a bag of fluid which was placed in an elevated position. Gravity ensured that the fluid would run into the peritoneal cavity. After a certain amount of time, the valve would be switched over and a second tube would be attached to it, allowing the fluid to run out again, taking the body's toxins with it.

It all sounds very simple, but I still have vivid memories of screaming with pain when too many litres of fluid ran into my peritoneal cavity too quickly, and my doctor tried desperately to get some of it to run out again! The external valve was continually getting blocked, leaving me feeling extremely bloated with fluid, and writhing in pain with a stretched peritoneal cavity. Despite my protestations, they hoped that running in more fluid would somehow unblock the valve. The doctors tried again and again to reposition the catheter to see if that would help, a procedure carried out in those days without any pain relief.

This was my first introduction to the rudimentary medical technology that was dialysis in 1969. The doctors were doing their best to treat my condition with large doses of the anti-coagulant heparin six-hourly, as well as tetracycline to prevent peritonitis. This was when I first started to take a cocktail of prescription drugs which I still take more than half a century later.

Over the next couple of days, the peritoneal dialysis started working well enough to remove some fluid from my body, halting any further decline in my condition. Unfortunately, by Thursday 18th July, my blood pressure was too high, I had additional purpuric rashes, and peritonitis had developed so they had to stop dialysis. Without the dialysis I became more and more confused, unable to recognise my surroundings or the nurses, as well as developing generalised grand mal fits lasting over 15 minutes.

My recollections of lying in a small cubicle on Bowring Ward, with various Disney and other cartoon characters painted on the glass walls, remain vivid. I could always tell precisely when a fit was coming because my entire body started to become rigid. The fits were incredibly frightening. They usually started in my legs, before moving up my body, which would then start to shake violently and uncontrollably. The nearest nurse or family member would respond to my shouts for help and try to hold me down on the bed, grabbing my ankles to stop me hurting myself. The convulsions ended as abruptly as they started, occurring regularly during the day and night. My parents were distraught at the sight.

My condition went further downhill on Saturday 20th July when I started to complain of sudden blindness. At 2.30pm the attending doctor commented in my notes that I shouted out several times 'I am blind' after he had just witnessed my recovery from one of these fits. This compounded the terror that I had already felt due to the convulsions. My kidneys had now stopped producing any urine and this, coupled with the vomiting and sweating during the fits, made me very dehydrated. I was no longer able to respond to commands and was slipping quickly into a coma.

The stark reality was made clear in the hospital notes when my doctor reported that I became comatose, with pupils unresponsive to light and of variable size. At 8.45pm I was admitted to the Intensive Care Unit (ICU) and, despite the peritonitis, underwent peritoneal dialysis once again. That evening, whilst I was comatose, the first (of many) Scribner shunts was inserted into my right arm to allow me to have haemodialysis as soon as possible.

Reading these accounts over half a century later has been a very emotional experience. In less than two weeks, I apparently went from being a normal child about to start swimming practice to one at death's door. The medical notes have also brought back all sorts of memories I had previously blanked out, from images of school and swimming, to brief recollections of Torbay Hospital, through to lying in a children's cubicle having uncontrollable fits and being held down by adults. I realise now how desperate the situation was.

The Scribner shunt that saved my life on this occasion was a major innovation brought about in 1960 by a Dr Belding Scribner, working with Wayne Quinton and David Dillard. Scribner perfected this Teflon device which allowed a patient to be connected repeatedly and continuously to a haemodialysis machine. He was a strong advocate of home dialysis and he was finally rewarded for this work in 2002, sharing the prestigious Albert Lasker Award for Clinical Medical Research with Willem Kolff. This award was given for 'the development of renal dialysis, which changed kidney failure from a fatal to a treatable disease, prolonging the lives of millions of patients'.

Scribner made other important contributions to nephrology. For instance, while working under Scribner, Henry Tenckhoff created the Tenckhoff catheter which improved access for peritoneal dialysis. Scribner had strong views about how patients should be treated within healthcare systems and passionately believed that healthcare should be non-profit-making and universally available. True to his vision, none of his innovations was patented. Hence, he has also been credited with being the father of bioethics. It was his campaigning, along with support from Washington Senators Henry Jackson and Warren Magnuson, that led to the creation of the Federal government Medicare End-Stage Renal Disease Program in the USA in 1972.

The success of Belding Scribner's shunt created unimaginable problems for dialysis units such as Seattle. For the first time people with kidney failure had access to a treatment that could prolong their life. Seattle, like other places, was inundated with patients wanting haemodialysis. To deal with this issue a selection committee was established in 1962, officially called the 'Admissions and Policies Committee of the Seattle Artificial Kidney Centre at Swedish Hospital'. It comprised seven unpaid, anonymous members of the local community, including a lawyer, minister, banker, housewife, state official, union representative and a surgeon. It met in secret every two weeks for the following four years to decide effectively who would live and who would die. At their first meeting, the committee decided only those patients aged between 18 and 45, with no other health problems, could have dialysis. Those under 18 years were specifically excluded as it was thought they would never survive the haemodialysis treatment.

There were 80 people who fulfilled the criteria but only 60 places available for dialysis. By the third committee meeting, the members decided to publish the criteria they had used to come to their decisions. These included age, gender, marital status and number of dependants, income, net worth, emotional stability, patients' ability to accept the treatment, educational background, occupation, past performance and future potential. People soon started calling it the 'God Committee'. It was soon to feature in *Time* magazine, as well as a 1965 NBC television documentary entitled *Who shall live?* These criteria were also used in the UK right through the 1970s and even beyond. My own acceptance onto the dialysis programme at the RDE was only four years after the last meeting of the Seattle 'God Committee'. I will always be grateful that my RDE consultant Dr Hall had the foresight to offer me a place in the RDE unit.

The RDE had an original Willem Kolff dialysis machine which resembled an old-fashioned washing machine. Willem Johan Kolff was a young Dutch doctor working at Groningen University in 1940 when war broke out and the Netherlands was quickly overtaken, with Nazi sympathisers being installed in both government and hospital administration. Looking for a place to work, Kolff found a position in a small hospital in Kampen. Here, he became interested in the treatment of kidney failure after attending a young patient who died a horrible death from the condition. He understood that it was the high concentration of urea in the blood that had led to his death. Kolff was determined to find a solution to treating kidney failure and this meant returning to Groningen.

Previous studies in animals had showed that cellophane could be used as a filter for solutions of small chemicals. By experimenting with blood and sausage casings – and using a variety of objects (including parts from an old washing machine) – Kolff succeeded in making the first 'artificial kidney'. The blood was forced through a filter using gravity and the tubes were rotated around a drum into a solution of dialysate.

Kolff tested his device on patients who were already dying from kidney failure. In the first study he recruited fifteen patients, and, despite some minor successes, they all died within days. As he refined the treatment, he was able to keep patients alive longer. Success came with the sixteenth patient who was already in a coma. In 1945 Maria Schafstad became the first patient to be successfully treated with the artificial kidney, after which she lived another seven years.

Near the end of the war, Kolff returned to Groningen to complete his PhD, using his research on the 'artificial kidney'. As well as working on his medical research, he was involved with the Dutch Resistance, helping hundreds of people escape the Nazis. After the war, in 1947, he sent a dialysis machine to the Mount Sinai Hospital in New York and soon began collaborating with researchers there. This led to his immigration to the United States in 1950, after which he took a position at the Cleveland Clinic.

While I was comatose, my parents were able to stay overnight in a room along the corridor from the ICU. They had been told to 'expect the worst' and they went to nearby Exeter Cathedral to pray for my recovery. Many other relatives and family friends were also hoping beyond hope that I would have the strength to pull through. It must also have been agonising for the medical and nursing staff who had witnessed my rapid deterioration, despite their interventions.

My parents spent a great deal of time talking to me and encouraging me to wake up so that we could go and buy the new bike I had wanted so badly before becoming ill, but which we could not really afford. They were worried about me riding it in all the busy traffic. However, they knew I really wanted a bike, and the medical and nursing staff had suggested they use it as a tool to try to get me to wake up.

There was a black and white television in my bay and the ICU nurse was watching the moon landing when I suddenly woke up from the coma on Sunday 21st July 1969. Even all these decades later, I can vividly remember looking up at the ceiling and seeing Neil Armstrong taking 'one small step for man, one giant leap for mankind', then asking the ICU nurse where my bike was.

These images are crystal clear, including my family then coming in to see me and lots of discussion about the bike! Considering that I'd been in a coma for the previous two days, and in and out of consciousness before then, it is extraordinary that I woke up fully alert. My treatment and medications had not changed, other than the additional peritoneal dialysis session. It seemed it was simply not my time to go, and everyone's prayers had been answered.

As I had pulled through, the doctors decided to start dialysis immediately. Later that morning, they placed me on a Kolff machine with a newly inserted Scribner shunt. It must have been a very steep learning curve for all the health-care professionals. The very few controls on the machine needed to be adjusted manually. My first haemodialysis session started at 11.55am and continued through the afternoon, finishing at 5pm. The Kolff dialysis machine almost certainly helped my recovery; together with the prayers and the thought of having a bike! Which of these interventions did the trick, we will never know, but I can attest to the fact that unconscious people can hear, so it's important to keep talking to them.

Over the next couple of days, I had more dialysis sessions, with six-hourly injections of 100mg hydrocortisone. The doctors were desperately hoping that my own kidneys would now start to recover, but each day they produced a miserly 100ml or less of urine which contained abnormally high protein levels.

Proteinuria, a classic sign that something is severely wrong with the kidneys, had been described by physicians some 140 years previously. In 1827, Sir Richard Bright published several research papers linking proteinuria with other clinical signs of kidney disease, a condition which became known as 'nephrotic syndrome' or Bright's Disease.

There was a glimmer of hope on Saturday 27th July when my urine output increased to over 260ml. It is fascinating that my notes contain handwritten calculations of kidney function, including blood and urine protein and creatinine concentrations. The doctors had to work all these out by hand, based on the clinical laboratory reports. There were no calculators so they probably sat at a desk on the ward, using a slide-rule. They clearly had to be good mathematicians. I wonder how many of today's doctors would be able to carry out such calculations.

There was a major setback on Tuesday 30th July. My dialysis on the Kolff machine ended abruptly when the dialyser and my new Scribner shunt both became clotted. Due to this, I lost a massive amount of blood, which in turn resulted in my becoming 'very shocked', according to my medical notes. Another attempt to perform dialysis was made, using my femoral artery, and I was given blood, plasma and saline to replace that which had been lost in the dialyser. It worked briefly, but there was no time to lose, as femoral artery dialysis was merely an emergency holding position. Down I went to the operating theatre, where another Scribner shunt was inserted into my left arm.

Once I'd recovered from this ordeal, the doctors redoubled their efforts to get me on the road to recovery. They prescribed a daily cocktail of drugs, including large doses of heparin, hydrocortisone, phenobarbital (to control the seizures) and the steroid, prednisolone. My miraculous recovery continued over the following days, and I became much more aware of my surroundings. By now I was receiving 60mg prednisolone each day. This was a vast dose, but my kidneys had suffered devastating damage and could produce only 250–300ml urine each day at this point.

Thankfully, within a few days my urine output started to rise and soon reached around 2000 ml per day (2 litres). This must have been a huge relief for all the doctors, who had never seen anything quite like this before and were performing a difficult balancing act – trying to maintain my kidney function while enabling me to stay off dialysis. Indeed, my kidneys improved sufficiently to allow me, albeit briefly, to return to a normal diet. However, I think this improvement was partly wishful thinking because I started to retain fluid again and the dietary change was quickly overturned.

Nevertheless, my improvement did mean that by Wednesday 13th August, the dose of prednisolone could be reduced to a mere 10mg per day. This was helpful as my blood pressure had started to rise and become a problem, a known side effect of steroids. The heparin treatment continued. Amazingly, by the evening of Friday 15th August, I had recovered sufficiently that a hospital car took me home to spend my first weekend in more than five weeks with my family.

It must have been a weekend of mixed emotions for my parents. They had me back home after a long time in hospital. I had been critically ill and now, for them, my relatives and friends, it must have felt as if all would be well. No doubt I felt the same. My mum went to great lengths to try to reproduce my salt-free, low-protein diet. To begin with, the whole family had to eat salt-free vegetables, but – having tasted them – Mum agreed to cook separately for me.

When I arrived back on the ward on Sunday 17th August, the doctor wrote in my notes, 'child had a good weekend at home but looks poorly and kidneys just maintaining status quo'. My family had been delighted to have me at home, but I suspect there were grave worries and a few tears about what the future might hold. At this stage I had received only a few sessions of haemodialysis, and I doubt that anyone was really prepared for what this would entail in the long term.

To try and help my kidneys recover enough to stave off dialysis, I had been placed on the infamous 'Giovannetti protein-restriction diet'. This is essentially a starvation diet, devised in the 1960s by Dr Giordano Giovannetti and used for patients with chronic kidney failure. It limits the protein intake to around 18 to 20 grams per day, to keep levels of blood creatinine and urea as low as possible. To give you an idea of what that means, one boiled egg has approximately 13 grams of protein.

Most of the calories in the diet came from carbohydrates and I had been prescribed Hycal to provide them. Hycal came in a 175ml bottle, containing 106.5g liquid glucose, and it was available in six flavours. It was designed specifically for people with kidney failure who required a high-calorie, low-fluid, low-electrolyte diet. It tasted foul. My mum tried to make ice-lollies with it, but the high sugar content prevented them from freezing.

However awful it may sound, this diet did keep people with chronic kidney disease alive for many months when no other treatments were available. It was obviously a necessary addition to my treatment plan, and it did stave off dialysis for a week or so. But this all changed after my return from the weekend at home. On my first day back, the medical team realised that my kidneys were no longer coping, despite the awful Giovannetti diet, and I was quickly deteriorating.

The fits had returned with a vengeance. As well as the six-hourly large doses of intravenous heparin, 70% magnesium sulphate was added to the phenobarbital to try to control the seizures, but neither truly helped. By the end of my first week back, on Friday 22nd August, the vomiting returned, my eyesight was deteriorating, with blurred vision, and my blood pressure had risen substantially to 135/105 mm mercury (mm/Hg).

My body was also retaining water at an alarming rate, causing retinal oedema and papilloedema (swelling behind my eyes), so Lasix (Frusemide, a potent diuretic), was added to my drug regime. The decline in my condition continued unabated over the weekend; and by Monday my blood pressure had risen again. Blood was coming from my nose and was also in my vomit. In desperation, the anti-hypertensive drug Bethanidine was added to my drug regime.

Bethanidine, first discovered in the early 1960s, acts peripherally to block the alpha (α)-2a receptors and causes vasodilatation, resulting in a drop in blood pressure, which is sometimes sudden and symptomatic. Its precise mode of action is not clear, but it can be beneficial in severe hypertension, and has fewer side effects than its predecessors in this class of drug. It also decreases blood pressure by suppressing renin secretion.

The way drugs are made available for use in patients has changed a great deal over the last half-century. Back then, there were very few large-scale clinical trials and the mechanism of action of the agents was often poorly understood. However, some argue that the current regulated clinical trials process is too cumbersome; it is certainly very costly and time-consuming. Many initially promising compounds are discarded long before they ever make it to clinical use, either at the animal testing stage or at any of the three human clinical trial stages.

The first well-designed, randomised, controlled trial actually took place in 1747, when James Lind successfully tested the effect of citrus fruits on treating scurvy. In 1943, the UK Medical Research Council (MRC) performed one of the first double-blind controlled trials of a substance called patulin as a possible cure for the common cold. And in 1946 the MRC set up a landmark trial of streptomycin for use in pulmonary tuberculosis, performed with precise design, implementation, patient enrolment criteria and data collection. Since then, clinical trials have grown in sophistication and influence. There have been many advances in ethics, guidelines and regulations that provide protections for participants. No doubt even more ethical and legal questions will be raised in the future. Society constantly needs to strike a balance between the demand for new drugs and medical technologies whilst protecting the rights and safety of the patient.

Until I saw my medical notes, I had not appreciated the extent of concern about my eyesight, with the retinal oedema and blurring of my vision both getting worse during this period. The hypertension was a major contributory factor to the eyesight problems and it was associated with terrible headaches. I do remember from time to time being taken to the West of England Eye Infirmary, located across the main road from the RDE. On one occasion I recall a nurse taking me there in a rickety old wheelchair, covered in blankets to protect me from the weather, and having to make a dash across the busy main road that was as hazardous then as it is now.

By the end of August, my overall condition seemed to stabilise, except for persistently high blood pressure and worryingly heavy proteinuria. But this all changed over the next few days, and my condition suddenly declined. On Tuesday 2nd September, my mother's birthday, I had become very confused and disorientated, having spent all day in bed with bad headaches and vomiting. At 9pm the on-call physician wrote in my notes, 'he was twitching, quickly followed by a full-blown grand mal attack that lasted for around two minutes'. At the end of these fits, my blood pressure would rocket to dangerous levels. The doctor prescribed 5ml paraldehyde twice a day to be given rectally, in the hope of stopping the grand mal fits.

Paraldehyde was first introduced into medical practice more than a hundred years ago, as a sedative, hypnotic and anti-epileptic agent in patients having continuous fits (Status Epilepticus). It is no longer licensed in the UK but can be used in children in special situations as an 'off-licence product'. It can dampen down the nervous system, thereby suppressing the fits and leading to drowsiness. I do not remember this, but it sounds rather unpleasant!

The fits and confused state continued into the next day and were compounded by the side effects of the paraldehyde which produced nasty skin rashes. The medical team therefore stopped the paraldehyde and switched to repeated doses of 20mg of intravenous Valium. The precise cause of my fits remained a mystery but this perhaps reflects the medical team's lack of experience of treating a child with kidney failure. I still remember being in the side ward cubicle, knowing that a fit was about to start and feeling very frightened. These fits might have appeared to be like those I had experienced during the first weeks of kidney failure, but to me they were far more intense and lasted longer.

Again, desperate measures were needed. With my urine output dropping, the doctors put the prednisolone dose back up to 45mg per day. The good news was that the continuous intravenous Valium was working its magic and the fits were drastically reduced, apart from some annoying twitches in my left leg. Prednisolone had presumably also had a good effect as, by Saturday 6th September, the dose was back down to 15mg per day. I had also continued to receive the intravenous heparin although the dose had been halved.

The emotional rollercoaster lurched again when I was told that my kidneys could no longer keep me alive, and a return to haemodialysis beck-oned. This was a major setback, not just for me, but for everyone involved in my care, including my family. Hope had been building only a few weeks before that I might have turned the corner and be on the road to recovery. Unfortunately, the disease had other ideas and had once again taken me on a nightmarish journey.

It was now going to take considerable resolve for me to keep going. Words like 'determination' and 'will to live' were often mentioned at the time by my parents and my healthcare team. They meant inner strength, which was now needed in abundance, and they gave me encouragement with phrases such as 'keep determined' and 'maintain your resolve' and 'keep fighting'. I did not need to be reminded of the importance of not giving up – but it was still reassuring to hear supportive, encouraging words from people who simply wanted me to beat this crippling condition.

By Monday 8th September, despite large doses of intravenous Valium, the fits had returned with gusto. I was also becoming confused, slipping in and out of consciousness with dangerously high blood pressure. I can imagine the doctors thinking that I was now a lost cause. My notes mention that they spoke to my mum, presumably to spell out to her how my condition had deteriorated. I never realised that any of this had taken place until I read my medical notes.

My left leg had become very painful, with large haematoma-like rashes. Meanwhile the arterial end of my Scribner shunt had clotted during the day and at 9pm I was taken to theatre for another emergency shunt replacement. The doctors were clearly running out of access options for dialysis – and this was to become a major issue.

At 9.40am the next morning, Tuesday 9th September, my fits had worsened, and I was once again unconscious. They kept me in my cubicle on Bowring ward, rather than transferring me to ICU. Thanks to enormous efforts by the medical and nursing teams, my condition was temporarily stabilised, but by 5.25pm I was once again deteriorating rapidly. My retinae were now reported to be very swollen and, while unconscious, I was quickly put on haemodialysis which continued throughout the night using the infamous Kolff machine.

This was yet another occasion when my mum was phoned at home and told that my condition had become critical. I was obviously 'out for the count' but it must have been dreadful for everyone. For reasons that have never been disclosed, I was again alone on the ward, perilously close to the end of life.

Amazingly, by the next morning, my vital signs had improved and I was able to respond to the spoken voice. I had somehow pulled through, and my family's prayers had once again been answered. By 2pm I was fully awake and conscious, the dialysis again having saved my life. I was not comfortable though, still complaining of blindness, and a very painful abdomen, with vomiting, and pain going into my loins and all around my kidneys.

By 9pm my conscious state had improved sufficiently that the doctors considered me out of danger. They commented in my medical notes that I had no recollection of the previous two days. Maybe this had been a far more serious episode of coma than the one in July when I could recollect being told 'to go and get my bike'. If the same technique had been used, I had no recollection of it.

My kidneys were now barely functioning, having produced only 90ml urine in the past 24 hours. Nevertheless, the improvement in alertness continued and by Friday 12th September the notes say that I was well orientated but had high blood pressure and still complained of tenderness over my kidneys. This improvement continued over the next few days, although I had now gained a massive 6kg in excess fluid (10% of my body weight), despite the extensive episodes of dialysis.

There were more serious problems a few days later and my condition took another turn for the worse when I developed a fever on Wednesday 17th September. By the following day, my notes describe how I had become septic with a temperature of 103.6 degrees Fahrenheit, with a very rapid pulse of over 166 beats per minute and a decreased jugular venous pressure. My kidneys were now only passing a few ml of very dark urine. Today, we would recognise this cluster of clinical signs as those of sepsis, a cause of considerable morbidity and mortality.

As expected, the doctors initiated intravenous cloxacillin and ampicillin every six hours while the nurses continually sponged my body with tepid water to lower my temperature. A chest X-ray failed to show any demonstrative signs of pneumonia so, like so many emergency episodes during this period of my life, the cause of the sepsis remained unexplained.

There were no ultrasound, CT, PET or MRI scans to help the doctors identify the source of infection – only simple X-rays – so they had to rely on their clinical experience, examination skills and judgement to come to a diagnosis. None of these doctors had previously used dialysis to treat a 12-year-old child with kidney failure; most had little experience even of dealing with adult patients with renal failure, other than with palliative care. Every time they made decisions about my care they were 'learning on the job'.

Over the next few days, the antibiotics seemed to get on top of the infection, despite its unknown source, and I stabilised, but became massively overloaded with fluid, leading to high blood pressure. My critical condition obviously meant that major decisions had to be made by the medical team on how to keep me alive.

According to my doctors, Professor Roy Calne (a pioneer in the field of organ transplantation) happened to be 'passing by' during a lecture tour in the Exeter area when – as a last resort – they asked him for advice about my treatment. Professor (now Sir) Roy Calne had studied medicine at Guy's Hospital, London, before serving in the Royal Army Medical Corps from 1954 to 1956, and then learning orthopaedic surgery at Oxford and the Royal Free Hospital in London.

While carrying out postgraduate surgical research in London, he conducted experimental kidney transplants on dogs, using one of the earliest immunosuppressant drugs to suppress the body's natural immune reaction against transplanted tissue, which would inevitably result in graft rejection. The results were encouraging, and he went to the United States to learn more about immunosuppressant drugs and organ transplantation. From 1960 to 1961, he worked at the Harvard Medical School and Peter Bent Brigham Hospital in Boston, Massachusetts, under Dr Joseph Murray who had carried out the first successful human kidney transplant between identical twins on 23rd December 1954. Calne and Murray collaborated with future Nobel Laureate George Hitchings of Burroughs-Wellcome pharmaceutical company to develop and test improved immunosuppressant agents. The result was Imuran (azathioprine), which Calne and Murray found resulted in the extended survival of dog kidney transplants.

On his return to England, Roy Calne was appointed lecturer in surgery first at St Mary's Hospital and then at the Westminster Hospital, in London. He published an authoritative text on kidney transplantation in 1963 and joined Cambridge University in 1965 as Professor of Surgery, later becoming department head. There, he improved kidney transplantation techniques and developed ways of transplanting the liver. Continuing his interest in immuno-suppression, Calne and his junior associate, Dr David White, carried out animal and then human trials on a new drug supplied to them by the Swiss scientist Jean-Francois Borel of the Sandoz pharmaceutical firm. The trials proved the effectiveness of what came to be the standard drug for suppressing rejection of organ transplants, ciclosporin (or cyclosporine), and Professor Roy Calne was knighted for his achievements in 1981.

Roy Calne's advances of course built on earlier vital work by other pioneers, and it is instructive to trace the progress of this area of medical innovation over time. Until the work of Alexis Carrel in the 1900s, there was no real technique for attaching an additional organ to the recipient's artery and vein. Carrel invented a technique known as 'suture anastomosis' while working with Charles Guthrie at the University of Chicago. Together they perfected a technique known as 'vascular triangulation and replantation of major vessels'. The key to their success was impeccable aseptic technique to prevent infection and careful handling of vessels ends, as well as the use of fine silk sutures coated with Vaseline. Carrel was awarded the Nobel Prize for Medicine in 1912 for his work on anastomoses.

He later developed the first modern form of tissue culture, claiming to have kept a chicken embryo alive for 34 years. Carrel was a flamboyant character who also pioneered the cold storage of tissues, treatment of wounds and skin grafting. During the First World War, he was drafted into the French army where he was appalled by the poor treatment of soldiers who lost limbs through infection. Working with British-born chemist Henry Dakin, he created a wound management system known as the Carrel-Dakin technique that included using sodium hypochlorite solution, mechanical cleansing of the wound and debridement. This technique was very successful and became widely used by military and civilian surgeons.

On his return to the US and while working at the Rockefeller Institute, Carrel was approached by the famous aviator Charles Lindbergh to invent a heart bypass and perfusion machine. Lindbergh's sister-in-law had died from a heart condition called mitral stenosis, and the surgeons had said there was no way to operate without a temporary bypass machine. Using his apparatus, Carrel was able to keep organs preserved for many days if not weeks.

Carrel was upset at being forced to retire when he was 65 from the Rocke-feller Institute and decided to return to his native France, where he turned his energies to creating the Foundation for the Study of Human Problems. Once France fell to the Germans in 1940, Carrel continued with his plans with the blessing of the German occupiers and was accused of collaborating with them. Upon liberation in 1944, he was dismissed by the Allies and died in disgrace shortly after. It was a sad end for a brilliant innovator, who had worked along-side other famous surgeons including Harvey Cushing and William Halsted, but his genius could not save him from his eventual downfall.

Another brilliant innovator, Sir Peter Medawar, was born in Brazil to a Lebanese father and British mother. After the end of the First World War, he moved to England with his family, renouncing his Brazilian citizenship. He was later educated at Marlborough College, followed by Magdalen College where he studied zoology. After graduating he completed his doctoral degree supervised by Nobel laureate Howard Florey who inspired his interest in immunology. During the Second World War, he worked in Oxford as a senior research fellow before being appointed as Mason Professor of Zoology at Birmingham in 1947. He later moved to University College, London, and then in 1962 to the National Institute of Medical Research where he eventually became Head of the Transplant Section of the Medical Research Council (MRC).

His interest in transplantation had started during the Second World War when he had been asked to investigate why skin grafts taken from one individual and placed on another fail to grow, while skin grafts taken from another part of the same individual's body grow well. This work was essential to try to save the lives of airmen and others who required urgent treatment for their burns. His work in this area formed the basis of what is now called 'acquired immunity' and 'immunological tolerance'. As well as being critical for treating life-threatening burns, his work directly influenced Joe Murray, a plastic surgeon working in Boston, who performed the first successful human kidney transplants between identical twins. Medawar was awarded a Nobel Prize for his work in 1960 and later became known as the 'father of immunology'.

Joe Murray's interest in transplantation had begun during the Second World War while he was doing his military service as a plastic surgeon at Forge General Hospital, which had been requisitioned as a wartime trauma centre. Murray was stunned by the array of horrific injuries, particularly in the burns victims. He spent all his time on the wards performing reconstructive surgery on patients and learning about wound healing. His supervisor was so impressed by Murray's dedication that he put in a special request to the military to enable him to continue his work at the hospital for the rest of the Second World War. Murray's interest in the mechanisms of wound healing encouraged his study of skin grafts in the wounded airmen. Later he moved to the Department of Surgery at the Peter Brent Brigham Hospital in Boston and started working with Francis Moore, the Head of Surgery. It was this relationship that led to Murray performing the first successful kidney transplant between identical twins on 23rd December 1954. There were serious ethical questions to address, as subjecting a normal healthy person to major surgery for the benefit of someone else had never been done in modern times.

Following this success, Murray was at the forefront of transplantation over the next decade, performing the first living unrelated transplant in 1961 and the first cadaveric kidney transplant a year later. This procedure led to an urgent need to define 'brain death' and written criteria were eventually agreed that became law throughout the western world. In 1990, Murray was awarded the Nobel Prize for Medicine in recognition of his achievements in the transplant field.

Francis (Franny) Moore made his own enormous contribution as a pioneer in the early days of transplantation. He was appointed Surgeon-in-Chief at the Peter Brent Brigham Hospital in Boston at the age of 35 in 1948, a post he held until 1976. Moore provided the inspiration, encouragement and guidance that ensured the surgical pioneers around him could develop the transplant programme at the hospital. He was also instrumental in publishing seminal works on the metabolic care of the surgical patient. Indeed, his textbook The Metabolic Care of the Surgical Patient was an essential reference for all those involved in post-surgery care for many decades.

Thomas Starzl is justifiably known as the father of modern transplantation and even immunology. He began his career in neuroscience, before starting medical school at the John Hopkins where he pioneered the early treatment of cardiac pacemakers. Following a spell in Miami, he became fascinated with the metabolism of the liver and later investigated the possibility of transplanting it in patients with irreversible disease. At this time, before immunosuppression was understood, many doctors had become disillusioned with the horrendous rates of kidney rejection.

Starzl believed that rejection could be reversed and this proved to be possible after the discovery of azathioprine (Imuran) by Calne and others. However, when the world's leading transplant surgeons convened in 1963 under the auspices of the American National Research Council to review the first 200 kidney transplants, the results were dire. Despite using azathioprine since the early 1960s, only 10 percent of patients were surviving beyond three months. Many leading surgeons thought it was unethical to carry on the work. But when Starzl presented his own results from Denver at the very end of the meeting, they showed an 80 percent patient and kidney survival after one year. Some in the audience refused to believe these results from the 'new kid on the block'. Nevertheless, this was a watershed moment in transplantation and clinicians quickly followed the Starzl immunosuppressive protocol of azathioprine and prednisolone. This protocol would be used throughout the world for many years to come.

Starzl and Professor Sir Roy Calne pioneered the use of other novel immuno-suppressant drugs such as cyclosporin, and later tacrolimus and antibodies to cells of the immune system. After moving to Pittsburgh. these next genera-tions of drugs allowed Starzl to pursue his long-term goal of successfully trans-planting livers, having been the first in the world to perform the operation in 1963. Once he retired from the operating theatre, he continued to devote his time to trying to solve the riddle of immunological tolerance. Throughout this career, he was always tormented by memories of his patients suffering during the early years of transplantation.

In 1969, fortunately for me, Roy Calne was in the Exeter area on a lecture tour and was willing to give my doctors the benefit of his advice. After hearing my story, he said the only remaining option was to remove my own native, diseased kidneys. In the short term this would commit me to haemodialysis, but would hopefully control my blood pressure, stabilise my condition and give me a chance of staying alive, but in the long term I would need a new kidney. He told the medical team that, if I survived the removal of my kidneys and the subsequent dialysis, he would perform my transplant at Addenbrooke's Hospital if a suitable kidney could be found. Indeed, a plan was put in place to remove my own kidneys at the same time as doing the transplant if a suitable kidney became available. I knew nothing of these discussions at the time and can only presume that my family had some involvement.

During this time, I was obviously confined to Bowring ward and dialysing, when possible, at Whipton and had not been home since that weekend in August. Over the next week I entered the irreversible decline in renal function which had only one outcome. Despite dialysis, I was severely waterlogged, and the grand mal fits became more frequent, even during dialysis.

By Thursday 25th September, I once again needed regular doses of 20mg intravenous Valium throughout the day, with worsening high blood pressure. The fluid overload was now causing substantial facial swelling and, together with the signs in my eyes of papilloedema, haemorrhages and exudates, confirmed that I had malignant hypertension. No matter what the doctors and nurses did, there now appeared to be only one possible outcome. The time had come for the doctors to grasp the nettle and take Roy Calne's advice.

On the night of Tuesday 30th September, I was being fasted in preparation for surgery. It was still less than three months since I had first been taken ill swimming in Torquay. Early the next morning, Wednesday 1st October, the porters took me down to the RDE main theatres for my life-saving operation, to be performed by Mr Shaldon. I was later told that he had never previously performed a bilateral nephrectomy (removal of both kidneys), let alone one in a child! He did the safest thing and made a large incision straight down the front of my abdomen from the bottom of my rib cage to the top of my pubic bone.

The traditional surgical approach for a single nephrectomy then was a diagonal incision around the side from front to back, whereas today nephrectomies are often done laparoscopically, requiring only a small incision of 2 or 3 inches. Some are even done using robotic instruments, with the surgeon operating the robot from behind a screen. In 1969, bilateral nephrectomy was extremely risky; and even today surgeons are often reluctant to perform the procedure, although it is probably considerably safer than half a century ago. Today, the recovery period is usually just a few days, whereas in 1969 patients receiving major operations usually had to recover in hospital for up to two weeks once the clamps or stitches had been removed.

However, my surgery was successful and the effect of removing my diseased kidneys was dramatic. The following day, Thursday 2nd October, saw my blood pressure return to a normal 120/80 mm/Hg. It was so impressive that the following day I felt faint with regular blood pressure values of 95/65 mm/Hg or less. It was obvious that the right decision had been made. The major surgery, along with disruption to my homeostasis, inevitably led to clotting of both the arterial and venous ends of my Scribner shunt. However, for once, they were easily cleared, using injections of heparinised saline. A large syringe attached at each end of the venous and arterial lines was pushed and pulled until the clot either went into my circulation or was sucked up into the syringe.

This was a very unpleasant and painful procedure – and there didn't seem to be much concern about blood clots causing embolisms half a century ago! The immediate priority was to ensure that I could dialyse, and this took place later in the day using the faithful Kolff machine. This was carried out on the ward as I was too medically unstable post-operatively to be taken to the dialysis unit.

In the months following the removal of my native kidneys, it was very strange to realise that my body no longer contained these organs. I knew, even from this early age, that I would no longer be able to live like most other people. At the time there would have been only a handful of children and possibly adults with no kidneys. Some patients might have had kidneys that were diseased and no longer working, but the knowledge that I had none at all took a long time to get used to.

The realisation gradually dawned that I would be totally reliant on a machine in order to stay alive. This strange feeling persisted for many months, and I had a sense of emptiness where my kidneys should have been. I felt worst at low points of the day and night when I was alone. But I had little time to dwell on the issue as I was too focused on being positive in order to stay alive. There was never time to discuss my anxieties with my family or the medical team. Self-pity simply wasn't on the agenda. Everyone was just thankful that we were where we were, and we all needed to move on and hope that the future would be brighter.

Nowadays dialysis is a commonly accepted treatment for end-stage kidney disease. Haemodialysis units are not only based in large teaching or district hospitals; satellite dialysis units can be found in many small towns, within easy travelling distance for patients. If haemodialysis if not an option, there is an alternative treatment, using Continuous Ambulatory Peritoneal Dialysis (CAPD), which can take place either in a hospital clinic or at home.

In October 1969, there were few haemodialysis units and CAPD had still to be invented. Dialysis machines were expensive and there were only limited spaces available for patients. Home dialysis became the preferred option, but there was still a long waiting time before a patient could have a unit fitted. The patient's home had to be surveyed to identify a 'dialysis room' which was usually a spare bedroom. Alternatively, some patients had a Portakabin installed in their garden to house the dialysis machine, to keep the clinical dialysis separate from normal family life. Local charities were often set up to raise money to buy the machine and convert the patient's home.

Our local newspapers were aware that I was on dialysis and had been to our home in Wellswood to interview me and take the usual photographs. We had many kind offers from benefactors who wanted to pay for a home dialysis machine. The hospital also received a letter from one lady who wanted to donate one of her kidneys, but it was declined. Taking a kidney from an altruistic donor was deemed unethical half a century ago but is now a common occurrence in the UK and elsewhere. Sadly, the offers of financial help to buy a kidney machine could not be taken up for many reasons. We rented our home, and this made conversion difficult. Furthermore, I was a child, and the medical team was unclear as to what type of machine I would need.

As often happens, the publicity brought out both the best and the worst in people. The entrance to our basement flat in a Victorian villa was down a long path with a large wooden panelled fence on one side and the stone wall of the Coppice Hotel on the other. We just had an iron gate at the entrance. My parents became aware of somebody leaving piles of dog faeces down the path, along with various items of household rubbish. This was reported to the police, although the culprits were never found. The healthcare team thought it might have been done by someone grieving the loss of a relative from kidney disease who had been unable to get onto the waiting list for dialysis.

It is hard to believe today that many patients never got as far as being offered dialysis, never mind being considered for a transplant. There were too few facilities; patients not earning a place would be offered palliative care and helped to die. The UK was particularly poor at providing dialysis facilities, compared to other developed countries, and this situation continued for many years. The reasons for this are complex.

In the United States the growth of renal replacement therapies over the past half century has been phenomenal. In 1972 President Nixon signed into law the Federal Government End Stage Renal Disease (ESRD) programme which meant that all renal replacement treatments for US citizens would be paid for by the Treasury. When it was first implemented there were approximately 10,000 patients; and the 2018 US Renal Disease Registry recorded 554,038 individuals on some form of dialysis. In the UK, the figure for 2018 was over 65,000.

Over the first few days after having my kidneys removed, the swelling and haemorrhages in my eyes disappeared and, to everyone's delight, my blood pressure remained normal. Mentally, I was much more alert and the enormous operation scar in the middle of my abdomen healed up well, the last of the staples being removed on Saturday 11th October.

The following week, the team finally allowed me to go home for a couple of days in between haemodialysis sessions. It seems that I even felt well enough to attempt a return to school, but this failed spectacularly. A taxi picked me up in the morning but I had to return home a couple of hours later, suffering from dizziness, blurring of my eyes and loss of vision, necessitating another trip to the RDE. Although now ostensibly in the second year at school, I had yet to appear for any lessons. The problem with my vision had persisted from the very start of my kidney failure journey, becoming particularly pronounced during the grand mal fits. These problems continued for many more months. No one ever found a cause but I suspect that uraemia was partly, if not entirely, to blame.

I returned to Bowring ward as an emergency admission on Friday 17th October. The complete loss of vision in both eyes was transient and would resolve spontaneously after an hour or so. But the doctors suspected that I was fluid-overloaded and on Sunday 19th October they prescribed 2mg of spironolactone daily. Following additional dialysis sessions, my condition was stable enough to allow me to go home in a hospital car late on Wednesday 22nd October. Another lengthy dialysis session during the night of Friday 24th October was organised. Together, the spironolactone and dialysis seemed to do the trick and the next morning I felt much better.

It is hard to imagine now, but at that time dialysis sessions usually lasted between 10 and 14 hours and they were carried out two or three times a week, often overnight, using a non-disposable Kiil dialyser. These dialysers were in effect the artificial kidney and consisted of metre long boards of thin cellophane membranes that were clamped together with plastic boards. Blood would flow between the cellophane sheets whilst dialysate fluid would pass in the opposite direction in a separate compartment. As the blood and dialysate fluid pass over each other the poisons are removed from the patient. This meant arriving at the unit by hospital car in the late afternoon, waiting a couple of hours for the machine to be prepared and then waiting again for your turn to be 'hooked up'. In 1969 the unit had only around six bays with dialysis machines, some of which had already been used in the daytime. Cleaning, sterilising and flushing each machine with dialysate fluid, ready for the next patient, was an extremely time-consuming process.

It was not easy to sleep overnight, attached to such a machine with all its alarms and lights. These would be set off if you accidentally lay on the lines, preventing blood from going or returning from the dialyser. There were alarms for pressure and air bubbles in the blood lines, but these were relatively simple compared to the sophisticated ones found on today's machines.

Blood was pumped out of the body using a very basic 'Watson-Marlow' peristaltic pump machine. It looked and worked just like a pump you would find in an old car engine. It had three rods that rotated on a spindle, encountering the line, and effectively pushing the blood along and into the dialyser. It was all very primitive compared to the sophisticated routine monitoring of a patient's well-being that takes place today.

At the end of the dialysis session, great care had to be taken when disconnecting the arterial end of the lines, trying to reduce as much blood loss as possible by allowing blood to be pumped back into the body. Gravity was used to help drain the blood through the plastic tubing. It would have been all too easy for air to get into the lines and be pumped around the body, causing an air embolus. This would have been disastrous – and it was something you did not want to think about too much! The nurse or carer had to be quick with the clamps to ensure it did not happen. Blood pressure monitoring during dialysis had to be done by a nurse or carer and there was no easy way of measuring oxygen saturation levels. The tools were simply not available, but despite the lack of these additional measurements, dialysis worked and kept people alive.

For a couple of weeks, my condition stabilised but this sadly came to an end on Thursday 6th November, when I was readmitted as an emergency to Bowring ward with vomiting, headaches and blurred vision. My legs were swollen and the puffiness in my face and eyes had returned, together with 'florid' retinal oedema, with new haemorrhages affecting my vision. My blood pressure was extremely high, at 170/130mm/Hg, with a racing pulse of 124 beats per minute.

My last dialysis session had been a couple of days before, on the morning of Tuesday 4th November, but I was clearly suffering from severe fluid retention and overload. The faithful anti-hypertensive drug Bethanidine (10mg) was started to try to bring down the blood pressure, but my condition worsened and later in the evening my notes report that I became confused, disorientated and agitated, and was slipping in and out of consciousness.

Intravenous Valium was continuously given to try to stop the convulsions, but this time it had little effect. I was once again 'walking a tightrope' between life and death and my medical notes show there was increasing concern that I would slip into an irreversible coma. My body was so waterlogged that fluid was accumulating in my lungs. When I was conscious, I felt as if I was drowning from the water in my lungs. The nurses had made me sit upright on the bed; it was impossible to lie down anyway, as I would immediately start to 'drown'. It was the most horrible sensation, feeling completely helpless and slowly 'drowning' from within.

The staff could not get immediate access to haemodialysis so, instead, as it was clearly an emergency, the decision was made to try peritoneal dialysis. At 11.30pm, I started peritoneal dialysis on the ward. An hour later it had to be stopped, as I had haemorrhaged over 300ml of blood from the site of the peritoneal catheter. Blood losses on this scale were common complications of peritoneal dialysis in these early days.

The following morning, I was started on haemodialysis again, using a Travenol RSP machine. This was a fully integrated dialysis delivery system developed by Travenol Laboratories, and it was used both in hospitals and in patients' homes. It was ground-breaking at the time. When first introduced, each machine cost approximately US $1,400. Over 3,500 of them were produced and used all over the world.

This machine required a bath of 120 litres containing the dialysate to be mixed each time it was used, but at the time it was considered a big step forward. The patient only had to be attached to the unit for 6 hours, up to three times a week. The machine also used a disposable coil-type dialyser, rather than a Kiil. Whilst dialysing this time, I was given a transfusion of 2 pints of blood to make up for the blood loss during the failed attempt at peritoneal dialysis. The 6-hour dialysis session removed 3kg of fluid, nearly 5% of my body weight. On the morning of Saturday 8th November, I was allowed home but had to return to Whipton Hospital for overnight dialysis on Monday and Friday nights, with another daytime session on Wednesday.

Blood transfusions were regularly needed due to blood losses incurred during haemodialysis sessions and anaemia that developed because the damaged or absent kidneys couldn't produce erythropoietin, a hormone that stimulates the formation of red blood cells. Erythropoietin is now genetically engineered and readily available, so dialysis patients no longer suffer extreme anaemia.

At the end of the session, a saline solution would be used to wash out the lines and – more importantly – the dialyser, where there was always a considerable amount of residual blood. During the last thirty minutes of the session, the Kiil would be tipped from a horizontal to a near vertical position to allow the blood to drain; the arterial end of the patient was raised to the eleven to twelve o'clock position with the venous end at nearly six o'clock. Nevertheless, there would always be residual blood loss; and the peristaltic blood pumps were not particularly kind to the red blood cells, breaking them up as they went through. Added to all this, the patient always had raised urea levels, which led to reduced haemoglobin. My own haemoglobin levels were often as low as 4g/dl (rather than 11 to 15g/dl), and this made the production of new red blood cells exceedingly difficult.

There was also the danger of pathogens. The Australia antigen was the main pathogen screened for in 1969. This antigen had been discovered in 1963 by R. Blumberg who won a Nobel Prize. In 1968, the Australia antigen became recognised as a surface protein of hepatitis B but a vaccine for hepatitis B only became available in 1981 and this was quickly replaced by a recombinant DNA form in 1986. There are now also several anti-viral medications that can be used to treat infected individuals.

This was important because additional units had opened in the UK in the 1960s, with marked increases in hepatitis infection. The first outbreak occurred in Manchester in 1965, where three staff died from the infection. Over the next five to six years there were many such outbreaks, which sometimes required the closure of the dialysis unit – for example, at Guy's Hospital between 1969 and 1970. At the same time another serious outbreak occurred at the Edinburgh dialysis unit where eight patients and three members of staff died. Over the next few years, these hepatitis outbreaks caused extensive delays in setting up desperately needed new dialysis facilities.

The sources of infection were thought to be from blood donations, but there were additional factors such as over-crowding in the units, and the non-disposable Kiil dialysers which had to be sterilised with formalin after use. Some of the bottles were still made of glass and, together with the needles, also required sterilisation. The 1972 Rosenheim report into the hepatitis outbreaks made several key recommendations which formed the basis for good practice in dialysis units.

Meanwhile, the problems with my loss of eyesight continued. I suffered another episode on Monday 1st December, on yet another of the half-dozen days in the entire second year that I had made it to school. It was clearly not a good idea as things went terribly wrong, and I had to return to the RDE as a 'blue light' admission.

The clerking-in doctor stated in his notes that during class I had suddenly developed fuzzy eyesight that had lasted for about 45 minutes and had then gone blind. This episode is still very clear in my memory, as my PE teacher had to call 999 for an ambulance to take me to Exeter. Without any warning symptoms, I suddenly could not see anything. The images were hazy even though both my eyes were open, and this was followed by blindness.

It must have been a very odd situation for my classmates as well as the teacher. As the class was now streamed, most boys would have known me only by sight from the previous year and would not have been fully aware of how ill I had been. Some might even have thought it was a great whiz for getting out of a boring lesson! But I suspect most of them would have been concerned to hear one of their peers shouting for help because he was going blind. They kindly escorted me out of the class and to the staff room, where I waited for the ambulance.

At the hospital, my eyes were examined again; apparently the optic discs were very poorly demarcated, and the retina appeared pale and oedematous with copper wiring around some of the arterioles. This may have been pathological or perhaps it was a psychological response to the extreme conditions I was having to cope with, brought on by the stress of going back to school.

Chapter 2: Back to the Beginning

After this whistle-stop tour through my first shocking experience of kidney disease, you may be wondering about the person behind the medical notes. After all, before I became a 12-year-old patient fighting for his life, I was a relatively ordinary child...

I was born at Cross Oaks Farm in Borehamwood, Hertfordshire, on Monday 11th March 1957, and given the name Andrew Glenn Northcott. Born to parents Trevor and Margaret, I was very much the youngest of three boys. Brother Trevor was eight and John six years older than me and they were a tight-knit pair of 'compadres'. My early life was fairly uneventful, apart from living on many different farms around England as my dad was a farm labourer who constantly changed jobs.

My parents hailed from Yorkshire and by 1962 they had settled in a house on a recently built council estate in Mixenden, near Halifax. They had 'come home'. My dad now had a steady job working in the Halifax Borough Engineer's Office. He could also spin a good yarn which, on the plus side, won him the title of best salesmen for 'Belzona' polymer coatings for metal repair, and earned him an award of one of the first 'Teas-maid' automated machines.

In September 1962, when I was five, I attended Mixenden Primary School, now known as Ash Green Primary School. School life seemed an entirely natural progression. My mum trusted my older brother John to walk me to and from school in my first few weeks, but after that I became an independent spirit.

However, normal family life was sometimes interrupted by my dad 'running away from home'. When I was aged six in 1963, my dad disappeared over the Christmas holidays. He was eventually found sleeping in our rented garage by my brothers. All four of us went to retrieve him that sad, dull, Christmas Day morning. At this time Dad had a small shop in Pellon Lane, Halifax, selling a mixture of goods including wrought iron furnishing as well as carpets, but he did not make a success of this venture, accruing large debts, the downside of his 'gift of the gab'. I have never satisfactorily determined the reason for his intermittent disappearances, but beneath his jovial exterior existed a complex man.

Maybe it was not surprising that my school life was characterised by me playing pranks and getting into skirmishes, usually leading my peers astray! Tall for my age and well-built, and top of my class academically, I had a natural confidence and a competitive nature. I remember vying with one boy to see who could collect the most 'gold stars' in any week. In September 1965, now in my fourth year, the teachers rewarded us by putting us both forward to take the eleven-plus exam a year early, a challenge I needed. Dad, who had been to grammar school himself, bought me eleven-plus practice papers and helped me get my head down and enjoy doing the work needed for me to pass.

Despite the problem of my dad's absences, I have fond memories of family day trips to the seaside, to Filey on the North Yorkshire coast and Lytham St Anne's in Lancashire. There were also longer family holidays. In the summer of 1965, we spent a fortnight in a caravan at Caister, on the coast near Great Yarmouth, Norfolk. Whilst we owned little materially, that summer Dad was driving a Rover 90 car, which was big enough for all of us. This was a joyous time, especially making enormous sandcastles and burying Dad in the sand. I had no idea that this would be our last holiday together as a family.

In early January 1966, when I was nearly nine years old, Dad disappeared again, this time for many months, and my memories of Christmas 1965 are therefore bittersweet. There was all the anticipation that Christmas morning of going into my parents' bedroom to open my numerous presents, not knowing what was to follow. This was when I became the proud owner of my first model railway, given to me by my Auntie Kathleen and Uncle Peter, an 'O' gauge clock-work Hornby Dublo set.

By now, the Royal Navy had stolen my brother Trevor at the tender age of 15, leaving only John and me at home. Thus it was that I had to accompany my mum to the police station in Halifax to report my dad as a 'missing person'. The Criminal Investigation Department room was no place for a child. We later discovered that Dad had been declared bankrupt and was under threat of the bailiffs, and my mum organised a repayment scheme through the Court. Fortunately for us, many of the debts were written off and Mum recorded everything meticulously in an A4 black book until his debts were finally paid off. Dad had disappeared and we did not know where he was.

In June 1966 Mum finally received a letter from my father, now living in Brixham in Devon in the far Southwest of England. He had settled down a bit and was working for Centrax in Newton Abbot. He desperately wanted us all to join him, to start afresh. Mum agreed and he came back to Halifax to help us move to our new home in Devon. The plan had been for us to live in a three-storey fisherman's cottage in Brixham, Devon, but by the time we were ready to move in it had already been taken. Instead, we moved to 4 Dunolly, two-bedroom basement flat and former kitchens of a large Victorian villa, in Barrington Road, Wellswood, Torquay.

The first drive into Torquay, sitting in the back of our Rover 90, was mesmerising. The streets lined with palm trees made me think of exotic foreign lands, and buildings overlooking the parade as we came along the sea front spoke of a much grander way of life. The sun was shining, and the entire bay was reminiscent of a setting from a James Bond movie. This was a new beginning for all of us.

John and I shared a bedroom despite our age difference. The single bed was allocated to me, whilst John had a double, although he was expected to share it with Trevor when he was home on leave from the navy. Although the flat only had two bedrooms, it had an exceptionally large garden, spread over two levels, linked by the original Victorian steps. Across the road from where we lived was a footpath alongside beautiful woods.

There were many hotels in this part of Torquay and the five-star Palace Hotel was especially grand. A path led past the Palace to more exciting places such as Anstey's Cove and Redgate beach, situated at the bottom of a very steep hill, going down to the beach. In the last few weeks of the school summer term in 1966, when I was nine years old, I often followed that path to escape from humdrum home life. Despite my age, and perhaps because I was rather tall, I managed to persuade the boatman in charge of the pleasure boats on Redgate beach to give me free boat rides if I helped pull the boats in and out of the water.

The boats were actually just wooden catamaran 'floats' with a seat between the two hulls and paddled like a canoe. Later, I progressed to helping with the motorboats and pedaloes. Beaches are always full of flotsam and jetsam so, using old ropes I found on the beach, I created a superb swing spanning three enormous trees in one corner of our large garden. It felt like a magical life.

Reality hit in September 1966 when I had to start at Ilsham Primary School, a small Church of England village school a few minutes' walk from our home. It was very small compared to my school in Halifax. Indeed, I only realised it was a school when Mum sent me to do some shopping and I saw children playing in what was obviously a school playground. I told Mum and a few days later I was enrolled, ready to start in September 1966. My parents let the headmistress know that my old school had been planning to put me into the eleven-plus examination a year early but she refused even to consider this. There was only one class for the last two years and I felt trapped! Whilst I enjoyed school, the teaching and content of the lessons soon became boring, tempting me to become a bit disruptive. I felt I was just repeating work from the year before, and I often got into trouble and ended up being reprimanded by the headmistress who was also my form teacher.

Once summer term and school were over, and I had finished primary school, I found myself a job, despite being only ten. Not surprisingly, I looked for work on the pleasure boats at Redgate Beach. The owner paid me £2 per week and told me to tell no one except my parents!

Back at school, my misdemeanours continued to lead to reprimands from the headmistress; and the punishment was often to have to sit with her during morning break. In those days, pupils were each given a small bottle of full-cream milk to drink, and the headmistress made me drink mine alone with her. In my mind she was the original 'school milk thief' as she used any spare milk to make her morning 'milky coffee'. Watching her remove the milk's skin with a teaspoon and eat it made me shiver! There were only six or seven boys in the final year and the headmistress ensured that they were all (excluding me and two of my close friends) appointed as Head and Deputy Head Boy or Prefects. This tactic only encouraged my rebelliousness.

My most notable act of rebellion, I am now ashamed to recall, occurred during the summer term on the dreaded sports day. One of my friends, for whom I had wangled a job working on the pleasure boats, had formulated a plan to play truant and spend the day working on the boats at the beach. All went to plan, and we met up to go down to the beach, taking with us a change of clothes. Unfortunately, not long after we arrived, it started to pour down with West Country rain and there was nothing for us to do. We could neither go home nor go back to sports day! We just had to spend our time doing cleaning jobs.

Painfully slowly, the clock moved to 'going home time' when we wandered back up the hill and back to our respective homes. My mum had come back from work and was blissfully unaware of where I had been, innocently assuming that it was just another school day. Everything changed half an hour later when a knock was heard at our front door; it was the Reverend Rose-Price, our local vicar who was also attached to my school. He had a quiet word with my mum and then confronted me about where I had been all day; all had to be revealed.

Somehow the headmistress had rumbled our plan. She was speaking to my friend's parents at the same time as the vicar had come to our house. We could not have planned for the cancellation of sports day due to the weather. My mum and dad were annoyed but understood how bored and frustrated I had become at school. I did attend the rearranged sports day the following week, being allocated only the egg and spoon and three-legged races in which to take part!

Despite my being bored and a bit naughty, I duly passed the eleven-plus and went to Torquay Boys Grammar School in September 1968. There was a strict school uniform policy and my mum had taken me to the school outfitters in Union Street, Torquay, to buy me an expensive Beau Brummell blazer. That blazer saw me through the whole of my school life as it had plenty of growing space and, though I did not know it then, my growth would be stunted by kidney disease.

Thankfully, starting at the grammar school was a fantastic experience. I settled in very quickly, making new friends and enjoying the academic subjects, the sport and singing in the choir. Previously, whilst at primary school, I had joined the local St Mathias Church choir. This choir had a good reputation and I had quickly developed my singing abilities and been promoted to senior choirboy, a position which attracted the grand sum of 15 shillings per term (75 pence in today's money).

We always ensured that we had a piece of paper and pencil hidden under our cassocks to be used for playing 'hangman' and 'noughts and crosses' during the dreaded sermons. Unfortunately, I had been dismissed from that choir, along with the choir master's son, for pushing another boy into the laurel bushes whilst waiting for the church to open for Evensong. We both pleaded innocence, as the boy in question had been bullying some of the newer members of the choir. Unfortunately, our protestations fell on deaf ears. It was definitely a miscarriage of justice.

I was somewhat surprised to find that the same choir master helped with music lessons and the choir at my new grammar school. Fortunately, he did not seem to bear any grudges, so I quickly established myself in the grammar school choir. In December 1968, I remember Mum and Dad coming to watch me sing the soprano solo at the Christmas school concert in Torquay Town Hall.

However excellent and challenging the new school proved to be, it could not take the mischief out of me, and I was always in the thick of any pranks, usually played on our unsuspecting form tutor and English teacher who was always clad in a traditional gown, had an RAF moustache, and at first appeared quite strict. We soon found out that this was not the case and in fact he found it exceedingly difficult to control the class. For instance, we used to enjoy making 'marble machines' by dropping a marble through the ink-hole in our old-fashioned, wooden, lidded desks. The marble ran alongside various rulers and books and out of the hole at the bottom, making a loud clunking noise as it went. The poor teacher never seemed to have any idea which of us was responsible.

Another time my two friends and I had caught the open-top bus from the harbour-side back home. We were supposed to wear our school caps outside school until we were fourth years (year ten now) but our caps were safely stowed in our school bags. On the bus, we made straight for the rear bench seat upstairs. It was a lovely sunny afternoon and we started larking about whilst the bus started its journey up the hill to Babbacombe. We entertained ourselves making faces and rude gestures to the car driver following the bus. It was all great fun, or so we thought.

The following morning, at school, nothing seemed untoward until the end of assembly when the headmaster made his announcements. He obviously left the best till last when he asked who the three boys were on the upstairs rear bench of the open-top bus destined for Babbacombe the previous day, boys who were not wearing their caps and were making rude gestures. Unfortunately, the car driver following us had been our headmaster! We all owned up and headed for his office to receive our punishment. We got away lightly, with whacks of a yard ruler on our backsides and detention for the rest of week. Luckily, my parents never found out.

Being part of the Cub Scouts at Mixenden was one of my great pleasures. Going to Cubs involved catching a bus into Halifax on a Friday night to get to the Scout Hut, and afterwards we would use our pocket money to buy chips from the 'chippie' near the bus stop. The Cub pack in Torquay did not seem the same and I never settled and soon left. The grammar school had its own Scout troop which was exclusively for its pupils. The Scout master, who was also a teacher at the school, made a big point about how privileged we were to have our own troop. Once again, I started to really enjoy Friday nights at the Scout Hut. This time, it required two bus journeys to get home as the hut was located a few miles from school and we had to wait by the bus stop on the main A380 road from Newton Abbot.

On Friday 1st November, just before Bonfire Night, I was waiting at the bus stop after Scouts along with some other friends. We had acquired some 'bangers' from some of the older boys, later banned from sale in the UK. We decided it would be great fun to start lighting them and putting them inside metal railings on the pavement alongside the main road. Of course, a police car soon stopped. We were in Scout uniform and easily identifiable. Names and addresses were taken, and we were driven home. Fortunately, my dad was the only one at home and I received only a mild rebuke from him, but that was the end of Scouts for me and the others.

My passion for railways was apparent from an early age. My mum worked as a housekeeper at the Clarence Hotel, Torre, when we first moved to Torquay and, before starting school, I sometimes had to accompany her to work. The hotel was situated opposite the railway station, and it was there that my interest in 'train spotting' started.

In my last year at primary school, I started building an OO-gauge railway using my saved-up pocket money and the money hard earned by working on the pleasure boats. It was built on an 8-by-4-foot baseboard and my mum allowed me to keep it on the sitting room floor in our flat in Dunolly. Unfortunately, our old television started to get black and white streaks of 'snow' across the screen, as well as a buzzing noise, whenever I ran my train. The faster my electric model locomotive went, the more interference there was on the screen. Consequently, I could only run my train when the television was switched off.

Various school sports captured my interest, including football, rugby and cross-country in the winter and spring terms, and athletics and cricket in the summer. As things turned out, I never had the opportunity to participate a great deal in the summer sports. However, I distinctly remember walking back during the last part of the cross-country course. It was a typical wintry rainswept Wednesday afternoon and a few of us started to practise being goalie and diving through the enormous muddy puddle in the goal keeper's box. We arrived back at school, completely covered in thick mud. My mum was not impressed and even Persil's 'whiter than white' could not remove all the grime.

Despite my high spirits, I was quite capable academically, achieving reasonably good results after the Christmas exams and particularly enjoying history and geography. The Head of History was a tall, distinguished-looking man who always wore a black gown and leather-soled shoes that could be heard coming, menacingly, along the corridors. He brought history to life with his stories of battles, using colourful language that would be frowned upon today. Our Head of Geography was a similarly smart man and extremely fierce. Blackboard rubbers and rulers would often come hurtling towards us if he thought we were not paying attention. This type of discipline was in stark contrast to my previous school – and the stricter environment suited my temperament and enabled me to thrive.

I had joined the school Railway Society when I started at Torquay Grammar School in September. Their plans to build an OO gauge railway in the massive loft of the main school building really excited me. The baseboards had already been built and there was still a considerable amount of preliminary work to carry out. My form master had organised a school Railway Society trip to London on a school day in July towards the end of the summer term. Several other railway enthusiasts (otherwise known as train spotters or anoraks!) were going on the trip, which would be leaving Torquay early on Tuesday 15th July, bound for London, Paddington. We would visit all the major London railway stations and various engine sheds before returning home to Torquay late in the evening. This was incredibly exciting for anyone interested in railways and collecting numbers – I had saved up all my pocket money over many weeks and could not wait for July!

Sadly, I would never go on that much-anticipated trip. As you already know, a very different journey awaited me – on ambulances rather than trains.

Chapter 3: Back to Hospital and Haemodialysis

Living with kidney failure in the late '60s and early '70s was unspeakably difficult. For patients today, it's hard to imagine how people dealt with the many problems that could arise from both their disease and the dialysis. Those who had access to a dialysis machine were considered lucky, as machines were in such short supply. I was certainly lucky to be in the right place, at the right time. The dialysis unit at Whipton Hospital had only recently been established and in July 1969 there very few units that would treat anyone under the age of 18 or over the age of 55. A patient with any co-morbidities, such as diabetes or heart disease, had little or no chance. Rationing of dialysis facilities was normal practice at that time.

Having gained access to a dialysis machine, I had to lie on an old iron hospital bed for 10 to 14 hours at a time, hooked up to the machine, two to three times a week. Haemodialysis in 1969 required access via an artery and a vein, usually in the arm or leg, via a Scribner shunt. Patients at Exeter were fortunate that some 'Parker Knoll' reclining chairs had been bought from charitable funds for dialysis. Despite the relative luxury of the chair, the daytime sessions were still incredibly monotonous, starting at around 8.30am and lasting till late afternoon. In some ways, the night-time sessions were a little better as there was at least a possibility of being able to snatch some sleep, but that was not easy when you were surrounded by masses of buzzing and flashing paraphernalia, as well as an uncomfortable bed! There was no bedside TV to watch, and iPads, Kindles and other electronic devices had yet to be invented.

Dialysis inevitably left me feeling like a rag doll, washed out and dizzy with low blood pressure and feeling nauseous, if not being physically sick. These symptoms will still be recognised by many of today's dialysis patients. My salt-free, low-protein Giovannetti renal diet was still in force even while I was on dialysis, although some years later it would be relaxed at these times, allowing for some little treats. Sadly, after my own kidneys had been removed, I suffered from similar symptoms, even when not dialysing. The fatigue and sickness were ever-present, but I also had postural hypotension. This meant that my blood pressure dropped suddenly when I stood up, and I would faint if I did not sit down again quickly. All these factors made it extremely debilitating. Having such low blood pressure may well have contributed to my shunt clotting on numerous occasions. This was a continual cause of anxiety, resulting in many emergency ambulance trips to Exeter, and endless worry about what might happen if all my access sites packed up.

The nursing staff constantly reminded me to take care of my shunt, and I certainly took this advice on board and tried my best to keep the shunt in working order. They had shown me how to check for blood clots and infection and how to use the stethoscope to listen for a pulse and a 'whooshing noise', as well as changing the Melonin dressing using the aseptic technique. These were all tasks that had to be carried out by the patient, even at 12 years old. There was a strong ethos of 'patient ownership' of the condition and the treatment, which was critical if you were going to survive the arduous dialysis treatment that was keeping you alive.

The importance of resilience, inner strength and honing my survival instincts, came to the fore in two episodes in my early days dialysing at Whipton. The first occurred when a middle-aged lady was also 'on the machine', dialysing in the bay opposite mine. Suddenly, awful screaming noises emanated from her cubicle. The nurses immediately went to her bay, while another nurse drew the curtains round mine. There was a great deal of commotion and eventually my curtains were pulled back, together with those in the opposite bay. The lady was no longer there, and I later found out that she had died, presumably from a heart attack. I doubt that many 12-year-old boys have had to face the reality of death at such close quarters.

A second episode occurred around the same time and involved a young man, probably no more than 20, who often dialysed at the same time as me. One Monday evening I was expecting to see him, as we usually dialysed overnight together. I asked the staff where he was and received evasive answers. I thought no more about it, but he remained absent from the unit over the coming days. I eventually found out that he had effectively committed suicide by spending an entire weekend gorging on dark chocolate. This ultimately caused his heart to stop, due to absorbing excess potassium. When my mum found out what had happened, we all had great sympathy for him and his family. It was a terrible thing, but he simply could not face any more dialysis and had given up the fight to survive. My mum also told me, in no uncertain terms, that I must never do that! I had no intention of following suit; in fact these experiences only hardened my resolve to fight with every breath in my body to come through this. Such experiences were all too common within the kidney failure community at that time.

The task of ensuring that the Scribner shunt was working took an enormous amount of my time and returning to any sort of normality was still out of the question. The first few months of 1970 were filled with problems with clotting shunts. It started almost immediately on Friday 2nd January 1970, when I was admitted to Bowring ward with a Scribner shunt which had become clotted at both ends. The venous end was successfully cleared, using heparinised saline in a 20ml syringe, which enabled a long stringy clot to be pulled out. But the arterial end was not so easy to clear, even using the new 'clot buster' medicine, urokinase. Without today's stringent regulation of drug use, it was possible then to use a drug such as urokinase in areas outside its original licence with relative ease. But, despite treatment with urokinase throughout the day and the evening, it remained completely blocked. Some hours later, the clot eventually cleared, which was essential as I needed to go on dialysis again that night.

There was an added complication in that my white blood cell count had become exceptionally low, probably because I been prescribed the antibiotic Fucidin. This had to be stopped so that I could have a sternal bone marrow aspiration to look for any underlying abnormalities before the next dialysis session. Don't let anybody ever tell you that bone marrow aspiration is not a painful procedure! It is. Fortunately, the result came back as normal. With the shunt now working, I was transferred to Whipton Hospital to be put on dialysis for my overnight shift. When I was taken off the machine late the next morning, I was able to enjoy my delicious salt-free breakfast of a boiled egg with inedible salt-free bread. Sadly, salt-free bread is useless for making 'soldiers' to dip into the yolk, as the bread just crumbles. The hospital car then took me home.

This was the beginning of weeks of ambulance trips, following 999 calls, from home to Exeter. Often, I had only been home a few hours when, on checking my shunt, I would find it blocked, with no 'whooshing' noise. Sometimes there would be two trips in 24 hours, while others would follow my dialysis session. If it was impossible to clear the shunt, it meant a general anaesthetic and a longer stay in hospital were needed. This inevitably meant running into another dialysis session, with no time to return home in between. By now, urokinase was often needed and being used at great expense but, equally often, to no avail. All these attempts to remove clots from the shunt caused considerable pain. The nurse had to grab hold of my arms and legs while the doctor (usually Dr Peter Bisson) pulled on the syringe. Looking back, I don't know why pain relief such as Entonox was never offered. I think that it would be now, but at the time everything was being done 'on the hoof'. Pain relief was low down the list of priorities compared to the need to get my shunt working again!

It wasn't only the clotted shunts that were becoming a problem. It was obviously difficult removing the correct amount of fluid (and electrolytes) at each dialysis session. The fact that I was a young teenager presumably made this more difficult, the calculations were based on adults as under 18-year-olds would not have been offered dialysis. Consequently, there were even more occasions when I had to return to Exeter as an emergency, with extreme swelling in my face and ankles, and waterlogged lungs.

One of these incidents happened in the early hours of Sunday 1st February 1970, when I woke at home feeling feverish, having felt unwell for the previous few days. As well as the fluid overload, I had a racing pulse of 110 beats-per-minute, vomiting and a return of the epileptic seizures. Once on the ward, I became delirious, and the doctors thought the massive oedema and water-logged lungs must be due to left ventricular failure of my heart. It was another very frightening experience.

Things worsened during the morning, as I progressed into congestive heart failure. My jugular veins became distended, a classic clinical sign of poor filling of the right ventricle. My condition required drastic action and the faithful Kolff dialysis machine was brought out of storage for my use. The old machine came to the rescue and by 9pm that evening it seems to have successfully removed a lot of fluid. My condition must have improved, as it stated in my notes: *'he is as cheeky as ever!'*

Sepsis was another life-threatening risk. Dialysis was performed without the benefit of today's single-use plastics and infection-preventing safety processes. One such episode occurred during an overnight dialysis session on Monday 9th February, barely a week after I had recovered from the heart failure and fluid overload. During the early hours of the night, I had become feverish with a temperature of 103 degrees Fahrenheit, shivering, with a pulse of 140 beats per minute. The doctors were called and expressed concern about these signs of potential sepsis.

The dialysis session was completed, and I was taken off the machine the following morning and transferred by ambulance to Bowring, where I slept all day. I remained stable and the next day, Wednesday 11th February, I was transferred back to Whipton Hospital for another overnight dialysis session. The next morning, I still had a fever and a terrible headache and was continually vomiting. The medical team wondered whether my underlying sepsis was due to bacteria infecting the dialysis fluid. The sepsis could also have entered via the entry portal of the shunt in my skin. The venous end of my Scribner shunt felt tender, so swabs were taken from both ends as well as blood cultures. Once again, I was prescribed Fucidin as a precaution.

My condition deteriorated the next day, Friday 13th February, and I was still feverish, but this time was also vomiting up 'green sputum' and had developed diarrhoea. My temperature was still raised, at 103 degrees Fahrenheit, and my pulse was racing at 112 beats per minute. Despite feeling feverish and possibly having sepsis, I still needed to have dialysis that night. It was simply not possible to miss any sessions.

The next morning, after coming off the dialysis machine, I felt much better and my temperature and pulse were almost back to normal. This was some positive news. The blood cultures and swab results had also come back from the microbiology laboratories, showing *Staphylococcus Aureus* at one end of the shunt. The infection was sensitive to cloxacillin so I would spend another week incarcerated on the ward, taking intravenous antibiotics.

Having recovered from the infection, any hopes of my problems being over were dashed within 48 hours. I had gone to Whipton Hospital on Friday 20th February for my usual night-time dialysis session. The next morning, Saturday 21st February, I was allowed to go home for the first time in nearly two weeks. But, before I even had time to take off my coat, I was back in an ambulance, with another blocked shunt! It was about 11pm when the faithful Dr Bisson met me on the ward. He always seemed to be on-call and invariably dealt with my emergencies. Both Peter and his wife Margaret (Peggy) were totally dedicated to their work and practised medicine in a truly pioneering era. Without their selfless work and dedication, I would never have survived these early, tortuous days of dialysis.

The next day, Sunday 22nd February, they were initially hopeful that the anti-coagulants might work. However, there was disappointment again, as it quickly became apparent that the heparinised saline being pushed in was simply leaking into the tissues under my skin, from the clotted end of the tube. The skin itself was now waterlogged, breaking down and creating another potential site of infection.

Consequently, at 5pm I was taken down to the operating theatre to have yet another Scribner arterio-venous shunt inserted. With all the access points in my arms used up, it was now time to start on my lower limbs! This time the shunt was inserted into my left leg, using the tibial artery and the long saphenous vein. At only 12 years old, once again I was getting ready to go down to operating theatre for my new Scribner shunt alone, my mother having given verbal consent over the phone. Circumstances were such that written consent was not always possible. As the shunt was in my leg, I now had to use crutches to get around, being allowed to put only a small amount of weight on it. The shunt was also protected by a Plaster of Paris cast. I had to remain on Bowring ward for another ten days until the stitches were removed, and I could finally return home.

Plans had, however, been made for me to have haemodialysis at home and my family had spent time in the dialysis unit being trained in how to operate the dialysis machine and learning how to attach the blood lines that ran from me to the dialyser. I would be using a Travenol RSP machine, with a disposable twin coil system, at home. While this was a different machine from the ones in the unit, it was a massive improvement on the conventional Kiil systems being used in the dialysis units and by most people who were on home dialysis. In many ways, I was lucky!

On my thirteenth birthday, on 11th March 1970, I had my first home haemodialysis session. My grandma had died the previous summer and my mother had received around £4,500 from her estate. Mum used it to purchase a four-bedroomed house at 79 Warbro Road, Plainmoor, around a mile from our two-bedroomed flat in Wellswood. It was an ordinary Victorian terraced house, but it had four double bedrooms, a living room, dining room and breakfast room. The rear bedroom looked out on to Torquay United football pitch, where there was an alley separating our small back garden from the football ground. The house had been purchased in February while I was in hospital, and I had not been around for the move from our old flat. I was given the second largest bedroom at the rear, while my brother John had the smallest one that faced out on to the front. The bedroom that overlooked the football pitch was to become my dialysis room and the main bedroom at the front was for my parents.

Home dialysis in 1970 was the preferred option, due to the limited number of dialysis machines in the unit. It was thought that it might also be a superior form of long-term treatment for the patient and their family. Of course, to be selected for home dialysis, you needed a home that could accommodate the dialysis machine and all the stores. If there was no spare room, the hospital would provide a Portacabin. It was also essential to have a family member or friend who would assist with putting you on and taking you off dialysis. If you were using a Kiil, this had to be washed and sterilised with formalin as soon as the dialysis had finished. It could take several hours to take apart the Kiil plates, clean, sterilise and then reassemble them. This was an extremely demanding task that put great strain on many families; and it became a major drawback to home dialysis using non-disposable dialysers. Fortunately, someone at Whipton Hospital, together with my family, must have decided that it would be preferable for us to use the disposable twin coil machine.

A maintenance team came to convert the rear bedroom into a clinical dialysis room in February. The floor and skirting boards were made watertight, using materials identical to those used in hospitals. There were numerous storage shelves along the left-hand side for all the dressing packs, saline bags and other paraphernalia required for dialysis. The hospital also provided a standard wrought iron NHS bed with a mattress and linen.

On the morning of my birthday, 11th March, the dialysis machine technician and staff nurse arrived to help put me on dialysis. Due to my size, it had been decided to use only 'half' of the twin coil and the length of time for the dialysis would be reduced to 6 to 8 hours. This was great in theory and all went well for the first session, but reality started to set in over the next few sessions. My mum had enlisted the help of her great friend, Margaret Potter, a woman in her early twenties who worked in the newsagent in Wellswood. Margaret had helped our family from the beginning of my illness, running errands and helping with my care. She later went on to join the police specials and the regular police force.

I was totally reliant on my mum, my brother John, and friends such as Margaret to provide the nursing assistance needed to get me on and off the dialysis machine. The unit had provided a telephone land line, paid for by the NHS, to contact someone in the unit to deal with small queries and problems. However, for most practical issues it was still a case of trial and error and dogged determination. In a matter of a few weeks, my 'support team' had to become clinically competent in disconnecting arterial and venous blood lines, where a single error could have been catastrophic. My life was literally 'in their hands'.

Similarly, the dialysate and other fluids needed to be checked and double-checked before infusing aseptically into me or into the machine. The access holes in the skin for the arterial and venous Scribner shunt tubes required great care to keep infection at bay. The sites where the PTFE Teflon tubing came out of my limb often leaked serous fluid and small amounts of blood which formed crusty clots between the dialysis sessions. A gauze dressing would be used to cover up the entry points, then the whole thing would be wrapped in a crepe bandage. This was done in such a way that the rubber connection between the arterial and venous tubes was visible, together with a small amount of each line.

The wound holes had to be cleaned at the beginning and end of every dialysis session. I had been encouraged to do for myself if the Scribner shunt was easily accessible, using both hands. As the shunt was now located in my leg, near my ankle, it was possible for me to reach and do this for myself. Everything had to be done using aseptic technique with 'Regency' sterile gloves, masks and dressing packs. The gauze would often get stuck to the serous fluid that had oozed out. Removing it required some care, moisturising the gauze with saline.

The wound hole would then be cleaned using EUSOL (Edinburgh University Solution) or a similar agent. EUSOL was invented in 1916 as an agent to combat sepsis in war casualties, and it was made by adding water to bleach and boric acid! The 0.5% hypochlorous acid solution releases chlorine, which sterilises the tissue. It was certainly vicious on the skin, and I tensed up every time I had to use it to clean the area. In 2008, research reports were published showing that, while EUSOL worked in preventing sepsis during primary wound treatment, it impaired secondary healing by inhibiting the growth factors and cytokines that promote healthy tissue. It also became apparent that, in combination with gauze these side effects were more obvious preventing the healing of a wound.

Cetrimide (yellow antiseptic solution) and chlorhexidine (pink antiseptic solution) were also commonly used for cleansing. All these solutions had to be prepared in glass bottles by the hospital pharmacy and sterilised by the Central Sterilisation and Storage Department (CSSD). In today's NHS, these solutions (like many others) would be purchased in bulk from an external supplier and supplied in single-use plastic bottles. Clearly, this is more convenient for the hospital, but comes with additional financial and environmental costs.

Today, there is a vast range of dressings available for many different wounds. Most home first-aid kits now have versions of Melolin, which has a plastic film to prevent the dressing from sticking to the wound and is perforated to allow the exudate to pass from the wound into the body of the pad. In the early days of renal dialysis, these types of dressing were not readily available. And when they did become available, they were incredibly expensive and used only sparingly. Similarly, Micropore is now found in every first-aid kit, but half a century ago it was also treated like gold dust, every roll having to be accounted for. Any attempt to use it for tasks other than those for which it was intended was frowned upon and led to a reprimand from Sister! I suspect that renal and dialysis wards were allowed to use these expensive new products, while Elastoplast was the norm for everyone else.

After the initial euphoria of my first home dialysis session, things started to become more difficult. It soon became obvious that the new dialyser was too powerful for my 60kg teenage body. I can still vividly remember how, after around 90 minutes, I would start to develop horrendous cramps in my legs.

When the cramp first started, it felt like one normally occurring after taking part in a lot of exercise. However, the intensity soon increased massively, and my limbs would be 'locked' in spasm. It was excruciating, and I would scream with pain on the bed, pleading for the nearest person to rub my legs. This never worked and the cramp and pain would continue. It must have been upsetting for my care team, as there was nothing they could do to help. The unit was contacted but they could offer no solution, other than rubbing the affected limbs. Often, I would be pleading to be taken off the machine, but my mum and others would insist that I had to carry on. Dialysis had to come first.

Eventually, the pain I suffered from the dialysis proved too great to bear and I was taken off this machine altogether. At the end of even the shortened session I would be exhausted and suffering from the effects of low blood pressure. The dialysis was just 'too strong' and in a short space of time removed far too much sodium and potassium, hence the debilitating cramps. It was impossible to walk the ten to twelve steps from my dialysis bed to my proper bed. If my brother John was there, he would pick me up and carry me from one bed to another; otherwise, it was a two-person job.

I saw little of my elder brother Trevor during this period, as he was away at sea. Consequently, unlike the rest of my family, he never saw my dramatic decline, from a normal 12-year-old boy to someone who was effectively house-bound, frail, pale and continually having to make trips to hospital. His lack of awareness of what had happened to his 'little brother' came to a head one evening. Trevor had gone out with John for a few drinks and, on his return, saw me lying on the settee in the living room feeling completely washed-out, hypotensive and occasionally vomiting. He immediately started to shout and bellow, telling me how pathetic I was and that I should get up and do something useful.

There were many similar explosive tirades from him. John and my mum would try to calm him down and explain why I looked and felt as I did, but to avail. Trevor remained extremely angry, and I usually made a quick exit to my bedroom. The situation remained tense until he returned to sea. It was never talked about after the night in question. However, I have spent a lot of time thinking about it and have concluded that Trevor was just deeply upset at seeing me so ill. He had missed being around during the many life-and-death situations, so he simply wasn't prepared to see me as I was, and it clearly affected him badly.

Over the next few months, the medical team decided to discontinue my home dialysis. In addition to the issue of the twin coil, I was still having access problems with my shunt as well as other medical issues. Although I didn't know it at the time, my mum and dad were also effectively living separate lives. When I was admitted to Bowring ward, my dad would make special arrangements with the Ward Sister to visit me at breakfast time; there was never a time when both my parents would visit me together. If for any reason he was unable to visit me he would post a letter to the ward with handwritten stories that I have kept to this day. The stories nearly always revolved around our dog Chum (or Chumbo) and me getting up to various mischievous antics. When I was at home with my dad, he would always take part in any board games that were played.

The Scribner shunt in my left leg was still clotting at regular intervals, which often led to emergency trips by ambulance back to the RDE. For all my routine dialysis sessions at Whipton, the hospital organised a Hospital Car Service driver to pick me up and take me home. I was obviously grateful for this but it sometimes meant being in a cramped car with other patients for a long journey. I would wait with trepidation, peering through the window of the front room to see who would be taking me. The journey home was worse, still feeling horrendous from the dialysis. If I had to sit in the back with others, it would not be long before the driver had to stop for me to be sick at the side of the road. This was very embarrassing. Dialysis treatment was still an unknown entity for most of the public and there was little point trying to explain about the treatment I had just endured to all and sundry, even if I had felt able to share it with a car full of strangers.

On one memorable occasion I was picked up from Whipton after my dialysis on a Friday evening by a lovely elderly couple. They quickly engaged with me and took pity on the hardship I was having to endure. When they stopped for petrol at a garage a few miles to the west of Exeter, they came back with a can of Coca Cola for me. For some unfathomable reason, I accepted it and drank it on the way home. This was like drinking poison – Coca Cola was strictly forbidden for anyone with my condition as it was full of sodium and potassium. When I got home the couple met my mum at the door and mentioned that they had bought me a drink. Oh dear! My mum was furious, not necessarily with the couple who thought they were doing their best, but with me. All the good work from the dialysis session had been undone by one can of Coca Cola. After a brief discussion with the hospital, it was decided to wait and see if there were any consequences. My renal diet suddenly became even stricter but, fortunately, there were no major issues and I dialysed again on the Monday.

A few days later, on Friday 10th April, I had dialysed at home and had checked my shunt at 10.30pm before going to sleep. However, when I woke the next morning, I found the shunt was once again clotted and we had to dial 999 again for the ambulance to take me to Exeter. Riding in the back of the ambulance with its blue lights flashing was perhaps the only endearing feature of blocked shunts. Half a century ago, the bypass around Newton Abbot had not been built. Sometimes, particularly during holiday periods, the A380 trunk road from Torquay to Exeter had a few bottlenecks, particularly around Kingskerswell and Newton Abbot. On some occasions, inconsiderate drivers refused to make way for the ambulance, despite blue flashing lights and sirens. The ambulance men would then turn the air 'blue', as they took down the offending car registration numbers to report them to the police. I was by then a regular customer of theirs. When I arrived on Bowring ward, the medical team quickly tried to flush through both ends of the shunt with large quantities of heparinised saline. Eventually, after a lot of pushing and shoving with 20ml and 50ml syringes, large clots were removed from both ends.

They kept me on the ward as I had started to feel unwell. By the next day, I had developed diarrhoea and was vomiting all day and became extremely hypotensive with 60/20mm/Hg blood pressure and a pulse of 90 beats per minute (BPM). The doctor prescribed 1 litre of intravenous saline to try to increase my blood pressure and eventually it settled at 80/30mm/Hg with a steady pulse of 90 BPM. Hypotension had become an additional major problem for me that continued for many months. While at home, between dialysis sessions, it had become severely debilitating; and on standing up from a sitting position, I would often become faint when it dropped further. Once the faintness had gone, I was able to move around the house, but only with grab rails to hold on to.

The tubing being implanted inside my body for shunts at this time was very different from the medical devices that are now used to provide safe, effective, reliable access for the delivery of fluids, drugs and of course dialysis. In fact, intravenous therapy originally evolved in the late Middle Ages when physicians started attempting to transfuse blood between patients. The first recorded example of intravenous therapy took place in 1492, when a doctor caring for Pope Innocent IV in Rome gave him an infusion of blood from three healthy young boys. Their veins were surgically joined to the Pope's veins but unfortunately they all died, almost certainly from blood incompatibility, which wasn't understood then. However, it is Sir Christopher Wren, the famous architect, who is known as the father of intravenous therapy. In 1658, he devised an infusion device, using a pig's bladder and quill, to infuse a cocktail of fluids (including opium) into a dog, who tolerated it well.

In 1843, the famous French physiologist Claude Bernard experimented with infusing sugarcane syrup into dogs. He spent the next 20 years perfecting various solutions and realised the importance of protein in maintaining a healthy diet. However, modern intravenous treatment would not have been possible without the development of needles and syringes. The hollow needle was perfected by Francis Rynd in 1845 in Dublin and shortly afterwards a French doctor, Charles Pravaz, developed the first metal syringe. In 1876, Sidney Ringer developed the first true physiological solution for perfusion, consisting of sodium, potassium chloride and calcium. This is still one of the most widely used infusion solutions in hospitals.

The next major step forward came from the well-known Baxter Travenol Company in 1933, when they marketed the first intravenous solutions in glass vacuum bottles, thereby substantially reducing the risk of microbial growth and bacterial infection. Rubber tubing was initially used to administer the solutions, but by the 1950s this had been replaced by plastic and by the 1970s plastic bags were generally used to store and sterilise the intravenous solutions. This also reduced the risk of an air embolism caused by air venting into the glass bottles.

In the 1950s, intravenous giving-sets still consisted of reusable steel needles with a stylet inside to keep the lumen open. The plastic revolution in medical technology began in 1950 with a landmark discovery by Dr Maasa at the Mayo Clinic, USA. He shortened a 16-gauge Becton Dickinson needle and inserted another steel needle as an inner stylet. Over the top of the needle was a PVC catheter that was shrunk to fit, using ethyl acetate which hardened the plastic. This was the first device that allowed fluid to be delivered into the blood vessel after venepuncture. It was quickly followed by improved versions, made by the pharmaceutical company Deseret, including individually packed. sterilised needle sets. Then, in the early 1960s, plastic syringes and disposable needles were introduced into the American and Western markets by Becton Dickinson and others.

PTFE Teflon medical tubing was introduced in 1969 and dealt with the problem of 'stickiness' of the cannula. The Teflon cannula slides easily over the metal needle and thereby threads it into the vein. Teflon was revolutionary at the time, as it was both self-lubricating and flexible. It began to appear throughout the home, coating kitchenware amongst other things. It was also non-toxic and tissue-compatible, making it ideal for use in medical devices.

Further major developments included the first precision machine-tipped catheter in 1974, which massively improved the comfort of patients who were undergoing venepuncture (puncturing of a vein). Polyurethane was introduced in 1983 as the outer covering of the needle and this reduced trauma to the patient's veins as well as the risk of phlebitis and blood clotting in the catheter lumen. There were more technological advances over the next few years, including greater protection for healthcare workers from needle-stick injuries and exposure to blood products. There are now filters, electronic fusion devices, drop counters and all kinds of alarms. Closed intravenous systems enable drugs and fluids to enter the patient's veins while preventing access for bacteria. Healthcare professionals have control of the system, maximising safety and comfort for all concerned.

In July 1969, I was unable to benefit from most of these major advances. I was, however, fortunate that PTFE-Teflon was used in the Scribner shunt, and this provided a lifeline for me to access dialysis. It seems primitive in comparison to today's array of intravenous catheters and access devices, but at the time it was the only available mechanism that could provide reasonable access.

However, my shunt problems continued throughout April 1970. On Thursday 23rd April, I had to take yet another emergency ambulance trip to Exeter. The venous end was blocked, with a large clot and a decision was made to X-ray the shunt. This revealed marked kinks at the internal tips of the shunt inside my blood vessel. It was rare for the doctors to bother X-raying the shunt – they usually just got down to the job of trying to unblock it as quickly as possible. However, with my access sites running out, they obviously felt they had to do everything possible to save this one. I was kept on the ward as I was due to dialyse the next day, but the shunt was difficult to manage, and the team finally concluded that I needed to have a new one created, on the inside of my right calf.

It took less than a week before my new shunt clotted, on Thursday 30th April. I had been on Bowring ward and using crutches since this shunt had been inserted. I knew that it was critical for it to last, as access sites were becoming more and more of an issue. The clot was removed, and the usual heparin flushed through but this time urokinase was also added to the mixture. It was usually physical pulls and jerks on syringes that worked.

Dialysis and transplantation were still experimental areas of medicine in 1970, and doctors and surgeons needed to 'think outside the box'. How were they going to save my remaining vascular access points? Fortunately, the next day the shunt was still working but I was kept on the ward for a further three weeks as a precaution. On Friday 22nd May, I finally went home after dialysis, nearly a month after I had first been admitted. All this time I was still having to use crutches to protect the shunt in my right leg. It is hard to imagine hospital managers in today's pressurised NHS allowing doctors to keep a patient in a bed just as a precaution. But it was the right decision, as I was in 'the last chance saloon' for vascular access.

Meanwhile, unbeknown to me, on Thursday 28th May, my dad underwent an arteriogram to check the vasculature of his kidneys. Although dialysis was keeping me alive, there were major concerns about the sustainability of this treatment, as I was fast running out of vascular access sites. Peritoneal dialysis was crude and only being used as an emergency, due to the considerable risk of peritonitis. The peritoneal catheters and tubing were incredibly basic and put together with whatever the doctors could find on the shelf at the time. Continuous ambulatory peritoneal dialysis (CAPD) had yet to be developed. The ever-present hypotension and anaemia were limiting my ability to do anything when I was not dialysing and this was having a severe impact on my quality of life.

When I was at home, the day would start with my low-salt, low-protein breakfast, usually consisting of a boiled egg and a slice of crumbly, tasteless, salt-free bread. I would then be left on my own until after lunch. My dad and John were at work, as was my mum, who worked as a housekeeper at the Anstey's Lea Hotel in Wellswood. With the postural hypotension making it difficult to get around the house safely, having fainting episodes even when I could stand up, I was also limited to using crutches to get around. Entertainment was non-existent; there was no daytime television, and commercial radio stations and computer games were still nearly a generation away. My general medical condition made it difficult to concentrate on reading for any length of time, although I was still able to do reasonably simple jigsaw puzzles, something which I still enjoy doing to this day.

Academic work was out of the question. While I had attempted to attend school at the beginning of my illness, all notion of doing this (other than sporadically) went out of the window. The education authorities had organised a taxi to take me to and from Torquay Grammar School; all it needed was a telephone call the day before. Nevertheless, during the entire second year I probably only attended on a handful of occasions, and even then, it was just a morning or afternoon, because I felt ill and either had to return home or go directly to hospital.

An entry in my Lett's Schoolboy's Diary for Monday 3rd November states that it was the first time I had been to school for five months, but the next day I recorded that I felt terribly ill. The only other time I went to school before the end of 1969 was on 8th December, when I went in the morning but had to dialyse at Whipton Hospital in the evening. It was physically extremely demanding being in a school environment. Just walking on crutches along the corridors was exhausting, never mind the problem of climbing crowded staircases. My haemoglobin levels were often as low as 4g/dl, making it impossible to walk more than a few short steps.

The school had a policy of streaming pupils after the first year, when the boys had been assigned to one of three classes based on their location within Torquay. I had already been ill for the final first year exams, but – based on my coursework and perhaps my eleven plus score – I was placed in the top class for the second year. This meant taking Latin O-level, rather than woodwork. I distinctly remember sitting in my new Latin class, being handed my textbook and being completely baffled, having missed all the previous lessons. I just sat there in a daze.

I was also incredibly nervous about accidentally knocking my Scribner shunt. When it was in my arm, I would usually wear a sling with a triangular bandage and when it was in one of my legs, I would be using crutches. However, all schoolboys (even in grammar schools!) push and shove when going in and out of classrooms. It would have been catastrophic, possibly even fatal, if my shunt had been pulled out, causing a massive bleed from the artery. I was fully aware of the medical emergency this would create, and it obviously made me incredibly nervous when I was moving among the other schoolchildren.

The danger of pulling out one of the shunt tubes became a reality on 12th January 1970. I remember the entire episode very distinctly. It was late morning and I had been dialysing in the unit for a couple of hours while sitting in one of the Parker-Knoll chairs. One of the nurses had asked me to help with a stationery project and I was trying to open an envelope using my right arm. I pulled at it – and at the same time pulled the arterial tube out of my arm! Suddenly, blood was spurting everywhere. The dialysis alarm did not go off immediately on the machine and I had to shout to get the attention of a nearby nurse. The shunt was close to the surface, making an easy exit for the blood, and I was bleeding out extremely fast.

The Sister quickly came to help, grabbed the top of my arm and squeezed it hard until a tourniquet could be found and applied. I was swiftly disconnected from the dialysis machine, thereby losing further blood in the Kiil and tubing. An ambulance had been called to take me straight to the RDE for emergency surgery. It seemed to take an eternity for the ambulance to arrive; all the time Sister sat with me, calmly reassuring me that everything would be fine. After the event, she told me that the only thing that had concerned me was ensuring that the ambulance's blue flashing lights and sirens were kept going. That incident, together with having to have the blood transfusion, was dealt with very efficiently, as I was already on the dialysis unit. Thankfully, that was the only time such an incident ever occurred, but it shows how precarious these things could be. Were it to have happened at home or at school, the outcome could have been catastrophic.

When I did manage to get to school, I was also acutely aware that most of the class were relatively unknown to me. It must have been almost as difficult for them, having a new person drop into their midst once in a 'blue moon'. I got the feeling that the school did not really know what to do with me during this time and I don't blame them! I doubt if any discussions had taken place between the school, the doctors and my parents. The school were just trying their best to accommodate me when I appeared, not knowing if I would ever come back.

On a very few occasions, no more than two or three times, we had a visit from the school truancy officers. One afternoon, I recall them knocking on the door at home unannounced and being let in by my mum. I was at home recovering from a dialysis session and feeling rough, with hypotension and all the usual symptoms. They came into the living room and bombarded me with questions. The initial confrontation seemed hostile and my mum was accused of keeping me away from school. They quickly got the sharp side of her northern tongue and soon realised what a dreadful mistake they had made. They were completely ignorant of my medical condition, but – having seen me with my shunt – they did a rapid about-turn and offered their sympathy. Funnily enough, there was never a discussion about the possibility of having a home tutor. I suspect the educational authorities thought I was a lost cause and it was not worth trying.

Around this time, I made an unusual alliance with Reverend Thomas Rose-Price, the Assistant Vicar from St Matthias Church in Wellswood, where I had been a choirboy, who had also been attached to my primary school. He used to come to see me when I was at home and reasonably alert. When we were choirboys, my friends and I had been quite frightened by him. He was very tall and thin and had snow-white hair on top of a rather pointed head. He always wore his black cassock and spoke with a noticeably quiet voice – and his aura enabled him to command the attention of the congregation or a group of rowdy choirboys. During his visits, he would play chess with me. I had never realised that he was an accomplished chess player who had competed in regional championships. This radically changed my opinion of him. I had expected him to be boring and rather dreary, but he was actually quite the opposite. This taught me not to make assumptions about people before getting to know them. He very kindly gave me his travel chess set that he had won in a competition, together with books on how to play the game, and I still have them to this day.

From time to time, the local Salvation Army representative would pick me up on a Sunday afternoon to take me to their 'Young Soldier' church service, but invariably my general fatigue or not being at home limited the number of visits. I had some other visitors during the daytime but none on a regular basis. If I wasn't hospitalised at the weekend, my school friends from the first year would come over to play board games and eat my salt-free toffee! My mum made around 2 pounds of toffee every other day. It was also a favourite with the nurses on the ward and dialysis unit.

During the spring of 1970, discussions must have taken place between my parents, my brothers and the medical team, regarding the possibility of kidney donation. The British Transplant Society Guidelines are now contained in a massive document numbering some 292 pages. But in 1970 there were far fewer guidelines and the whole process was very different. It gradually became apparent that my dad had been selected to donate his kidney. My mum was apparently ruled out because of angina, while my eldest brother, Trevor, was in the Royal Navy and it would presumably have meant an end to his career if he had donated a kidney. I know John always said he would have donated his kidney, but I cannot recall any discussion about that. I was certainly aware that it was critical to get a transplant, and I knew it was a waiting game. At 13 years of age, I was not included in any of the discussions. Maybe it was felt that I was too young to be able to make such a decision; how things have changed.

From the middle of 1970, the need to create new access sites became critical. Without any access it would be impossible for me to dialyse, in which case palliative care would be the only option. Central line catheters were not available until 1979, when Hickman published the first use of a large calibre implantable device used in a bone marrow transplantation trial. For me, it was either a Scribner shunt, rudimentary peritoneal dialysis or palliative care, and I was quickly heading for the final option, having had peritonitis and a major haemorrhage during the last attempt at peritoneal dialysis.

Thankfully, once I had returned to hospital dialysis, although the sessions were longer, they were less demanding on my body, and I finally had a calmer period. With the possibility of a lifesaving transplant from my dad, I desperately wanted to build up my health in readiness for what I knew would be a major operation in a relatively experimental field of medicine and surgery. I would still be far younger than nearly all the other patients receiving either a living relative's kidney or a cadaver kidney. When it came, the operation would take place in uncharted clinical waters.

43

By the summer, plans were being put in place by Dr Hall in Exeter and Dr Evans in Cambridge for me to be transferred to receive a kidney from my dad. Strangely, I have few memories of family discussions about this. I am now aware, reading my hospital notes and correspondence between the two hospitals, that the transfer should have taken place in early September 1970, but the consultant urological surgeon who would remove the kidney from my dad was away. Nevertheless, after a few weeks, I would finally get the 'gift of life' that would give me a fighting chance of survival.

Chapter 4: The Gift of Life

Saturday 26th September 1970 was a momentous day. Early that morning I was transferred from the RDE and admitted to Douglas House Renal Unit, part of Old Addenbrooke's Hospital, Cambridge. My dad had accompanied me in the ambulance to Cambridge; he was giving me his right kidney and the operation was to be performed by Professor Roy Calne (who was later knighted).

Oddly enough, I was not at all apprehensive about going to Cambridge or about what lay ahead. I mainly remember being disappointed that we had to travel by ambulance and not by my beloved train! It would be a little while before I would be able to make the trip by rail. The unit at Douglas House had first opened to patients in February 1966, initially with seven beds, but expanded over the following years to offer individual rooms for patients, each including a private bathroom. According to the nurse's admission notes on 27th September, I settled in quickly and had a good day, making friends with all the nurses and other patients in Douglas House.

The thing that thrilled me most was that the renal diet at Cambridge was less rigid than the one I was used to in Exeter. My mum had sent me to Cambridge with a wholesale pack of Wrigley's chewing gum, one of the only 'sweets' that tasted nice on a renal diet. She also included a large Quality Street tin full of her legendary salt-free toffee. This would usually be demolished by staff and patients within a few hours unless I protected it well. When I dialysed in Exeter, it was a great favourite with the nurses, patients and everyone else. Douglas House deserved nothing less!

Pre-transplant dialysis was planned for Wednesday 30th September at Douglas House. Thankfully, the Scribner shunt in my right leg was working well and I was allowed to eat a normal diet for the first couple of hours of dialysis. At the start of the session, I eagerly devoured a delicious plate of baked beans on toast, a meal I had not tasted since July 1969.

On the evening of Wednesday 30th September, my dad and I were transferred to Old Addenbrooke's Hospital in preparation for our operations. It was nice to spend a little time chatting and we were both feeling incredibly positive about the next day and the future. For me, this major operation was just another boulder I had to clamber over, on my kidney journey. I certainly wasn't afraid. My overwhelming thought was that, if I was to have any chance of surviving the coming months, let alone years, this operation was essential. I had already withstood many operations over the previous 15 months. I was acutely aware that this one was special and carried significant risks, but I had overwhelming faith in my medical team.

My dad and I had no formal counselling beforehand and we dealt with the situation as well as we could, supported by good wishes from fellow patients, relatives and healthcare staff. We didn't delve too deeply into our situation and simply buoyed each other up with positive thoughts about the hoped-for outcome. He was doing this for me, his son, and we both accepted that this was my best chance of survival, but I have no idea what personal fears he might have had. Now, being a parent myself, I know that I would do exactly the same for any of my children.

The operation, on Thursday 1st October, lasted most of the morning. After recovery I returned to the ward at 12.15pm, with Dad's right kidney now placed in my right pelvic area. It was exactly one year to the day that I had had my own kidneys removed in Exeter. For the entire year I had relied on a machine to stay alive. Once it had been plumbed inside me, my new kidney immediately got to work making urine on the operating table and in the first 24 hours produced an amazing 5,500ml!

My operation went ahead with just a simple cross matching of blood groups and a test to ensure that my serum had no antibodies to Human Leuco-cyte Antigens (HLA) that would bind to the outside of the cells of my dad's kidney and kill them.

The next day, Friday 2nd October, it was still going strong, producing 3,000ml. The only complication was that my temperature rose to 99 degrees Fahrenheit and this continued throughout the night. A rise in temperature so soon after my transplant might simply be a response to the major surgery, showing that healing was underway. Or, more worryingly, it could indicate infection or rejection of my new kidney. I slept for long periods that day and the shunt was causing problems with clots and needed continuous monitoring. Late that evening the doctors had to unblock it again using the usual tried and tested methods; and the shunt survived to fight another day.

The next morning, Saturday 3rd October, an ambulance returned me to Douglas House via the hospital X-ray department, where I had a renogram (a procedure which at that time used a radioactive isotope to view the blood vessels). My chest had become congested overnight and, on my arrival at Douglas House, the physiotherapists started work immediately to clear any fluid or sputum. The healthcare team were concerned that I might have developed pneumonia.

After the operation I was 'reverse-barrier nursed'. The objective was to protect me from any infections that could potentially be transmitted by health-care staff or relatives. Before entering my cubicle, staff and visitors had to wash their hands with Hibiscrub, don a surgical gown, facemask and gloves, which made them look like creatures from outer space. The gowns were non-dispos-able so, after use, they were immediately sent to the hospital laundry to be washed and sterilised. What a contrast to the extensive array of disposable personal protection equipment used during the Covid-19 pandemic. The policy post-transplant was for reverse-barrier nursing to continue for ten days, which meant that I could not leave the room except for medical treatments such as dialysis. Nowadays, a transplant recipient might be on an open ward and will often be back home after a week or less.

In October 1970, transplantation was still very much in its pioneering days. With only a handful of units performing these operations, each procedure was almost an experiment in itself. It was still only 7 years since Tom Starzl had presented the first successful results of cadaver kidney transplants using azathioprine together with prednisolone. A conventional, straight up-and-down, surgical laparotomy technique was used to open my abdominal wall, leaving me with a 12-inch-long scar. 'Keyhole surgery' was still a pipe dream.

A Riches drain had been inserted through my abdominal wall to deal with any loss of blood and excess fluid. This had been invented by Sir Eric Riches, recipient of the Military Cross in 1917 and a pioneering urologist who also made an eponymous and revolutionary cystoscope. The drain was a funny contraption – brown-coloured rubber tubing exited the abdominal wall with a rubber bulb at the end. Fluids drained into the bulb, which could be removed and emptied, and then re-attached to the end of the tubing. There seemed to be no concern about sterility of the rubber bulb, although the nurse dealing with it wore a gown and sterile gloves.

The large surgical wound and drains made movement excruciating for the first few days and the nurses tried their best to help me out of bed. To even sit me up in bed, two nurses were needed, each inserting an arm under one of my armpits and pulling me up the bed, while I pushed back on my heels with my bended knees. This technique has since been banned, as it puts a great deal of strain on the nurse's back and the patient's arms. They then placed several pillows around me, to create an 'armchair'.

The metal bed had a grille hinged from the headboard, to ensure that the upper part of the body could be upright. Occasionally, a horizontal metal bar would be attached above the headboard, from which a 'monkey-bar handle' extended, by which a patient could lift themselves up by their arms and upper body. This was my preferred method when it was time to use the metal bedpan! Everything relied on mechanics; there was no electric button to raise or lower different parts of the bed. During the first few days, even small movements requiring the use of my core muscles induced a sharp pain. However, I knew that it was essential to mobilise, despite the pain, to reduce the chance of developing complications such as bed sores or chest infections.

There were no compression stockings to prevent deep vein thrombosis, nor ripple mattresses to keep the blood moving. Prevention of deep vein thrombosis and prevention of foot and pressure ulcers are now at the forefront of nursing care for post-operative patients and those with limited mobility. Even though the importance of such preventative methods wasn't yet understood, the nursing staff in 1970 were acutely aware of the possibility of these post-surgical complications developing, so every few hours they would roll me over on to my side, check for sores and then move me back again. This was not much fun, with all the tubes and the surgical incision, but it was a case of having to grin and bear it; I knew it was doing me good! In between times, I was encouraged to move my lower limbs and wiggle my toes – anything to keep the circulation going.

Even that first afternoon, within hours of returning from surgical theatre, the physiotherapist came along to persuade me to cough and bring up phlegm from my lungs. This was a tortuous task, and the mere sight of the physiotherapist entering my room soon induced great fear and trepidation! My first attempts at coughing were rather pathetic, but with practice and resolve I was finally able to muster productive coughs that pleased the physiotherapist and would hopefully stop me developing chest infections.

The staff insisted on steam inhalations at least twice a day and encouraged me to request even more. The inhaler looked rather like a white teapot with a glass pipe curving out of the top, covered by a tea cosy, containing extremely hot brown liquid, rather like Friar's Balsam. I had to suck in briskly to inhale the vapours (which had a pleasant aromatic smell) with a towel over my head, all the time breathing in the fumes. There is nothing wrong with some old-fashioned remedies; and this one definitely worked.

A few months earlier, my mum had bought herself a red Mini with some of the proceeds from her mother's estate. The car was essential to enable her to visit me in hospital, although she was unable to drive herself. It was down to my brother John to be the chauffeur, as Trevor was still away at sea with the Royal Navy. As with most families, the car was often a source of tension and there were many arguments between my mum and John, as he assumed that the car was rightly his. It was John who had driven my mother up to Cambridge on the day of my operation, but they had to go home on Saturday 3rd October and they last visited me at Douglas House that morning as work in Torquay beckoned. Neither my mum nor John were allowed much time off work and the household bills didn't stop just because I was in hospital. Our family members were all far distant so I was on my own at Douglas House. My dad was still recovering on an adult ward at Old Addenbrooke's Hospital half a mile away, and John and my mum were driving back to the South-West while Trevor was somewhere on the high seas.

On the afternoon of Saturday 3rd October, after my mum and John had left, I was doing as I was told, sitting out in a chair all afternoon drinking, consuming 90ml fluid every hour, and looking forward to scrambled eggs for supper. Things were going to plan, and my urinary output was steady. However, sleep did not come easily that night and the nurse gave me 5mg Mogadon at midnight, a sleeping tablet (nitrazepam), to knock me out. According to the nursing notes, it worked with 'good effect'. These tablets were extensively used in hospitals and nursing homes over this period to help patients sleep. It still seems odd that a 13-year-old would have been prescribed them, though I don't think they had any long-term effects on my health. Their use as sleeping pills was subsequently phased out, when studies showed the addictive power of benzodiazepines.

By 1am on Sunday 4th October, my temperature had once again spiked to 101 degrees Fahrenheit. This time, sputum and blood cultures were taken as a precaution, though my urine output continued to be good, as I had produced over 3,000ml in the previous 24 hours. My condition briefly settled down early the next day and I was up and about within the confines of my room. However, the pyrexia continued, with a temperature of 99 degrees Fahrenheit by teatime and during the night, and drenching sweats throughout the next day.

My notes remind me that I was complaining of 'fullness' and pain over my pelvis. By 8pm, my temperature had increased again to 102 degrees Fahrenheit, and more blood cultures and urine catheter swabs were taken. Paracetamol was used to lower my temperature and Mogadon was prescribed to help me settle. By 6am the next day, my urine output had started to decrease while my temperature had risen further, to 103 degrees, with a racing pulse and respiration rate, a raised blood pressure and vomiting. These clinical signs, taken together, are consistent with sepsis and my condition continued to deteriorate, with a constant temperature of 103 despite taking paracetamol.

The clinicians had decided to perform a renal biopsy on Sunday 4th October to see what was going on in the transplanted kidney. This decision was not taken lightly as the procedure had to be done without ultrasound guidance in 1970 and was therefore quite risky. I was told that complications occurred in approximately 1 in 100 kidney biopsies, which were usually performed with a large, 14-gauge Tru-Cut needle. Fortunately, in my case the biopsy resulted in only a small amount of bleeding.

However, another chest X-ray revealed a left lobar pneumonia for which I was prescribed intravenous antibiotics, in addition to the intravenous fluids and drug cocktail I was already on. My urinary output decreased further and my weight dropped by 4kg, due to the vomiting, diarrhoea and sweating. The team must have been concerned, as the frequency of my routine observations increased to every hour, while the physiotherapists came every two hours to perform chest physio even during the night. It was exhausting, as there was no opportunity to sleep despite the Mogadon tablet. My observations at 6am on Monday 5th October were no better; with continued fever, a racing pulse and a respiratory rate of 46 breaths per minute.

The nursing notes for this day describe me as being 'rather miserable and fed up' and 'wanting a great deal of attention'. The staff understood that I was feeling awful, with either sepsis, rejection, or both, on my own in unfamiliar surroundings, nearly 300 miles from home. My dad was still in another hospital and there were no other relatives around. Looking back, it is quite remarkable that a 13-year-old was left alone in a hospital, considering I had just gone through a very risky, major surgical operation. I liked to think I was mature enough to look after myself, as I appeared to cope with everything that was being thrown at me medically. However, in other ways, I was still just a boy and suffering emotionally.

By 10pm my temperature was 102 and stayed at this level throughout the night. More blood cultures and urine samples were sent for analysis. The night nurses brought in a fan and started to sponge my body with tepid water in an effort to bring down my temperature, which had now reached the dizzy heights of 104. The physiotherapist was also working on my chest intensively during the night to clear my lungs.

Nothing changed throughout Tuesday 6th October. The tepid sponging and intensive physiotherapy continued every couple of hours. My urine output had fallen further and there were now very real worries that, as well as the bronchopneumonia, I was rejecting my dad's kidney. I cannot recall much of this but, based on my medical notes, there is no doubt that my condition had seriously deteriorated. Indeed, it is only now, reading these notes over half a century later, that I realise how close I came to losing the kidney and perhaps even losing my life.

Over the next 24 hours, my condition worsened and my temperature rose to 105 by 11pm. The nurses and physiotherapists continued to make hourly observations and provide regular chest physio. A dry unproductive cough had developed, my pulse rose to over 140 beats per minute, respirations were shallow at 40 breaths per minute, and I was vomiting bile. My newly transplanted kidney had suffered what today would be called an 'acute kidney injury', with reduced urine output, but it may also have been rejection, or both...

There were no biochemical markers then (other than blood urea) for measuring kidney function, which left the doctors in the dark about precisely what was happening with my kidney. Blood creatinine was used later as the gold standard way of measuring renal function, and decades later this was overtaken by estimated glomerular filtration rate (eGFR).

As well as having limited ways of finding out if a kidney was in trouble in 1970, there were very few anti-rejection drugs, other than steroids and azathioprine. In my case, the doctors decided to use high-dose steroids. A course of 200mg intravenous prednisolone was prescribed, in the hope of preventing the rejection process. The steroids reduced my ability to fight the infection, but my clinicians had to use their clinical judgement and experience to make the best decisions for me, as they did for all their patients. They needed to save the kidney, and save my life, and sometimes it was hard to balance the two. It must have been exhilarating when things went well, but heart-wrenching when their methods failed, as my healthcare team had very few tools in their armoury to combat rejection. They must also have provided me with emotional support and comfort, as I had no one else by my bedside. My family were all absent and none of the other patients would have been able to enter my cubicle while I was being barrier nursed.

My condition finally improved by 6am on Friday 9th October, as my temperature had dropped to 99 degrees, with improvements in my pulse and respiration rate. I appeared to be out of danger and my conditioned had stabilised. I was still having considerable volumes of intravenous fluids as well as regular large intravenous doses of prednisolone. They kept an eagle eye on my shunt, monitoring it every half-hour, as they knew they would soon need to use it for emergency dialysis. A 14-hour overnight session started that evening, which I seemed to tolerate reasonably well despite my fragile condition. Fortunately, the vomiting had stopped but my temperature was still 99 degrees and I was still taking intravenous antibiotics (ampicillin and cloxacillin). The intravenous steroids had now been switched to twice-daily doses of 60mg intramuscular prednisolone. This was all part of the anti-rejection regime, which lasted four days.

By Saturday 10th October, I was finally turning the corner and feeling much better, although my temperature remained high. The steam inhalations continued, as well as the two-hourly pounding on my chest by the physiotherapists. While my condition continued to improve over the next two days, the same could not be said for my kidney, which was now producing little urine, 40ml on Sunday 11th and a mere 21ml on Monday 12th. My dad had only just recovered from giving me what should have been a wonderful chance of life – and I was now facing the possibility that it might all have been for nothing. I don't think my dad ever realised that giving me his precious right kidney might end in failure.

The urinary catheter had been in place all this time and had been essential to make careful measurements of urine volume. It was finally removed the next day, after another overnight dialysis session on Tuesday 13th October. Catheters had never bothered me either emotionally or practically (for example, with urine infections). As a 13-year-old boy, the catheter was just one of the many tubes coming out of my body. Today, it is highly unlikely that someone would have a urine catheter for nearly two weeks after an operation, as catheters are linked to a higher risk of urinary tract infection. As I had not passed any urine for 12 months, my bladder now needed 'retraining'. This was not as easy as it sounds and took a lot of concentration and 'mind control' to overcome inhibitions and 'tell' the bladder and the sphincter to open! Having the catheter in place for so long just delayed this recovery.

On Wednesday 14th October, my urine output had fallen to a miserly 13ml in 24 hours, although I was feeling a bit better and was by now taking only oral antibiotics. That evening the shunt in my right leg clotted, but thankfully it was removed using heparinised saline rinses with the syringe. The next day, it clotted again, and – after many brave attempts by the doctors – it finally gave up the ghost. Another dialysis session was planned for 5pm but this could not take place as I no longer had a functioning shunt!

It was now imperative for the doctors to gain new vascular access for dialysis, as my kidney was not working. An emergency operation to insert a new Scribner shunt into my right arm was planned for the next day, Friday 16th October, so I was to be nil-by-mouth from midnight and another general anaesthetic awaited me the next morning. The nurses had given me the usual pre-med, comprising 10mg Valium and atropine at 7.30am. The operation went well and the shunt had good blood flow in both the arterial and venous ends, although there was a haematoma (damaged blood vessel) under the skin where the venous end of the tubing entered my arm. The shunt was used straight away that evening for a 12-hour overnight dialysis session. There was no time to wait for the joining of the Teflon tubes to the artery and veins to heal.

One of the major milestones following a transplant is to be released from the machine, when the kidney finally works and is keeping you alive by itself. Finding that I needed a new shunt seemed like a massive setback, but I had no alternative. Gone was the euphoria of the first few days post-transplant, when I was producing litres of urine; instead, I was back on dialysis, with a new shunt and my kidney producing just a dribble. I was on an emotional and physical rollercoaster, with only the healthcare team and some other patients to support me. Grit, determination and a few prayers were needed. However, despite the setbacks, I had to remain positive, calling on all my inner strength to get me through. I had to cling to my deep conviction that my new kidney was going to work, as it represented my only chance of a long-term future in this world.

Sixteen days after my transplant, on Saturday 17th October, my condition was finally improving. I was feeling well for the first time since the operation and I was up and about in Douglas House. My right arm was still very sore, with the new shunt, and there were some worries about the haematoma. Consequently, I was treated with 6,000 units of heparin every six hours throughout the day as an anti-coagulant. I still had a slight temperature of 99 degrees Fahrenheit, so I had been prescribed gentamicin intramuscularly as well as the other oral antibiotics. The haematoma continued to be a worry the next day, so the heparin treatment was continued. Passing only 147ml urine in the past 24 hours was disappointing, but I tried to be optimistic and see this as a positive sign. I am not sure the doctors and nurses were quite as optimistic as I was.

Because kidney failure treatment was still at an experimental stage in 1970, they would have been familiar with the awful life and death scenarios facing patients, families and carers. But most units never saw teenagers or children. Having a 13-year-old boy in a critical condition, with the possibility that my transplant operation might end in failure, would undoubtedly have caused tremendous grief among all those fighting to save me. At the time of my operation, I was one of the youngest transplant recipients in the UK, if not the world. While the doctors and nurses might have had some private doubts about my long-term prospects, they always took care to give me positive, encouraging messages. I still had complete faith in them and had no doubts about my future. Everything would work out – my kidney just needed time.

After a good night's sleep my temperature was near normal and I was beginning to feel better. This surely meant that my body was finally healing. The only caveat now was that some 'red serous fluid' was leaking from the new shunt, presumably from the underlying haematoma, and it still needed regular dressing. It caused great excitement when my urine output crept up to

280ml in 24 hours, nearly double the amount I'd produced the previous day. The haematoma had improved enough for the heparin therapy to be swapped for warfarin.

The next day, Tuesday 20th October, was another good one, my urine output increasing substantially to 520ml. The blood urea and other biochemical markers were still not good enough to avoid dialysis and I had to endure another overnight session, but thankfully this passed with no problems. The next day my new kidney produced 570ml of urine and during dialysis I lost a further 0.45kg fluid.

Another milestone was reached on Thursday 22nd October. Sixteen days after becoming critically ill and three weeks after my transplant, I finally reached a urine output of 1000ml. The nurses recorded in their notes how delighted I was about this! My early interest in measuring things was now finding an outlet. I had been measuring my urine output obsessively every day, right down to the last ml. But, despite the increased urine volume, the urea was still far too high, at 139mg/dl (23.1mmol/L).

Later that same day, another renogram was performed to check my kidney function following all the insults it had suffered over the past couple of weeks. When I finally got back to Douglas House, I had to have yet another overnight dialysis session. My 24-hour urine output had increased massively, to 1350ml, and I lost an additional 1.6kg fluid while on dialysis. I was now definitely on the mend. The next two days, 25th and 26th October, saw more big increases in urine output.

You cannot imagine how excited I was! My kidney had finally started to work efficiently and I no longer needed dialysis. This was the first time since 21st July 1969 that I would not have to rely on a machine to stay alive. The relief was palpable and the sense of freedom exhilarating. Dialysis had kept me alive for 16 months and I was grateful for that, but it had come with unspeakable difficulties. These were sometimes so great that, at times, it was debatable that I would survive long enough to be able to receive a cadaver kidney. All that was now in the past and I could begin to concentrate on an exciting future and getting back to normality.

Over the following week, I went from strength to strength, with urine outputs in excess of 2,500ml and sometimes as much as 4,400ml. I was by no means the only transplant patient who obsessively measured their urine, as we all knew how important it was to see the output increase following the operation. To an onlooker it might seem bizarre that a group of people could be so fascinated by this topic! It was the policy of the transplant unit that we should drink 500ml on top of the previous day's fluid output, to keep in fluid balance. Once the kidney had 'opened up', it was hard work keeping up with this fluid input; it was only a month since my total daily fluid allowance had been a miserly 500ml and I was not used to drinking so much. The nursing staff made it a big priority to urge me to drink. In the nursing notes, they described how I had become much more alert and was chatting to them and other patients. It really did feel as though I was on the road to full recovery and a normal life.

I was not quite over it all though, nor fully recovered; things were still very delicately balanced. On Tuesday 3rd November, I developed another infection, in the urine this time, and was prescribed Septrin. The infection drained my energies, and I felt very tired. Fortunately, my urine output remained excellent. Despite having a raised temperature, again due to the infection, on Thursday 5th November I was allowed to join several patients and staff from Douglas House to watch the firework display from the Old Addenbrooke's Hospital site. This was after having had another renogram that day to check the kidney's function.

On Saturday 7th November, my urine output was still more than 4,000ml a day, but I had another blip in temperature. Despite this, the nurses and doctors were now planning my discharge from Douglas House and my return to Exeter by Monday 9th November. Still aged only 13, I was in charge of taking my own medication (35mg prednisolone and 75mg azathioprine) each day. During the first few days following the transplant, the prednisolone dose was as high as 65–75 mg, all taken as 2.5mg tablets. This amounted to 25–30 tablets, and it was quite a feat to swallow them all while my fluids were restricted! The dose was usually split, morning and evening.

My urinary tract infection finally went away and by 10th November I no longer needed antibiotics. But I did have another setback the next day, when I developed a deep vein thrombosis in my left leg which was managed conservatively. This was now my only medical issue, apart from looking after the Scribner shunt in my right arm.

Friday 13th November was my last night at Douglas House and I was filled with a mixture of sadness, trepidation and excitement. On the Saturday morning I had my last breakfast in the room that had been my home for almost two months, since my arrival by ambulance on Saturday 26th September, with my dad, who had given me the precious gift of life. I was to be accompanied on my journey home by a British Red Cross ambulance man, going via the renal unit at Exeter, with my dad's kidney finally working successfully. At this stage, I was still unaware that my mum and dad had separated. It was only later, when I got home, that I realised Dad was now living on his own in a single room in Newton Abbot. It was strange to think that we had started our journey to Cambridge together but on departing we had taken separate paths.

I have very fond memories of Douglas House. Looking back through my hospital notes today, I realise how dangerously ill I was for the first six days post-transplant. It was another episode in my life where I had survived alone, despite the odds stacked against me. Being immunosuppressed to counter rejection, I was lucky not to die from the pneumonia. Today, live related transplants are extremely safe for both the recipient and donor. The array of drugs we now have, and the technology for monitoring patients and the transplanted kidney, simply did not exist in 1970. After all, it was a time when intravenous fluids still came in glass bottles!

I had grown accustomed to spending lengthy periods alone since July 1969, including overnight dialysis sessions in Exeter, staying on the ward for weeks at a time following surgery. Being on my own for most of my stay at Douglas House was therefore nothing new. I was a 13-year boy who had been thrown into an adult world because of my illness. In many respects, I enjoyed this adult world, as other patients and the medical staff treated me as an equal, rather than a young teenager. In the last few weeks at Douglas House, I had even been allowed to take walks outside in the grounds and walk into Cambridge city centre.

I had also grown close to the staff and patients in a way that excluded the rest of my family who were hundreds of miles away. I had been dependent on this community not just medically but also emotionally. They had seen me through a critical part of my life when self-belief and inner strength were needed to come through, fight off the infection and overcome the rejection of my kidney. This was followed by the joy of seeing me return to something resembling a normal 13-year-old. These were, and still are, cherished moments that changed my life forever.

Such experiences are unlikely to take place in today's NHS. Patient welfare concerns, particularly for a 13-year-old, would take precedence nowadays. There are of course some risks involved in giving a patient ownership of their condition – a fine line to be drawn between medical staff either neglecting the patient's care or taking it over completely. However, the NHS may have become too 'risk averse', to the detriment of patients with chronic diseases such as kidney failure, who do better if they have ownership of their disease. Indeed, perhaps it is the phrase 'patient welfare' that needs to be redefined. Whatever one may think about these questions, there is no doubt that the healthcare team looked after me and gave me excellent care, even in those difficult, pioneering days of kidney transplantation.

Chapter 5: Return from Cambridge

On the evening of Saturday 14th November, I arrived for observations at Whipton Hospital, from where I was discharged the following Monday. My facial features were now very Cushingoid (as in Cushing's syndrome), with a classic 'moon face', thin legs and stretch marks and bruises all over the skin on my upper arms. All these effects were caused by the exceedingly high doses of prednisolone that I had been taking for so long – I was still on 35mg a day, with a rather small (75mg) daily dose of azathioprine. My daily fluid output was over 4,000ml and the Scribner shunt inserted in Cambridge was still functioning, so a pragmatic decision was made to wait until it clotted before removing it.

I went back to school on Monday 13th December 1970, having had the Scribner shunt removed the previous Thursday. Two notable milestones had been achieved – I had returned to school and I was completely free of medical contraptions related to my previous kidney failure. It was now the end of the first term of my third year (year nine today). The school had sensibly decided that I should not pursue Latin as an academic subject, as I had missed nearly the whole of the second year! However, this meant I had to be put into a lower stream, in a form taking woodwork instead. Separated from most of my old friends, who were in classes taking Latin, and having been away from school for almost 18 months, I found going back extremely difficult. I was constantly reminded of my recent life-and-death experiences in a predominantly adult world. In addition, I didn't know many of the pupils in my class and had to go through the whole process of making new friends. This was not easily done as most of the boys already had their own friendship groups.

Returning to school in January 1971 after the Christmas holidays, my drug regime had not changed. I was still taking extremely large (35mg) daily doses of prednisolone and 75mg azathioprine. Between November 1970 and the beginning of May 1971, I gained 12kg, and went from 55.8 to 68kg. I put on 6kg over the Christmas holidays, without any increase in height, remaining 1.6m tall. I was constantly ravenous and raiding the cupboards for food. This was partly because certain foods had been out of bounds for years, but also because the steroids meant that my appetite was out of control.

On top of this, my protein-starved body was having to make up a lot of muscle mass. For instance, even after having a substantial evening meal, I would sneak into the kitchen and heat up a can of Heinz soup – chicken, tomato, mushroom, any flavour would do – to eat with two or three buttered slices of bread. It's not surprising that my weight increased, with such a high calorie intake driven by the large steroid dose, especially as I was still unable to exercise very much.

By Friday 15th January 1971, I was tipping the scales at 64.4kg and my weight reached 68kg on Tuesday 4th May! Clinical photographs taken of me at this time were used by the doctors to teach students what a classic case of Cushing's syndrome looked like. Many people who had not seen me since before my transplant failed to recognise me. I had turned into a medical curiosity for all the wrong reasons. Within a few months, I had changed from a pale, jaundiced, sickly-looking boy into a 'Billy Bunter' lookalike and I was now facing a completely new set of emotional traumas being a target for bullying with people referring to me as 'the freak' or worse.

I gradually began to readjust to the routine of being in class and managed to get my head around the various subjects. There were some subjects I found interesting, and it was quite easy to get back into those, including history, geography, biology and – to a certain extent – chemistry and physics. But I was all at sea with French. I could make neither head nor tail of the lessons, although I tried my best. I had been reasonably good at French in my first year, but by now there was just too much to catch up on. Certain aspects of maths and English seemed within my grasp, but art never captured my imagination, and I am ashamed to say that I was not always on my best behaviour in these lessons. In retrospect, I was pleased to have been put into the woodwork stream, as I really enjoyed these classes and learning Latin might have been a step too far.

The PE department did not really know what to offer me, as they were concerned that I might be injured if I was knocked in the area around my new kidney. My PE teacher was the same man who had taken me home, and organised an ambulance, when I had lost my vision on a brief return to school in the second year. He was being cautious on my behalf, aware that the doctors had advised me to be extremely careful about getting knocked in the pelvic region. In these early days of life free from dialysis, I had taken all this advice to heart, including avoiding crowded shops or walking along street pavements. I was hyper-aware of people around me and could sense what they were about to do.

There was also the risk of infections from crowds so I tried to avoid getting close to anyone who might have any virus, even a common cold. (Half a century later, we have been given the same warnings during the Covid-19 pandemic.) My doctors had warned me about the risk of acquiring infections while I was severely immunosuppressed, and that some infections might prove difficult to treat. If this were to happen, they explained that the steroids might have to be withdrawn to treat the infection and save my life, but this could lead to rejection of my kidney. Doctors then had very few weapons to combat bacterial, fungal and viral infections, as anti-viral drugs were still many years away from being developed.

My PE teacher kindly put together a modest fitness regime for me to do on my own during Wednesday afternoon classes, as my fitness levels were very low after 18 months at death's door. It was extremely difficult to really achieve anything without guidance, but I would take out some weights in the school gym and do what I could while the teacher looked after the rest of the class. In hindsight, I would have benefitted from having a personal trainer. However, Jane Fonda fitness videos did not arrive until 1982, followed by the BBC *Green Goddess* aerobics breakfast show in 1983, and such role models were absent in the early '70s. I was becoming deeply self-conscious about my new physical appearance, including the gross obesity and 'moon face', the operation scars covering my body, and the hirsutism (excess body hair) caused by the steroids. It was a good job that I had initially been tall for my age, as my ill health and high steroid dose stopped my growth over these 18 months and I remained pre-pubertal, while many of my peers were already having growth spurts and entering puberty.

Over the months leading up to the summer holidays, I remained an outsider and did not really establish any friendships. But, once the holidays arrived, I was able to return to working on the pleasure boats, a job I loved passionately. By then, I had regained some of my fitness and the Cushingoid features had abated somewhat. My ravenous appetite had also been quelled. It's hard to believe that I was still taking 27.5mg prednisolone a year after my transplant. Today it would be unthinkable for a young teenager to receive this enormous dose of steroids for such a long period, but in 1971 the doctors had no clinical trials to call upon. Consequently, they erred on the side of caution.

At my regular outpatient clinic at Exeter, on Tuesday 7th September, Dr Peter Bisson challenged me to go on a weight-reducing diet. He was clearly concerned about my increasing obesity, as I still weighed over 66kg. As well as the physical health risks of being obese, there were also severe psychological effects. I hoped my transplant would return me to a degree of normal life but I would struggle to live happily unless my weight was addressed. I certainly did not want to become a 'freak', to be pilloried by my peer groups.

I had a meeting with the renal dietician, and we went through a diet sheet which I have kept to this day. It was essentially a diet of 1,000 Kcal per day, plus a daily pint of milk to enhance my growth. I started the diet, religiously sticking to all the restrictions. I did not have school meals, although I would have been entitled to free ones, and instead made my own packed lunches. Every day thereafter, and for the foreseeable future, I would eat two Ryvita biscuits made into a sandwich containing Shippam's meat or fish paste with tomato or cucumber, and an apple or banana to finish. Breakfast and evening meals were scaled down, with little carbohydrate. I became a big fan of Marmite, as I could have salt again, and would sometimes have it on toast for my evening meal or as a drink. An evening meal of tinned tomatoes or sardines on toast replaced the family meal. That year I experienced only a few medical issues, but these included headaches which were attributed to stress, as my home life was far from settled. My mum now had a new boyfriend from Glasgow who had moved into the house. He was a seasonal worker and much younger than her.

One effect of my large steroid doses was demonstrated on Friday 24th September, when I was admitted to Bowring Ward with an infected right index fingernail. It had appeared completely out of the blue, with no previous injury to the finger, although I was being plagued at the time by hard red lumps in front of my ears which, on reflection, were obviously infected areas of skin. My GP had prescribed ampicillin three times a day, earlier in the week, but the finger had worsened.

Dr Bisson decided the nail needed to be removed urgently and put in a local anaesthetic nerve block. He then yanked the nail off with forceps while I looked in the other direction! It was all done very quickly and efficiently. The pus under the nail was able to drain and, when cultured, showed a *Staphylococcus Aureus* bacterial infection that was resistant to ampicillin. The treatment was quickly changed to 150mg clindamycin (Dalacin) three times a day. They found me a bed on Bowring Ward overnight, and a hospital car took me home the next morning. This is the sort of procedure that would almost certainly be carried out as a day case today, even in an immunosuppressed child, as it is now recognised that a hospital can be a major source of infection and perhaps not the highly sanitised environment it was years ago.

The infection with *Staphylococcus Aureus* was not surprising, given the exceptionally large doses of prednisolone I was still taking. A couple of weeks later, on Saturday 9th October, I was again admitted to Bowring Ward at 11pm with an inflamed area on my abdominal wall to add to my inflamed right index finger. The areas on my abdomen had hardened, suggesting that pus was collecting at these sites. My right ear was swollen again with a possible abscess, and I was prescribed clindamycin and ampicillin, and the swabs came back showing an ampicillin-resistant Staphylococcus Aureus. Hexachloride was used to bathe the areas every day, which meant I had to stay on the ward until Wednesday 14th October, when I was discharged home. However, I was back in again the next day with worsening symptoms, including pus oozing from my index finger. Other than the infection sites, there were few signs of sepsis, as I had a normal pulse and temperature.

However, over the next few days, the infection refused to go away and by Sunday 18th October Dr Bisson realised that there was underlying osteomyelitis in the finger. He sought a surgical opinion and the next day Mr Mike Golby, a surgeon interested in transplantation and newly arrived in Exeter, carried out an exploration of my finger under Valium sedation and local anaesthetic. It seemed that the end of the finger needed to be amputated to remove the infected bone, an operation which was carried out the following day under another general anaesthetic. Following the operation, the nurses bathed my finger in Eusol every 30 minutes. It felt like plunging my finger in bleach! It seemed to do the trick, though, as all the abscess sites cleared up over the next week and I was allowed home. Once again, the swabs from the excised bone showed infection with Staphylococcus Aureus.

This stay in Bowring was to be my last on the children's ward. I was now 14 and, having spent a considerable proportion of the previous two years in an adult environment (including being on my own in Cambridge while receiving my dad's transplanted kidney), an open children's ward did not seem appropriate. Instead, I was given a large cubicle on the ward – partly, I suspect, to ensure that I did not succumb to any more infections and partly for my privacy. It still had all the Disney characters painted on the glass windows but the cot was exchanged for a conventional hospital bed.

The cubicle was quite different from the one I had been familiar with during my previous stays. Most importantly, from my point of view, I was able to use my old transistor radio to listen to Radio Luxembourg in the evenings! Radio Luxembourg was the first commercial 'pop' radio station, originally formed in 1933, and it broadcast in English on '208 long wave' from 7pm every evening. Many who later became household names as disc jockeys on Pirate and BBC radio stations started here, including Kenny Everett, Noel Edmonds and Kid Jensen. While on Bowring Ward, I listened to Radio Luxembourg excerpts from the newly released *Jesus Christ Superstar* album, written by Andrew Lloyd-Webber and Tim Rice. The music completely overawed me. I remember struggling to make sure that the radio was tuned in properly so that I did not miss any of the excerpts. A copy of the LP went on to my Christmas list. It was not cheap at the time and would be my main present.

Meanwhile, my finger recovered and has never troubled me since. It is still not uncommon for patients on steroids to develop spontaneous unexplained episodes of sepsis with abscesses. With no substantive clinical trials to guide the appropriate effective doses of immunosuppression, everything had to be trial and error, steered by a clinical sixth sense.

That year I attended the Addenbrooke's Kidney Patients' Christmas Party, held at the beginning of December. My dad, who I had hardly seen during the past year, wanted to join me at the party. Despite protestations from my mum, he travelled up by car while I went on the train. Dad had organised bed and breakfast for both of us in a pub in Trumpington, as the party was going to be held in the Occupational Health Department at New Addenbrooke's Hospital. My train fare was paid for by the hospital's Social Work Department, by way of a travel voucher. They managed to do this by cleverly co-ordinating a 'hospital check-up' on the Sunday morning at Douglas House!

Dad and I spent Saturday afternoon helping to organise the evening buffet and drinks. He was working at the Cider Bar, Newton Abbot, at that time and had brought barrels of cider with him. Sister Sally Taber had asked him to take charge of making the punch and running the bar. He was in his element, with his larger-than-life character. He made a fabulous punch and ran the bar like a professional. This was the first time that we were able to enjoy each other's company without me being seriously ill. I had obviously matured enormously since we had spent time together in October 1970, when he had given me his kidney, and we were now able to have something resembling a proper father-son relationship. I was proud that he was doing such a great job at the party but this was the one and only time that he came up and stayed for the weekend. Nevertheless, at subsequent Christmas parties, several people, including Sister Sally Taber, would fondly talk about the punch he'd made. Sadly, following this weekend, we gradually started to lose contact.

Christmas came and Trevor had shore leave from the Royal Navy. We all enjoyed a fantastic Christmas dinner, the first time we'd been together for a long time, and I was delighted to receive a copy of the *Jesus Christ Superstar* LP as a Christmas present, which John immediately commandeered! John was very keen to attend the Sunday Boxing Day fox hunt near Widecombe on Dartmoor. Many of his friends, who also knew Trevor well, were meeting at a Dartmoor pub. John was still using Mum's red Mini, registration 55 COP, a number that I will always remember. Five of us packed into the Mini, including my mum's Glaswegian boyfriend, setting off late morning, with my mum in the front passenger seat and me immediately behind her. The weather was overcast, after rain earlier in the day. I was quite excited to be going out as a family, as it was something we had not done for many years; and at 14, I was underage for the pub! The banter flowed as we sped through Newton Abbot on to the A382 Newton Road.

John was a great motor racing enthusiast and felt entitled to drive at speed as we were passing through Bovey Tracy out towards Dartmoor. The road straightened, he put his foot down and the car sped forward at an alarming rate. As we went over a brow in the road, the car suddenly lost traction and weaved a little before apparently rolling over a few times and coming to rest, upright and still on the road. I must have blacked out, as I still cannot remember the car rolling. When I came to, I was alone in my original place at the rear left side of the car, but everyone else had gone. The front and rear windscreen and windows were broken, and the roof was very buckled. Outside a crowd of people were milling around, including police, fire and ambulance crews. My legs were trapped by the front passenger seat, and I was unable to move.

After what seemed like an age, an ambulance man and policeman came to speak to me through the open front passenger area. The front door had become detached. They checked to see if I was all right and told me to stay put until they could get me out. I was dazed but not in any pain and waited patiently for what seemed like 10 to 15 minutes. Eventually, an ambulance man and fireman together removed the front passenger seat. They asked me to move my legs and come out from my seat and at that point I let out an enormous scream; my right femur was obviously broken. They told me to take a deep breath while they got their arms under my legs and manoeuvred me out of the car. The pain was excruciating, and I blacked out again.

There was no pain relief on offer, and no airbag splints to immobilise the limb. In 1971, emergency services personnel were given less scope than today's paramedics to carry out first aid. I was taken on my own to Torbay Hospital by ambulance; my brothers, my mum and her boyfriend had all been taken separately from the crash site. As I have no recollection of the journey to hospital, or of being admitted or taken to the operating theatre, I suspect I remained unconscious due to the trauma and pain.

I presume I was given sedatives and pain relief once I got to the hospital but I have no idea who signed the consent form for my surgery later that evening. My first memory of being in Torbay Hospital was waking up the next day, on Monday 27th December 1971, and finding myself on an open, adult, male orthopaedic ward, with various weights and pulleys attaching my leg to the end of the bed. The first few days were very confusing. Trevor had gone back to sea and John was working. Nobody from the medical or nursing teams came to explain what had happened to me or where my family was, and I had no idea why this strange contraption was attached to my right leg. Someone, I don't recall who, did tell me that I could not see my mum, who was apparently on another ward suffering from concussion and bruising to her face and body. After a couple of days, the nurse from Mum's ward brought her in a wheelchair to see me. It was an emotional reunion, and I was still confused about my own situation. Mum was able to go home a couple days later, but not me.

One afternoon soon after that, the awful reality was brought home to me. I asked a staff nurse when I could go home and she replied very acidly that I would be in traction for at least 12 weeks, followed by many weeks in a plaster cast. She then just walked off, leaving me utterly distraught and tearful. No one had told me; I had thought that I would be home in a week or so at most. Her manner and tone were horrible, as if she were enjoying rubbing salt into my wounds. All I wanted was to be alone so that I could cry, but that was impossible on an open male ward. Instead, I pulled the bed sheet up and quietly sobbed into the linen. This was the only time I can recall being emotionally traumatised by the actions of a healthcare worker. She had managed to shatter my outer shell of resilience and pierce the soft core of my inner emotions, something that no one had previously done despite all the life-and-death experiences I had already gone through. It was a cruel lesson and I vowed I would never let it happen again, even though I was still only 14. I can still recall this nurse's unfeeling behaviour as if it were yesterday. Words have consequences and no patient ever deserves such treatment.

It was a massive shock to discover that I would be tied to a hospital bed for the next three months, and the next week was extremely hard, both physically and emotionally, with little pain relief on offer. Fortunately, as open male orthopaedic wards can be very noisy during the night, I was prescribed Mogadon. Moving around the bed was extremely difficult, though I did have the infamous monkey bar to lift myself up, and, with the help of a nurse on each side of the bed, move on to the pillows. The traction system consisted of a nail inserted through the distal end of my right femur. Cords tied to each end of the nail were directed through pulleys at the end of my bed, which were on iron poles at height, while weights pulled the cords down to floor level. It was quite a simple idea – by pulling the end of the leg using weights, the ends of the fractured bones could be kept apart, allowing the bones to heal correctly. However, it also meant that I was totally reliant on the nursing staff to take care of my basic bodily functions, including washing and toilet requirements. This was new to me as, even after the nephrectomy and my transplant, I had been able to take charge of these matters myself.

Gradually, I adjusted to the routine of the ward. There was little to do during the day, other than engage in banter with my fellow patients, who were mostly young men ten years or more older than me. My school, although aware of my being in hospital, provided no schoolwork and the hospital had no one able to provide lessons. Thankfully, my mum and family friends, such as Margaret Potter, brought me some books and puzzles. The fact that I'd had a transplant appeared to have little impact on the way I was treated on the ward. As time went on, I became immersed in my fellow patients' banter, much of which was of a rather adult nature! The other patients were all of sound mind and otherwise fit, simply waiting for bones to heal. Dr Bisson visited once to check on how I was doing. I have no idea how often anyone at Torbay checked my renal function and it is certainly something that I cannot ever recall being discussed. Dr Bisson kindly brought me a hardback copy of The Hobbit, which I did not read until some years later, when I belatedly realised that it was a literary masterpiece.

Finally, ten days after spending yet another birthday in hospital, I was wheeled down (on my bed) for an X-ray to ensure that the bones had knitted together. Then it was off to the orthopaedic technician who dismantled the traction, removed the nail, and fitted my plaster hip spica cast. The cast extended from underneath my armpit all the way around my trunk, rather like a waistcoat, with an additional appendage going all the way down my right leg to my ankle. It took ages to construct, and I had to keep my right leg perfectly still while rolls and rolls of plaster of Paris bandage were wrapped around. It felt extremely heavy! And I was told I had to stay in it for another six weeks.

Before the cast was applied, I saw my right leg for the first time in three months, as it had been wrapped in crepe bandages and a light back-slab cast, within a metal cage to hold it in place. The physiotherapist showed me how to walk with my wooden crutches, and then I was allowed to go home by ambulance. This was the first time I had been home since Boxing Day the previous year. The house was little changed, and my dog Chum was pleased to see me. Pete the Glaswegian was still living with my mum, and John was now engaged to be married to Judith, although their relationship was rather rocky.

I was pleased to be home but it was difficult to readjust to family life, with all the different relationships it entailed. I had also changed significantly during those months in Torbay Hospital. Being exposed to the goings-on in the adult male ward, combined with my own awakening adolescent sexuality, had made me realise that I was rather naïve when it came to understanding physical relationships. School sex education at this time was still all about 'the birds and the bees'. Meanwhile, the banter among my fellow patients, particularly as they were allowed to drink beer, would sometimes get quite bawdy (often involving references to the nurses), but all the sexual innuendoes went right over my head!

On reflection, I'm astonished by the decisions that were made in relation to my care at Torbay Hospital. Unfortunately, the hospital policy was to destroy medical records long before I started writing this book, so I have no medical notes to check. However, it is telling that my notes from Exeter contain no copies of any medical letters from Torbay. Why was a decision made to put me in traction, and then in a hip spica, for a total of nearly five months? In those early days of kidney transplantation, my life expectancy would have been more or less unknown. My transplant was barely 15 months old, so committing an almost 15-year-old patient to five more months in hospital, apparently with little or no discussion with the renal team, seems extraordinary. I certainly had no input into the decision. Looking back, it was paternalistic doctoring of the worst kind that raised many ethical questions. It was also very strange that I was kept on an open male ward.

The six weeks in the hip spica were incredibly difficult and demanding. At the beginning, I needed both crutches to move around the house, but gradually, as I became fitter, I regained my balance and could eventually manage with a single crutch while holding on to the furniture. Balance was an important issue, as I had been in bed for so long and was very wobbly. My left leg had also become considerably weaker. The days were very boring. My mum was still working as a housekeeper at the Anstey's Lea Hotel and John was at work at Renwick's Garage, so I was left to my own devices.

I would get up after everyone had left the house and get myself down for breakfast. There was no daytime television to watch and only BBC radio to listen to. I still had no schoolwork to do, so the days were spent reading any interesting book I could find on the shelves. I did become competent at playing Patience, one of the few card games you can play on your own. Electronic games (including even the most basic 'Pac-Man' and 'Dig-dug') were still ten or more years away.

It was impossible to go outside in public with the hip spica, as the cast was too big to be covered by ordinary trousers, this being a generation away from when people could routinely wear tracksuit bottoms and even then I would have needed XXXL! My waist size was probably at least 50 inches, including the plaster cast! Baggy pyjamas were the order of the day for modesty. I became increasingly adept at moving around the house and finally dispensed with the crutches. While my physical well-being was clearly improving and my fracture was well on the way to being fully healed, the same could not be said for my mental and emotional health. I was becoming increasingly depressed, trapped inside alone with very little human contact. There was no one to discuss my feelings with, and I was just expected to get on with it.

My desperation is illustrated by an incident that I can still recall very clearly. As a keen railway fan, I had taken out a yearly subscription to the monthly

Railway Magazine, and I always waited eagerly for each new edition to drop through the letterbox. I would read it avidly from cover to cover over the following days. On this day, I was alone at home as usual when the postman delivered the May 1972 edition. For some reason, opening the magazine package sparked a furious response within me. I began to scream and became more and more agitated and 'out of control'. I tore the magazine into shreds with my hands and burst into tears. The crying continued for a considerable period. It was as if all the pent-up anger and frustration of the past weeks and months (perhaps even years) had erupted in this sudden outburst.

Later, when I had calmed down, I was embarrassed about my actions, particularly as I had destroyed my favourite magazine. There were articles and photographs of railway engines that I really wanted to see and read about. When my mum came home, I showed her the ripped-up magazine and tried to explain my feelings, but I was told not to be so stupid and to grow up. I don't think my mum had a great deal of what we would now call 'emotional intelligence'. Her support was essential but mainly confined to practical matters. I desperately wanted someone to buy me a replacement copy, but that was a futile wish, given the response I received – that it was ultimately my own fault. In response to this episode, I buckled down and decided to keep my worries to myself. This was the only time I had given way to my emotions and, having tried to discuss it with my mum, I was certainly not going to let my defences down again. There would be no more 'cries for help'. Everything would be kept under wraps and discussions about my health and wellbeing would be kept to a minimum.

Looking back, I think this incident shows how my relationship with my mum and brothers had changed. After my transplant in October 1970, I had spent a long time alone in Cambridge, as a 13-year-old in an adult environment, and this had sowed the seeds of our later estrangement. The car accident and everything that followed had served to reinforce these profound changes. Unfortunately, unlike my previous hospitalisations, I had no support from doctors and nurses. I was now back at home but running on separate emotional tracks from my family and increasingly distant from them when it came to my deepest feelings. On a more positive note, being 'emotionally independent' probably helped me develop the resilience to deal with chronic kidney disease.

I suspect no one wanted to discuss my emotions because such discussions would inevitably lead to unanswerable questions, such as: 'How long is the kidney going to last?'; 'Do you think I will still be alive in one, two or five years' time?'; 'Will I need to go back on dialysis?' and 'Will I ever be accepted as a normal person?'. When I was alone, these and many other questions would soon surface in my mind but they were quickly returned to my deepest thoughts as I knew they were topics that were not to be dwelled upon. In 1971, psychology was barely an academic subject and 'talking therapy' had yet to be invented. There was no psychologist or counsellor to help me unravel my deep-seated anxieties. I simply had to deal with my fears alone, which usually meant putting thoughts into black boxes that were not to be opened, until many decades later when I decided to write this book.

Eventually, towards the end of May 1972, the ambulance came and took me back to Torbay Hospital to have the hip spica cut off. It all went well and, following an X-ray, I was allowed to come home by hospital car. I was now free of my cast, although I still needed to use crutches as I was struggling to bend my knee. I was incredibly elated when I was able to walk again, using only crutches. The muscles in the right leg obviously needed strengthening, particularly those in the thigh, to compensate for the wasting over the months, though I had been doing basic conditioning exercises on my right ankle and lower leg while in my cast. A tremendous amount of rehabilitation would be required. I needed to regain confidence in walking, as well as muscle strength. I also needed to re-educate my muscles and brain to improve my balance and prevent me falling over. Because of my extensive time off and, as I was going to be reliant on crutches for a little bit longer, it was decided that I should stay at home until the beginning of my fourth year Autumn term. In any case, the end of term was only four to six weeks away and was usually dedicated to the end of year exams.

My physical rehabilitation started with simply aiming to walk again without falling over. This wasn't easy after spending months in traction and then plaster. The back of our house had a private lane where I could do my exercises. The hospital was unable to offer much support, apart from physiotherapists explaining how to walk with crutches and the basic stretch and extend exercises. Perhaps additional support would have been available if I had been able to go to outpatients at the hospital, but this would have been difficult to organise. Consequently, I had to use my ingenuity and resilience to work out how best to get my balance and strength back.

Once I had overcome my fear of falling over without crutches, by taking small steps and using my hands to balance against the wall, it was time to take the next step – starting to jog (a word not yet in use in 1972) and subsequently run. It might sound bizarre but, having not run for so long, I had a real mental block about it. A toddler naturally goes from walking to running and, if they fall over, they simply get up again; but teenagers and adults are aware of the danger of falling over. Similarly, toddlers can learn to ski very easily but adults usually find it daunting. One of my fears, after finally starting to run a few steps, was that I might fall forwards. My legs didn't seem to be coordinated with the rest of my body and appeared to race ahead. In the privacy of our back lane, I was able to take my first few steps, acutely aware of how embarrassing it would be if someone saw me staggering around as if I were drunk! Every morning, when I was alone in the house, I challenged myself to take an increasing number of steps. Gradually, my confidence returned, and I was finally able to run the 120 yards to the end of the lane and back. Now it was time to get back into the saddle on the bike Mum and Dad had bought me in 1970! This seemed easier, so perhaps it's true that one never forgets how to ride a bike.

By the middle of July 1972, my fitness and confidence had returned, and I was able to enjoy a few days working on the boats at Redgate Beach. This gave me immense pleasure. It immediately took me back to my old life when I was just a normal boy with two healthy kidneys of my own. Home life had become increasingly difficult, as my mum's previous boyfriend had moved out, only to be replaced by occasional dates. As money was short, Mum had supplemented her wages by offering lodgings to two (or sometimes three) seasonal male workers in the spare bedrooms while I had been in hospital. These chaps invariably worked in hotels and other tourist outlets. They had frequent parties, which often woke me up at night. On at least one occasion I went downstairs to ask my mum to turn down the music, but my request fell on deaf ears amid all the revelry. The invasion of my home by these lodgers caused me a lot of stress.

Trevor was now at sea on the Polaris nuclear submarines and spent little time at home, while John was usually out enjoying his own social life. This left me feeling very alone and desperately angry about the lodgers who seemed to be exploiting my mum's hospitality. The lodgers were only meant to use their allocated bedrooms, but things started to go missing from the kitchen and elsewhere. It all came to a head one morning after Mum had gone to work and I was alone with two lodgers, who were then joined by two of their male friends. I came downstairs to find them making long-distance calls using our home telephone, which was strictly forbidden. In 1972 the cost of morning long-distance calls was extortionate and our family had to be extremely careful about using the telephone because of the cost. The lodger swore at me when I asked him to stop so I cut off the dial tone, thereby ending the call. I was greeted with a 'Glasgow kiss', drawing blood from my head, which led to me dialling '999'.

The men all made themselves scarce long before the police arrived, and my mum came home. Later that day, John oversaw them moving out with their belongings. The one who had assaulted me later received a conviction for GBH. I don't know what came over me when I decided to confront him, but it had a positive effect as my mum took in no more lodgers for a considerable time, and when she did, the new lodger was a middle-aged woman. Looking back, I think I was angry that my mum was being abused both financially and emotionally and I decided to be the 'man of the house' and protect the family as well as my own privacy.

On Tuesday 16th May 1972, the hospital car took me to my first renal outpatient clinic appointment since the tip of my right index finger had been amputated. The letter from my Consultant to the GP mentions the problems I was having at home and raises the question of whether they should be contacting the social workers. When I attended clinic on 30th August 1972, these family issues were again documented in my medical notes.

The good news was that my weight had fallen considerably, to 52kg, and my 'moon face' had long gone, as well as the unwelcome hirsutism. To everyone's delight, I had also grown slightly in height, suggesting that I might now be entering a growth spurt. The prednisolone dose had been reduced to 20mg per day, though that was still a relatively high dose. During the late summer, my mum had become engaged to her new boyfriend Alan, who had now moved in. He was a nice person, though he was only in his early twenties. At the same time, Judith (previously John's fiancée) had become engaged to Trevor. All this was again recorded in my medical notes, as my doctors were clearly concerned about the impact of all these domestic changes on my wellbeing. Over the next few clinic appointments in Exeter, the issues surrounding my home life were noted by Dr Hall and Dr Bisson and included in the clinic letters that were sent back to my GP, Dr Imrie.

I'm sure all the events around the time of the car accident did have profound effects on my emotional wellbeing. However, I have since realised that they also helped prepare me to cope with my chronic condition. My mum was also dealing with her own emotional turmoil. She had a child who had nearly died several times and was now healthy, but only because he had received a kidney from her estranged husband. It was not surprising that she should seek affection and relationships to distract her from this nightmarish situation.

None of this has never been discussed. However, I remember that there were strenuous attempts to prevent me having any contact with my dad. Birthday and Christmas cards that arrived were all hidden. On the rare occasions when he rang home to find out how I was getting on, there was invariably a torrent of abuse from Mum usually regarding his non-payment of maintenance money for me. It is certainly true that he failed to pay the Court the maintenance money and this left my mum having to scrimp and save to pay the household bills.

On the other hand, I am now aware (having read my medical notes) that my dad offered to pay the costs for a trip to Addenbrooke's in late spring 1972 so that I could see Professor Calne and Dr Evans for a review following my fracture and spend a week or so at Cambridge. Sadly, my mum intervened and told the Exeter social workers to refuse any financial help from my dad, and that she would borrow the money from her employers if necessary. Like many children of separated parents, I fell victim to their sparring and the result was that I never made the trip to Cambridge. Eventually, my dad moved away from the area altogether, although he maintained contact with my brothers, who kept this secret from my mum. I am sure these issues will resonate with those caught up as children in the strong emotional currents surrounding marital break-ups. My situation was even more complicated because I had been given a life-saving organ transplant by my dad, which acted as a constant unwelcome reminder to all concerned.

Summer came and I was disappointed to find that my hoped-for work on the beach had been given to 'a friend of Mr Wheaton's family' even though I had been promised that my job was safe. Instead, I worked as first mate on the pleasure boat *Nomad*, owned by the Wheatons, which was used as a ferry service from the harbour to Redgate Beach, as well as for trips around Babbacombe Bay and Torbay.

Working on *Nomad* meant getting down to Torquay Harbour by 8 am every day. The skipper (a friendly ex-trawlerman in his forties) was a big chap who would often get me to row the two of us from the D-Day landing slipways on the east side of the outer harbour to her mooring by The Princess Theatre. There I had the job of cleaning all the previous night's seagull mess off her beautifully varnished and painted elm and teak decks. Sometimes we would come alongside the fuel quay for diesel before embarking on the 60-minute trip along the northern coast to Redgate Beach. On the trips my job was to tell our passengers all about the sights we were passing. This would sometimes bring tips but, often, just a thank you. I really enjoyed working on the *Nomad* and this was my first experience of being in a reasonable size boat. There were many times when we left Redgate Beach with a freshening wind blowing from southerly quarters; and it would be a rough trip back to the safety of the harbour. But *Nomad* was incredibly seaworthy and more than up to the task.

In September 1972, I returned to the fifth form (the equivalent of year eleven), ready to take up my studies again, after another break of nearly nine months. This was the second year of the O-level course. I buckled down and worked hard to make up time. It was easy to re-engage with some subjects, such as history and geography, which had a rigid O-level syllabus that had to be studied over the two years. There was no need to know any detail about the 'Tudors and Stuarts' if the syllabus was European History from 1840 to 1939, as mine was. This was also true, but to a lesser extent, for biology, chemistry and physics, which had distinct syllabuses, although some prior knowledge would have been helpful as there was some overlap between contents. But in English and mathematics it was a struggle to understand the lessons if you did not have a firm grasp of the fundamentals. English grammar sometimes left me dumbfounded. At times, it really seemed like a foreign language when I was trying to get to grips with verbs, adverbs, pronouns and nouns and adjectives.

Fortunately, my mathematics teacher willingly gave me tuition when I asked for extra homework to help me understand topics such as algebra, which had been covered the previous year. This really helped me to keep up with the lessons. My school reports for the Autumn Term, including the end of term exam, showed that I had made progress and was quickly attaining a level where I was likely to succeed at the following summer's examinations.

By now, I had decided that I wanted to work in the NHS and had started talking to the dialysis technicians at the renal unit as well as other medical staff. My history teacher at the time made the very thoughtful suggestion that I should go into teaching, particularly because of my medical history. He thought this would be something at which I would excel, and the working conditions would be helpful if I became ill again in later life. Meanwhile, a 'careers officer' who visited the school suggested I should be a carpenter; without meaning any disrespect to carpenters, this was his way of saying that I was unemployable! I ignored his advice but do still enjoy woodwork.

Christmas and New Year 1972 came and went. My passion for model railways and trainspotting was being rekindled and my small group of friends were all fellow trainspotters. We would spend our pocket money going to Exeter St David's and other railway stations in South Devon on a Saturday to collect numbers. Of course, I had been unable to develop this passion fully since I had developed kidney failure just before that longed-for school trip to the London terminuses.

During half term and other holidays, we would buy seven-day Rail Rover tickets, which allowed unlimited travel from Penzance to Bristol. Later, we became more adventurous and made trips as far as York, Crewe, Swindon and Derby. This was a time when British Rail had 'Open Days' for their maintenance engine sheds for anyone to come and enjoy. Society was less obsessed with risk and litigation and British Rail were happy to allow masses of people, many of them teenagers, to wander around the engine sheds and rummage in locomotive cabs. British Rail also ran occasional Saturday 'Mystery Tours' as well as special excursions to places like Blackpool.

Some trips turned out to be very eventful, and the trip to Blackpool was a case in point. Four of us caught the early-departure special excursion train from Torquay, which made only a couple of additional stops before travelling directly to Blackpool. As required by British Railways byelaws, we had letters from our parents giving us permission to travel such a distance. As minors, we needed these letters when travelling overnight on a train. We arrived at Blackpool and were delighted to see masses of new train numbers in the station, which at the time accommodated more than 20 excursion trains at any one time.

Next, we headed for the Pleasure Beach to eat our packed lunches, which were stashed in our duffel bags with flasks of coffee, although by the evening we were starving and needed extra fish and chips. Our return train was due to leave just after midnight, arriving back at Torquay at 6 or 7 in the morning, hence the need for the letter. We checked our watches around 10.30pm and decided we had just enough time to make one more ride before heading back to the station, which was a good hike from the Pleasure Beach. For some reason, our group had split up and the next thing I knew it was way after midnight and I was left with only one of my friends. The other two were nowhere to be found.

We made a dash for the station, only to find that our train had departed long before. We were both worried about our missing friends, but also desperate to get back to Torquay. We asked a station master how we could get home. We had little money and he told us that our tickets were no longer valid. Finally, he took pity on us and put us on an excursion train which was leaving for London, Euston; it was now getting on for 2am. He told us to make our way from Euston to Paddington and try to get a train home. The Euston train was packed and,

70

knowing our tickets were invalid, we spent the entire journey hiding, locked in the toilets. We arrived at Euston just as day was breaking, very tired, cold, hungry, and numb from sitting on a toilet seat for hours. We headed for the Underground and had just enough money to catch the tube to Paddington and grab some drinks and food.

At Paddington, we managed to persuade the barrier and platform staff to let us board the next train home, which was leaving quite soon. This was a time when very few trains travelled down to the Southwest on a Sunday, and fortunately there was space for us on one of them. The guard on the train was rather grumpy that we didn't have valid tickets but was persuaded by our story and allowed us to stay on board. We kept our heads down, feeling grateful. By Sunday mid-afternoon, we were back at Torquay Station. My travelling companion's younger brother had come with us to Blackpool, but he had caught the correct train home. He and our other friend had explained to their parents that we had missed the train and they were no doubt concerned for our safety. However, once we had phoned home from the station (we had not done this before because we were scared we might run out of money), our parents came to pick us up and take us home, where we could tell our story with all its embellishments. The ending was a happy one but could so easily have been completely different. Even during this epic adventure, I always made sure I took my medication on time and had plenty of supplies.

From November 1972 and into the following year, my kidney function remained stable. This meant that my prednisolone dose could be reduced in stages, from 20mg per day on 30th May, to only 5mg per day by 1st August 1973. This reduction was accompanied by a growth spurt amounting to more than 4cm over six months. There were also some signs that I was developing secondary sexual characteristics. Since my transplant, my doctors had worried about whether I would ever go through puberty with its accompanying growth spurt. There was little in the scientific literature to refer to, and very few people of my age had ever received a kidney transplant.

I was lucky to have inherited 'genes for tallness', and I was probably in the top 5 to 10 percent in my age group for height, being over 5 foot tall when I first went to Torquay Grammar School. The high-dose steroids had clearly affected me and delayed the start of puberty – and the reduced steroid dose was accompanied by my move through the stages of puberty. Everyone breathed a sigh of relief, myself included! As a teenager, the thought that I might never go through puberty and would be stuck as a pre-pubertal boy was a real anxiety. From my medical notes, it seems that my doctors also had concerns about this. I was quite simply a medical experiment, and no one knew what the outcome would be.

After Christmas 1972, I was finally able to lead a relatively normal teenage life. My train-spotting friends used to invite me to Friday night discos run by a local church, close to the Grammar School. These were extremely exciting! Although the disco was supposed to be alcohol-free, we found ways of obtaining Woodpecker cider, and other such drinks, to have before going to the event. I can recall having my first taste of illicit alcohol, all of us crouched among the gravestones in the cemetery. Inside the disco, we stood around watching the girls, feeling too embarrassed to ask any of them to dance.

Although my 'moon face' had almost disappeared, I was still very self-conscious about my body, as my numerous operation scars were very visible on my legs, arms and abdomen. They always drew a lot of attention, and I was conscious of people staring at me, particularly when I was working on the pleasure boats. Sometimes they would ask about the long, vertical, somewhat livid, scar running down my abdomen. I would usually reply with an off-the-cuff remark about having been 'in the wars'. I knew I was different from everyone else because I had been through near-death experiences and had received the 'gift of life' but I simply did not want to talk about my previous medical history. How could such matters possibly be discussed with people who did not know me? My small group of friends from school, I assumed, just accepted me as a mate. My past, present and future medical experiences were strictly off-limits, and this was a strategy I would use throughout my career.

Returning to school in the fifth form also brought back the problem of being a target for bullying on the way home. My journey back from school was around one and a half miles, most of it down a very steep hill. Riding a bike was out of the question because of this hill, but I was able to catch a bus. As I became fitter, I started to walk instead. This was fine, except for the last part of the journey which was close to Homelands Technical College. Here, groups of their pupils often stood around on street corners and I tried my best to avoid them. Sometimes they would catch up with me and call me vile names including 'the freak'. On one memorable occasion, a group of boys managed to push me to the ground and subjected me to 'a good kicking'. Once they had dispersed, I managed to get home just after my mum had returned from work. Both my shins were badly grazed, with deep cuts, and I had numerous bruises on the rest of my body. I was terribly upset, mainly because I had been subjected to this unprovoked attack simply because I was different, alone and an easy target. I went to the GP to get my injuries dressed although I should have probably gone to the emergency department at the hospital for the cuts on my shins to be stitched.

My mum contacted my school and spoke to the PE teacher, who happened to be the same one who had taken me home in the second year when I had gone blind. He was incensed when he heard what had happened. The next day there was some heated discussion between the headmasters of the two schools. I'm not sure if the boys who attacked me were ever identified, but it certainly caused a furore. My school offered to provide a taxi to avoid any possible repeat attacks, but I turned down this kind offer; I had to deal with this in my own way. The injuries to my shins took many weeks to heal. Following a check-up at Exeter, I was given vast amounts of dressing and Eusol to use daily to prevent infection. Painful though it was, this experience proved invaluable for the rest of my life, as it taught me how to deal with injustice and bullies.

I can only recall one incident of bullying in my own school. I had continued to have packed lunches and the school allowed those not having school dinners to eat their food in the form classroom. On one occasion I was sitting at the back of the room, minding my own business, when a very tall boy at the front started calling me horrendous names. There were probably a dozen or so other boys in the room, and there was total silence except for the poison coming out of the bully's mouth. He was revelling in being the 'ringmaster'. Some of the boys left the room, clearly embarrassed by the bullying, while others became party to the verbal assault. The name-calling revolved around me being a freak, with horrible comments about my physical appearance. Eventually, after many minutes of trying to ignore him, I picked up a nearby wooden chair and threw it at him. It was a direct hit, and the chair broke in several places. Amid a stunned silence, I gathered my belongings and walked out of the room. Afterwards I found a quiet spot, where I waited for the adrenaline rush to subside, and one or two of the boys came and made sure I was all right. The bully never bothered me again. He was supposedly a good tennis player and went to Millfield School on a sports scholarship, at the same time as the highly acclaimed player Sue Barker. He was never heard of again.

Meanwhile, Mr Wheaton had sold his business on Meadfoot Beach. The new owner, who lived close to us and had bought all the motorboats, pedaloes and floats, asked if I would like to be his foreman for the following season. I was thrilled and immediately said yes. The motorboats were wooden and needed painting, and the Stuart Turner two-stroke petrol engines needed overhauling. They were all stored in his garden and shed. He paid me to do the painting and showed me how to strip down the engines and rebuild them. I really enjoyed going down to his house to work on the boats, and working on Meadfoot Beach that summer was another glorious time.

By May 1973, it was time to think about sitting my O-level examinations. I had no real experience of taking exams, having missed so many at the end of each year. I certainly didn't know how to make revision plans and timetables or how to use my classroom notes to prepare. On reflection, I was very laid back. I had bought numerous revision books from WH Smith's and these were often presented in the form of key fact cards. Of course, what I should have done was create my own 'key fact cards' using my notes and the school textbooks. I also did not appreciate how much time I needed to devote to revision. I was still confident I would achieve reasonable success with the eight O-level subjects I was taking with the University of Oxford Local Examinations Board, having done reasonably well in the last set of mock exams.

Around the third week of August, the postman brought my results. I had passed only three subjects – geography, mathematics and biology – and I was extremely disappointed. I even bought a copy of the *Herald Express* to check the result, as I couldn't understand why I had performed so poorly. I was terribly embarrassed and dreaded telling my family. Mum just told me I had done my best, while John (in true older brother style) poked fun at me and called me a dunce.

Once I had calmed down a bit, and recovered from the disappointment, I decided to enjoy the rest of the summer working on the pleasure boats and return to Grammar School for the Sixth Form in September. I hoped there would be a way of retaking my O-levels while also starting my A-levels. Many of my friends were going off to find a job, as was common in the 1970s, but I was sure I could do better academically, and I was determined to try.

Chapter 6: Chronic rejection

September 1973 heralded my return to Grammar School to start the Lower Sixth. My teachers were extremely helpful when I discussed my disastrous O-level results with them and together we decided that in November I should re-sit those that I had failed. This would mean revising for them as well as starting the A-levels syllabus in physics, chemistry and biology. My teachers' advice was to focus on passing the O-levels first, rather than worrying too much about the first few months of the A-level syllabus.

By the time I was due to re-sit my exams in November, I had started to feel unwell again – mainly headaches and tiredness. These symptoms started gradually but they had escalated over a couple of months, so the doctors decided to admit me to Whipton Hospital on Wednesday 12th November 1973 to assess my kidney function. My blood results seemed fine, except for the creatinine level which had risen to 162μmol/l. (Creatinine had now replaced urea as the preferred measurement of kidney function. Values above 150μmol/l are above the normal range). At the time, my immunosuppressive regime was 5mg prednisolone (enteric coated) twice daily and 100mg azathioprine. The doses had only just been increased the previous week. I now weighed around 54kg, and was about 5 foot 3 inches tall, with a normal blood pressure of 110/70 mm/Hg. Other than the slightly raised serum creatinine level, there was nothing to suggest that anything was untoward with my kidney, so they discharged me on the Friday.

The symptoms of tiredness, dizziness and being generally under the weather persisted over Christmas and New Year. The Addenbrooke's Kidney Patients' Association (AKPA) Christmas party was an unmissable event, so I had attended that the week before. As with the previous parties, the senior renal social worker at Addenbrooke's had organised my rail fare from home to Cambridge. A lovely young couple from Trumpington, dentists with two young children, were 'Friends of Addenbrooke's' and offered me their spare bedroom for the weekend. They picked me up from Cambridge railway station on the Friday.

On Saturday I had a day to myself, and I spent it wandering around the shops and Cambridge market before the party in the evening. On Sunday, the blood tests and a check-up at the hospital were duly carried out and I left for Torquay early on Monday morning. As my regular care was not in Cambridge, these parties were a great chance to meet up with old friends and staff members I hadn't seen for a year. They were a celebration of the success of transplants in restoring a good quality of life to renal patients and offered a glimmer of hope for those awaiting a transplant. These parties continued for many more years, moving from the Occupational Health Department at New Addenbrooke's Hospital to Hills Road Sixth Form College to accommodate the increasing numbers of attendees. In subsequent years it also became a time to remember those patients who had sadly succumbed to kidney disease despite their transplants, as well as those receiving other organ transplants, such as livers, at Cambridge.

On Thursday 6th December, I had to attend the ENT Department at the RDE to have my hearing tested as I had been experiencing partial deafness for a few months. Mum and others would have said I was selectively deaf whenever there were jobs to be done around the house or the dog needed to be taken for a walk! However, I really did feel that my hearing was becoming impaired. The audiologist tested me and confirmed a slight loss of function in my right ear, which the ENT Consultant put down to gentamycin toxicity from treatment of previous infections in the early days after my transplant. This was followed by another renal outpatient appointment on Tuesday 18th December, where I discovered that my creatinine had risen to 210µmol/l and there was now a significant amount of protein leaking into my urine (protein-uria), a total of 4.5g in 24 hours. My blood pressure was also higher, and I now had borderline hypertension. This news was a very unwelcome Christmas present. The hospital sent me home with a mercury sphygmomanometer to monitor my own blood pressure and keep a diary. My haematological results were still normal, but these worrying signs indicated either chronic rejection of my dad's kidney or possibly a recurrence of my original disease.

At this stage, for reasons best known to themselves, the doctors decided not to disclose to me the full extent of my renal function decline; the first time I knew of any problem was when I started looking at my hospital notes while preparing to write this book. By late 1973, I very much wanted to be involved in my own medical care; I was what we would now describe as an 'activated patient', but there remained considerable mystery and a degree of paternalism surrounding the doctor-patient relationship in those days. I had already read numerous books on kidney disease, its biochemistry and pharmacology, some of which I had bought myself, while borrowing others from the school or town libraries. At the age of 16, I had spent the previous three years trying to live a normal life, always believing that my transplant would last a long time, particularly as it had come from my dad. The possibility of rejection was not something I wanted to confront at that point. Maybe my doctors were, in fact, well advised not to share every detail with me. I was pretty engaged with the medical and healthcare team during my out-patient visits, but outside the hospital environment I just wanted to be like other teenagers.

On Friday 15th February 1974, I was readmitted to Whipton Hospital with worsening dizziness and headaches. My blood pressure was now undoubtedly raised, at 150/100mm/Hg, and I was started on propranolol 40mg three times a day. Although propranolol (Inderal) had been discovered by Nobel Prize-winner Sir James Black in the 1960s for use in angina, it was rarely used regularly for hypertension until the early 1970s. There were no large clinical trials upon which doctors could base their prescribing judgement and certainly no National Institute for Health and Care Excellence (NICE) guidelines. Everything was done with the help of the British National Formulary, an invaluable encyclopaedia of medicines that can be prescribed by an NHS medical practitioner.

Persantin (dyprimadole), 25mg three times a day, was added to my regime. This drug was usually used to prevent blood clots after surgery and heart valve replacement, but in the 1970s there was a suggestion that it might be effective in preventing rejection. The hypothesis was that blood vessel damage in the kidney might be part of the rejection process, so the risk of rejecting might be reduced by Persantin. Apart from the dizziness and headaches, I remained relatively well.

However, over the next few weeks, my hypertension and renal function both worsened. In 1974 there were very few anti-hypertensive drugs available to treat raised blood pressure. Angiotensin converting enzyme (ACE) inhibitors, and subsequently their receptor blockers (ARB), would not be available for at least another 15 years. The doctors had already prescribed propranolol and frusemide, a diuretic. Other drugs were added, including hydralazine as my blood pressure became increasing malignant. My weight had also increased to 65.3kg.

This was my first long hospital stay since I had fractured my femur on Boxing Day 1971, and my first at Whipton Hospital – apart from the brief spell in November 1973. The unit had relocated so that it was within the hospital site and had also expanded since it had first opened in 1969. It now included several cubicles for in-patients as well as a separate haemodialysis unit. This time, I was given my own cubicle with washing facilities and a black and white TV – I was now addicted to the ITV programme, General Hospital, as well as the BBC1 programme Pebble Mill at One. My days were taken up with having blood pressure and other clinical readings taken and – from time to time – blood samples to check renal function. I had no schoolwork to do as I had just passed the chemistry O-level at the re-sit, although physics and English language continued to elude me. As my blood pressure control worsened, with systolic readings above 220mm/Hg and diastolic over 170mm/Hg, I became increasingly uncomfortable, with throbbing headaches, despite taking painkillers such as dihydrocodeine. Lying down became difficult, due to the intense, pounding in my head.

I well remember a young man in his late twenties from Bridgewater, Somerset in one of the cubicles near mine who had received his new kidney a few weeks before. We became good friends and kept each other company, sharing stories of life on dialysis, transplantation and hospitalisation in general. One of the funniest stories he told me involved the staff nurse who had admitted him for his transplant. As she was sorting out his personal belongings, a partly used box of Durex fell on the floor! It caused great laughter that, as a dialysis patient, he still had the urge and the means. He had also managed to persuade the doctors to prescribe a bottle of Mackeson Stout to be given at the evening drug round, supposedly to build up his strength following the operation. I decided I was also in need of this 'medication', which was duly prescribed, with additional bottles of stout being made available from time to time. I doubt that this would happen in today's NHS. There was also the small matter of prescribing alcohol to a minor; I was about to celebrate my seventeenth birthday in style on the ward.

During this admission, the Bissons regularly invited me to their big, modern house at the weekends. It was in Pennsylvania, a smart northern suburb of Exeter, and they were building a new swimming pool in the garden. Some of the groundwork had been carried out, but pairs of hands were needed to dig out the hole for the pool. The weather was settled that year and we had hot sunshine and blue skies even in March and early April.

These trips were an escape from the monotony of the ward, and I was also treated to some excellent home cooking and in a funny way felt part of their family. Their two children, who were a few years younger than me, also joined in the digging parties. Dr Bisson would pick me up in his car from the ward in the morning and return me late in the afternoon. Although I was genuinely helping them dig out the hole for the swimming pool, it was still incredibly generous for him to take me to his home. It reflected the close relationship that I had formed with him, and other members of the healthcare team. The doctors, nurses and patients were all part of a remarkably close-knit family and, even though I was by far the youngest, I was accepted just like any other adult. There was no doubt in my mind that we were all on a pioneering journey, pushing back the boundaries of medical knowledge. The trajectory of my kidney journey, which had started on 7th July 1969, had not changed. It had simply plateaued for a short time and I still had a reasonable quality of life.

Despite the welcome respite of weekend trips to the Bissons', the routine of being hospitalised and becoming increasingly hypertensive became more and more wearing. I had too much time to ruminate on what the future might bring. I still assumed that my dad's kidney would recover, and I believed each of these episodes were just small boulders in my path. This was yet another experience of being away from home and being treated like an adult, making all my own decisions and fending for myself. In many respects I was living in a rather unreal world, far from home and school, contemplating an uncertain future. The million-dollar questions ('What if my kidney rejects?' 'Will I ever get another kidney?') were always at the back of my mind but quickly shut out. In any case, the severe headaches caused by the hypertension would have made it extremely difficult to concentrate on academic work.

Towards the middle of April 1974, after I'd spent about ten weeks by myself in Exeter, my doctors realised that the anti-hypertensive treatment was not working, and they decided to transfer me back to Cambridge. This came as a relief, not because I doubted the quality of the care I was getting in Exeter, but because I knew Cambridge was an international centre for transplantation and the best there was to offer in the UK. It was a remarkably astute decision by Dr Peter Bisson to let me go and a generous offer by Dr David Evans to accept me. The letters they wrote each other, included in my notes, show their close professional relationship and the fact that they always had my best interests at heart. In today's NHS, with its focus on cross-charges between Trusts and other rigmarole, I wonder if such collaboration would be possible.

On Wednesday 24th April, I was taken by ambulance to Exeter St David's railway station for the start of another long journey back to Cambridge. This time, I was allowed to travel alone on the train (unlike previous occasions). I was looking forward to the trip from Exeter to Cambridge, a journey I had already undertaken on my own on previous trips to the annual Transplant Patients' Christmas parties.

The hospital at Exeter had arranged my whole journey, including an ambulance to meet me at London Paddington, the London terminal for West Country trains, to take me to King's Cross Station and ensure that I was safely on the train to Cambridge. Another ambulance crew met me at Cambridge Station and took me to New Addenbrooke's Hospital on the Hills Road site, as it was known in 1974. At the time, the hospital was situated on the south edge of the City of Cambridge; to the north was Cambridge with its numerous new housing estates, while to the west there were still arable fields right up to the hospital boundary.

I knew from the previous Christmas parties that the renal unit itself had moved from Douglas House to the new premises, although the dialysis unit remained there. The renal and transplant unit was now on Ward C9 at the top of a purpose-built hospital with numerous wards on all the floors. Even at the time, I remember noticing how different the atmosphere felt in the new building compared to my previous stay in Douglas House in the autumn of 1970.

The evening meal was waiting on the ward when I arrived, after which I was clerked in by the junior doctor and nursing team. According to the admission notes, I was taking a 'considerable' number of anti-hypertensive drugs, including bethanidine 50mg, methyldopa 200mg, hydralazine 25mg, propranolol 80mg, all four times daily, as well as prednisolone 15mg and azathioprine 100mg once a day. Clonidine had also been tried, but that had recently been stopped. My blood pressure on admission was sky-high, at 180/140mm/Hg with a pulse of 84 beats per minute.

I was now experiencing many hypertension symptoms, including feeling faint on standing up, a ringing in my ears (tinnitus) associated with a popping sensation, and severe, inexorable, pulsating headaches. There was also a strange numb sensation over my transplant site. These feelings were extremely disturbing. Sometimes it felt as if a blood vessel were about to burst – not so much a pain as a dreadful pounding sensation, making it difficult to put my head on the pillow to sleep. A stethoscope placed over my carotid artery detected a bruit, suggesting significant turbulence within the blood vessel;

and the inner surfaces and blood vessels in my eyes were also showing signs of damage from the persistent high blood pressure.

It was strange being on an open ward for the first time since the 12 weeks I'd spent in traction in Torbay Hospital. In this newly constructed ward, everything was very modern, including my bed (with hydraulic movement) and my own bedside locker! As usual, I was by far the youngest patient on the male side of the ward. Interestingly, I was still referred to as 'a school child' in the nursing records, which seems a little strange now, considering the vast amount of time I had spent in the presence of adults and how little time I had spent at school.

By the next day, Thursday 25th April, a treatment plan had been put in place, including numerous laboratory investigations and cross-matching of blood, ready for a kidney biopsy on Sunday morning, 28th April. The medical team did not involve me in formulating this plan, though they described it to me and I was allowed to ask questions. However, this was a monumental moment in my kidney journey, as it was the first time that I had personally signed my own consent form for the biopsy procedure. I am sure consent was overlooked numerous times when I was first treated for kidney failure in 1969. At that time, it came way down the list of priorities for all concerned. For me, taking responsibility for my own surgery was a big step forward and another move into the adult world, even if I was still officially considered a 'school child'!

The biopsy was performed by my Consultant, nephrologist Dr David Evans, with me lying supine on my bed in the ward. In 1974, a renal biopsy was still a high-risk procedure, done 'blind', using the 14-gauge Tru-Cut needle. Complications could be mild (such as developing haematuria) or severe, with severe haemorrhage into the kidney, blood loss or death of the patient. Ultrasound and other imaging techniques were not available to assist the doctor, as they are today. Success was purely down to the skill and clinical judgement of the operator. There was also the problem of ensuring that the biopsy needle, which was rather like a 'potato gun', was on target, hitting the part of the kidney where the suspected problem lay. There needed to be enough glomeruli and other parts of the kidney to give a true representation for the histologist to examine. Fortunately, there were no complications following my biopsy, but I had to spend the next 24 hours in bed to ensure my complete recovery.

A fellow patient in the next bed to me, who had recently received a transplant, was not so lucky. A routine ten-day post-transplant biopsy of his new kidney was performed on him in the late afternoon; and that evening he was lying on his bed, waiting for his meal. Suddenly he shouted out for a nurse, and I pressed the emergency button for him. By the time the nurses arrived, he was distressed. The curtains were drawn, the junior doctors ran in, and he was rushed off for emergency surgery. This all happened in the space of five to ten minutes. He returned later in the evening, having had his newly functioning transplant kidney removed. The entire ward, including patients, nurses and doctors, were in shock at these events but it was 'the luck of the draw'. He was incredibly positive about the situation and, while clearly upset about losing his kidney, was determined to move forward, and start looking forward to another transplant. Today, a renal biopsy (when done under ultrasound guidance) is a very safe procedure, with a complication rate of around 1 in every 1,000 (0.1 percent).

The results of my kidney biopsy came back the next day, Monday 29th April. Initially, they were inconclusive, but the full report on Friday 3rd May showed severe changes in all nine glomeruli present in the biopsy. There was no thrombosis or necrosis in the glomeruli and the tubules were all well preserved. The pathologist raised concerns that the changes might be a recurrence of my original disease and wanted to compare this kidney biopsy with the one from my native kidneys, removed at Exeter in 1969.

Fortunately, he was able to obtain unstained sections from Exeter to make a comparison, which confirmed that the changes in my transplanted kidney were due to chronic rejection, with added changes caused by malignant hypertension, and not a recurrence of my original disease. I don't remember ever being given this information at the time, and I had always assumed it was rejection. At the time my original diagnosis was haemolytic uraemic syndrome (HUS), which sometimes recurs in a newly transplanted kidney, this was exceptionally good news. It also confirms the subsequent misdiagnosis of my condition in later years. Today, there are immunomodulating factors that could be given in similar circumstances, to try to prevent the disease recurring.

Over the next few days, I continued to have severe headaches and related symptoms of malignant hypertension. Distalgesic was prescribed, a now defunct combination drug comprising paracetamol and dextropropoxyphene. In 2007, the MHRA withdrew the licence for all drugs containing dextropropoxyphene. My drug regime was modified from time to time, with certain drugs being removed when they were clearly ineffective, while diazoxide 50mg four times daily was added. Diazoxide is a diuretic as well as an anti-hypoglycaemic agent. In 1974, it was a relatively new drug and its mode of action as a diuretic was poorly understood. Again, there were no clinical trials to guide the doctors on its use. In later years it was no longer licensed for treatment of hypertension, although it is still used to control hypoglycaemia in surgically untreatable insulinomas (cancer of the insulin producing cells of the pancreas). While taking this drug, my blood and urine had to be monitored for excess glucose. The latter I did myself in the ward sluice, using dipsticks.

By Tuesday 7th May, I had the results of a nephrogram and arteriogram, which had been performed a couple of days previously. A nephrogram is a radiographic image of the kidney parenchyma (the functional tissue of the kidney) and is used to evaluate structural abnormalities. In 1974, radioactive Iodine-131 Hippuran was used to provide an image. This technique has now been replaced by CT and other scans. The arteriogram is still used today to examine the kidney blood vessels, particularly in patients with hypertension possibly caused by kidney disease or vasculitis. My arteriogram showed good major vessel blood supply, and I had a reasonable nephrogram. It was thought there might be damage to minor blood vessels in my kidney due to chronic rejection, although they still seemed uncertain as to whether this might indicate the return of the original disease. This could not be confirmed until later, when they received the histology results from my original kidneys.

A pattern emerged – reasonable blood pressure control for a couple of days, before it soared again. Reserpine 0.25mg twice daily was added to my drug cocktail on Friday 9th May. The doctors made me run up and down stairs to check the effectiveness of propranolol. Propranolol is a ß-blocker which is supposed to slow the pulse. In my case, my pulse went up from 72 to 120 beats per minute and consequently the dose had to be increased to 160mg four times daily. This is the maximum dose permitted under today's guidelines, although there are several long acting ß-blockers available. The head of my bed had to be raised in the hope that it would help control my blood pressure and give me a more comfortable night. My blood pressure stabilised for another couple of days, before becoming malignant again, even with increasing doses of drugs. Spironolactone was substituted for reserpine, which helped for a short time.

Despite all this, the healthcare team encouraged me to get out and about. I was drawn towards the railway and would often walk on a public path that went in a south-westerly direction from the south side of the hospital towards the London King's Cross to Cambridge railway line. The hospital superstructure, including the incinerator chimney, was a familiar site looking east out of the train carriage window, something a train enthusiast would notice. As it was late spring, the field to the south was full of wheat, which looked beautiful in the Cambridgeshire sunshine. Today, the hospital site spreads further out towards the railway line and this lovely view has been lost.

During this stay I had become close friends with another patient, a man in a bed near mine. He invited me to spend the weekend with his family who lived in a village close to Kettering and had a daughter who was a similar age to me. I was extremely excited to be allowed out for the weekend. We left in the family car on another sunny Saturday morning, me with an overnight bag rattling with bottles of anti-hypertensive drugs! His house was just over 60 miles away and the family lived in a recently built semi-detached house.

My friend had been dialysing at home in a Portakabin using a Kiil dialyser. He would dialyse three times a week overnight for ten hours in this outside portable building. His wife would help him get attached to the machine and then sit with him for a while before returning to the house to their daughter who, at the start of his illness, would have been on her own as a young teenager. This presented a difficult dilemma for his wife. For all patients enduring home dialysis at the time, there was often considerable stress on family relationships.

The daughter confided in me later that she had mixed feelings seeing her father shut up in the mobile unit overnight, away from the family, and both her parents having to deal with taking apart and sterilising the Kiil once the session had ended. On top of that, there were all the emergencies to deal with. On the other hand, the dialysis machine could also bring families together, as it was a lifeline ensuring that life could go on even if it was severely restricted. Our conversation made me realise that socialising could also be exceedingly difficult as a teenage child of a parent dialysing for long periods of time at home. It affected all members of a family.

Once we arrived at the house, I was shown to my bedroom for the night and it was time to take some of my many tablets! I still remember the lovely lunch his wife prepared for us, especially the delicious home-grown new potatoes, lathered with low-salt butter. We spent the rest of the day and next morning talking about all manner of subjects although our main topic was dealing with life with chronic kidney disease. My friend was hoping to receive a successful kidney transplant, while I was in the throes of dealing with Dad's gift of life that was now failing. This was, and still is, a very poignant memory – the generosity they showed when taking me into their family home for the night.

In these pioneering days of the late sixties and early seventies, the difficulties of chronic kidney disease, dialysis and transplantation created intense bonds between patients and their families. Everyone was aware that transplant patients were living on borrowed time, but this was never articulated. Instead, most remained stoic and kept hoping for a healthy future. For some, this might mean dialysing at home but for most it was the hope of getting a new kidney that spurred them on. The fear of death was ever present. Indeed, it was with great sadness that I received a letter from my friend's daughter a couple of weeks after I returned home from Cambridge that summer. I had written to her and her father when I got back to Torquay, thanking them for their generosity. In her letter, she told me that her father had become extremely ill with pneumonia and septicaemia. After becoming paralysed in his legs and arms through the infection, he had sadly died. Once she and her mother had got over the initial grief, they thought it was in fact a 'happy release', considering the immense suffering he had undergone.

While I was at Addenbrooke's, I was sometimes able to take the bus into Cambridge and spend a few hours wandering around colleges and the city centre, where I became fascinated by the enormous number of bookshops. This was my first opportunity to really appreciate Cambridge as a centre of culture and learning. I spent time just browsing and occasionally purchasing second-hand books, especially building up my collection of *Doctor Doolittle* Penguin classics.

Sally Taber was the Sister in Charge of C9 and quickly realised that she needed to keep me occupied – as I was so far from home, with no likelihood of any visitors – for her sake as well as mine! The entrance to the ward by the lifts had a table tennis table, to be used by patients, relatives and staff, and I would continually badger people to come and play table tennis with me. Although my blood pressure was still exceedingly high, there were times when it was controlled enough, and I would be on the lookout for able-bodied people to partner me. I would particularly pester sister Sally Taber to play. From time to time, she obliged, but more often would delegate the task to an unsuspecting nurse or even one of the housemen (junior doctors). Consequently, I became close friends with some of the doctors and nursing staff.

They were all kind to me. Even though I was only 17, I had spent so much time in adult company that I was happy to form relationships with members of my medical and nursing team, who were often a decade older than me. I obviously already had close relationships with the staff at Exeter, who had seen me grow up from the age of 12 to 17, surviving against all the odds. With a few exceptions there was a degree of protectiveness, as you might expect. As well as providing medical and nursing care, they had also had to support me emotionally. These relationships had changed substantially during my lengthy admission at the beginning of 1974 and with the arrival of new staff. The relationships I formed in Cambridge were also different, even in 1970, when I had my first transplant.

For instance, there was a newly appointed Staff Nurse who had just arrived from Lancashire, with whom I quickly formed a bond. She was also away from home and finding her feet in a new hospital. In 1974, like many hospitals throughout the country, Addenbrooke's had its own School of Nursing and the nurses lived and studied on the hospital site. New Addenbrooke's hospital had recently built accommodation blocks for the student and qualified nurses as well as junior doctors. Close to the accommodation blocks, there was also a new 25-metre indoor swimming pool and other sports facilities in The Frank Lee Centre. During the day I was able to go swimming in the pool with the Staff Nurse, with the blessing of the ward hierarchy. After swimming and at other times we would go to her self-contained flat in Barton House, one of the accommodation blocks, where we would have a coffee together and chat about life and the future. This was all very innocent, and I was grateful for the camaraderie. These were incredibly special times, away from the 'clinical sterility' of the ward, and the friendship continued for a number of years. Today, her flat houses one of the hospital administrative offices but the Frank Lee Centre is thriving and still providing a welcome resource for staff and patients.

My trips as a patient to the swimming pool and socialising with a female Staff Nurse in her hospital flat would break so many of today's rules and regulations. Yet this friendship provided me with the support I needed to deal with being alone away from home with a transplanted kidney that I knew in my heart was failing. I will always be grateful for the deep friendship, and the emotional and psychological support she provided to get me through these difficult times. Today, I suppose similar support might come from a counsellor, but in 1974 the nurses *were* the counsellors. She gave me an emotional outlet and our conversations enabled me to off-load many of the issues I had confronted over the previous years. Our relationship was based on mutual respect. I do not believe for one minute that she 'pitied me', and this was borne out by the letters we sent each other in subsequent years. Furthermore, she enabled me to engage in normal activities, such as swimming and socialising with another young person, albeit a nurse four or five years older than me.

It would not be long before all this would change for the worse and I had to enjoy every moment before I hit the slippery slope towards end-stage kidney failure that I knew was fast approaching.

There were special times with other members of staff too. Sister Sally Taber would take me out in her Triumph Stag open-top sports car, including trips to the Cambridge University Farm, where Professor Calne was undertaking research into transplantation using pigs. It was a real privilege to be able to accompany Sally on these trips. They fed my unquenchable curiosity and she was subjected to non-stop questioning about every aspect of kidney disease and its treatment.

On one memorable occasion, I went with Sally in her car and met other staff, patients and their relatives at a Sunday evening live television programme. We were part of the audience in a live question-and-answer debate on the ethics of kidney transplantation. The panel consisted of a Franciscan Friar in his plain brown habit, a former nursing sister from the hospital, and other religious figures. I still vividly remember the debate, which centred on whether it was ethical to remove kidneys from a body while the heart was still beating. The opponents, particularly the friar, argued very strongly that the heart formed part of the soul and it was a sin to carry out organ donation.

At the time, the kidneys were not removed until brain stem death had been established by senior doctors. The concept of brain death had first been proposed at Harvard Medical School in 1968. However, in subsequent years there were fierce debates about where a person's soul and spirit resided – the brain, the heart or elsewhere. These were important questions for heart transplant surgeons and their teams. There were also documented cases of critically ill patients who were thought to be 'brain dead' but then regained consciousness. External agents (such as opiates or other drugs), as well as hypothermia, might interfere with the unresponsiveness on which the testing of brain death relied.

During the debate on this Sunday programme, there was solid opposition to transplantation. This was particularly upsetting as transplant recipients (including me) were sitting in the audience – people who would most likely have been dead if they had not received a new kidney. In 1976 the UK Royal Medical Colleges issued new guidelines defining brain death as completely irreversible loss of brainstem function and specifying that the clinical criteria to certify brain death had to be observed by two independent doctors. Today, with 'opting out' of organ donation having become law in England, it seems very strange that a Sunday evening television programme would have a live debate on the subject, with people arguing that organs should be burnt or buried with the body, thereby denying thousands of people the chance to have a better quality of life, or indeed any sort of life.

By Friday 17th May, my night-time headaches had become so bad that I was prescribed Fortral (pentazocine), a strong opioid, an agonist of the kappa opiate receptor, in other words, a drug that mimicked the opioid effect. Over the next week or so, my symptoms worsened, and I developed swelling of my ankles and legs as well as occasional vomiting. Despite this, on Thursday 30th May, Dr Evans spoke to the doctors in Exeter about my possibly returning there on Saturday 1st June. These plans were thankfully shelved the next day, due to a marked rise in my blood creatinine and urea levels over the previous couple of days, coinciding with a urine infection due to E. coli. At the time I was unaware that any plans had been made for me to return home. It came as quite a shock to this in writing, as I knew in my heart that I had to stay in Cambridge even if the medical team had briefly thought otherwise!

Just a few days later, on Wednesday 5th June, my potassium levels blood had become critically high – at 7.8mmol/l (hyperkalaemia). An intravenous cannula had been inserted and I was given an infusion of calcium gluconate to try to overcome the dangerously high potassium levels. This was followed by intravenous hydrocortisone, insulin and diazoxide, emergency treatment which continued throughout the night. A decision had also been made that I should start back on dialysis as soon as arteriovenous access had been achieved with another Scribner shunt. A repeat test of my blood potassium at 11pm found it had now risen to 8.5mmol/l.

Thank goodness I had stayed where I was, in Cambridge. With no family around, my emotional support came from the patients and nurses I had befriended, and I had to rely on my own instincts, which had been telling me I needed to stay there. My 'sixth sense', knowing my own body, was proved right. Sixth sense defies all scientific logic, but I am a great believer in its existence. It proved to be right then, as it had on previous occasions. It would certainly come to the fore as I navigated the rest of my kidney journey.

My kidney function was declining rapidly over the first week of June, along with uncontrollable high blood pressure (which had 'stabilised' at more than 190/140mm/Hg), fluid overload, vomiting and a slight fever. Professor Roy Calne saw me on his ward round and, together with Dr David Evans and the other doctors, came to tell me that a decision needed to be made about removing my dad's kidney. Professor Calne explained that it was no longer sustaining my life and instead was making me extremely ill, particularly the extreme high blood pressure. It needed to be removed as soon as possible.

This was no surprise, as I already knew the kidney was no longer functioning, and had to come out. I had been aware of the marked change in my body a few weeks previously, which is why it came as a shock recently when I read in my notes that the doctors had briefly considered discharging me back to Exeter. A strange feeling had been growing inside me, a sixth sense that things were just not right. A dull ache had developed in my right iliac/pelvic area, over my rejecting kidney. It wasn't a pain or soreness, just a strange ache. My dad had made a great sacrifice when he had donated his kidney to save my life as a 13-year-old – and that same kidney was now killing me. That was not an easy concept to accept.

There have been many reports on the phenomenon of biofeedback and how it might be used to help relax certain muscles, slowing heart rate and blood flow, reducing blood pressure as well as perception of pain. Controlled clinical studies have usually failed to support the notion of biofeedback. However, the power of the mind over the body is certainly borne out by numerous anecdotal stories, which give it some credibility and substance. In my case, I had become aware of things going awry with my kidney before any changes in biochemical or physiological markers could be identified. This belief has stayed with me nearly half a century later. You just know when something is not right! I am sure countless readers will recognise this feeling themselves.

At the time I did not confide in anyone about my fears that that my kidney was coming to the end of its life. Outwardly, I continued to be my usual optimistic and cheery self whenever possible. This was important, as there were patients on the ward who had just had their transplant and needed encouragement, while others were seriously ill or on dialysis. For some unfortunate individuals, an early death lay ahead, but I saw my medical condition as just another obstacle on my kidney journey, and felt sure that I could navigate my way around it.

The next stage was to have a new Scribner shunt inserted somewhere in one of my limbs. The responsibility for forming this new shunt fell upon Mr David Dunn, a superb vascular surgeon, who had just been appointed as a Consultant Surgeon and University Lecturer in Surgery in Professor Roy Calne's transplant team. Mr David Dunn had recently returned from the US, where he had acquired the skills to create fistulas (invented by Dr James Cimino in New York) to enable easier access to haemodialysis. Mr Dunn had worked alongside Professor Calne in developing transplantation in Cambridge. He later went on to be a pioneer of surgical skills in his on right including work on endoscopic and laparoscopic keyhole surgery. He later developed unique audit processes to evaluate surgical complications that would help in making these novel techniques safe for the patient.

So, at 3pm on Thursday 6th June, I had my pre-med cocktail of drugs in readiness for surgery. I returned from the operating theatre at 6.45pm with a new Scribner shunt inserted into my right ankle. The operation note by Mr Dunn goes into some detail about the 'great difficulty' of finding any arterial access. Eventually a post-tibial site was found deep in my calf. This showed what a dire state my vasculature was now in, following the numerous shunts I had had when first on dialysis. At first there was poor flow in the shunt but with additional flushes it eventually worked. My recovery from the general anaesthetic was overshadowed by my doctors' grave concerns about my hyperkalaemia. It reflects how serious my condition had become that inserting a new Scribner shunt for access for dialysis took precedence over my dangerously high potassium levels. It simply had to be done, otherwise my death would have been inevitable.

My condition remained stable overnight, which was a relief as I was due to have dialysis first thing the next morning, on 7th June. This would be my first session since 23rd October 1970. The dialysis appeared to go smoothly, with my blood pressure dropping from 205/130mm/Hg at the start to 135/80mm/Hg at the end of the six-hour session. Consequently, some of the anti-hypertensive drugs were stopped. The nurse's report noted that my shunt needed frequent washing and, as it was in my leg, I was also back to being on crutches. Over the next few days, I had frequent dialysis sessions that greatly improved my blood pressure control, though both my legs remained very swollen. However, on Monday 17th June, the dialysis session was prematurely interrupted after only a few hours due to a major leak in the Gambro dialyser, which meant that I lost a large quantity of blood.

Thankfully, artificial kidney machines had changed out of all recognition since 1970. The 10- to 14-hour sessions using the Kiil had been replaced by 6-hour sessions using a disposable artificial kidney. This new design had been pioneered by Richard Stewart, using the reverse osmosis technology developed to enable purification of water. In 1961 the Dow Corporation had patented this technology for industrial use and Stewart quickly realised its potential for kidney dialysis. The size of this artificial kidney was tiny, compared to the large and cumbersome Kiil. It was a cylinder approximately 30cm long and around 12cm deep.

Within the cylinder were thousands of hollow fibres ('capillaries') that the patient's blood was pumped through, while between the fibres was the dialysate (the fluid). This had many advantages over the flat plates of the Kiil: the surface area for exchange of toxins from the blood was exponentially greater; there was less blood within the cylinder; and there was a reduced requirement for a blood pump. The critical practical benefit for the patient was that it was disposable – no more building and rebuilding Kiils.

Over the following decades, all dialysis was performed using Stewart's hollow-fibre artificial kidney. It was a massive step forward for patients, families and healthcare workers, and it contributed enormously to reducing the mortality and morbidity associated with dialysis. The increased efficiency of the dialysis, with drastically reduced dialysing times, was also of great benefit to the patient who was able to eat normally for the first hour or two into the session. In 1970, I'd had to follow the strict Giovannetti low-protein and no-salt diet throughout the whole 10 to 12 hours that I was hooked up to the machine. For anyone who has never been on such a draconian diet, this might seem like a minor detail. But having to eat such a sparse, tasteless diet all the time is incredibly depressing. The only benefit was that all the food had to be cooked from fresh, as all pre-packed food contains salt, sugar and other preservatives. However, many basic items, including most dairy products (except for cottage cheese), meat and certain fruit such as bananas and vegetables like mushrooms, were all out of bounds.

Another dialysis session followed on Wednesday 19th June, in preparation for removal of my dad's kidney the next day. In 1974 it was normal practice to shave the area the day before the operation and this was done after finishing dialysis. It is interesting how practices have changed, and shaving is no longer advocated. It is now thought that the skin bacterial flora that might protect from infection is disturbed by the shaving process, though not all surgeons agree.

I had signed my consent form and once again I was 'nil by mouth from midnight'. At around 6am the next morning, I was given an intramuscular cocktail of pre-med drugs to prevent vomiting, together with a sedative. A couple of hours later the porters came to wheel me down to the operating theatre. By this point in my five years of living with kidney failure, I had already had scores of general anaesthetics. The one joy I had from the experience of being anaesthetised was inhaling the sweet-smelling gas through the rubber mask and feeling the world around me change. People's voices in the anaesthetic room changed to a type of vibration and became very distant and then I was gone! The sweet smell of the gas, together with the rubber of the mask, is very distinctive and many people feel sick and claustrophobic. However, I had obviously been conditioned from the age of 12 to know what it entailed. Once I was anaesthetised, Professor Roy Calne reopened the original incision in the right pelvic area and removed the damaged kidney, detaching my dad's kidney from my body, before closing the extensive wound with sutures, and leaving a Riches drain in the abdominal cavity to remove the fluids.

The operation was a success and I returned to C9 Ward some hours later, just after midday. I had not been back on the ward long before my mum and her fiancé Alan came to see me. I had not expected to see anyone from home, as it was such a long journey. It was a terribly busy time for my mum, at the start of the peak holiday season, so they only stayed a short while as they had to get back home to Torquay that evening.

Although there was some sadness that my dad's gift of life had failed, I felt an overwhelming sense of relief that the organ that had been poisoning my body had been removed. I had known for many days that it had to come out, long before Professor Roy Calne told me during the ward round, but there was still an emptiness in the pit of my stomach. Having to return to being totally reliant on a machine for survival, with no kidneys inside me, was a weird feeling and required a big adjustment. No one comes along to your bedside after the operation and asks: 'Can you describe what it feels like to have no kidneys?', 'How do you think you will cope?', 'Will you ever be able to have a normal life?' As a person with kidney failure, you have to be relentlessly positive. There is simply no room for self-pity and all the 'What if...?' questions. You just have to get up, brush yourself down and start navigating round the next pile of rocks in your path. Fortunately, I knew that great strides had been made in the treatment of kidney failure since 1970. Dialysis could now be faced with less fear and trepidation; it would be a challenge, but it would be bearable.

During this period, my Scribner shunt had to be continually coerced to prevent it from clotting. There were several occasions when it almost completely clotted but the nurses and doctors worked extremely hard to monitor it and keep it open and flushed. It was the only vascular access I had to connect me to the machine. Some things had not changed for the better since 1970! In 1974 there were no arterial central lines or other inventive techniques to gain access to the vasculature for dialysis. The loss of access sites was a major problem and Scribner shunts were all that was available. Running out of sites for these shunts them would mean reverting to peritoneal dialysis, which was still very rudimentary and contributed to the high mortality during these times. Rationing of dialysis machines was also still evident, as it had been four years previously.

Following the transplant nephrectomy, I continued to improve – but I now had to deal with a catastrophic *drop* in my blood pressure! History was repeating itself from October 1969. I was no longer taking any anti-hypertensive drugs and was facing the challenge of being hypotensive instead. My legs were still swollen and during the week I had additional dialysis sessions to remove the excess fluid. The Riches drain was removed on Tuesday 25th June.

I was due to have a Cimino fistula created in my right arm the next day by Mr David Dunn, who was well acquainted with all the problems of creating vascular access sites in my body. There was no ultrasound or other imaging technique available to find the best possible site for the fistula on my limbs. He simply moved his fingers along my arms with a gentle touch, searching for pulses and veins. Eventually, he found a spot and decided to use my ulnar artery and basilic vein. He really was exceptionally skilled at working with arteries and veins that had been damaged by haemodialysis in the early days.

The development of the arteriovenous fistula, by Dr James Cimino and his colleagues Michael Brescia and Kenneth Appel, was one of the most important advances in the history of dialysis. It followed in the footsteps of Belding Scribner, who had devised the external arteriovenous shunt. Cimino recognised in the early 1960s that 'vascular access was the Achilles heel of chronic haemodialysis'. Healthcare professionals and patients had identified the problems associated with Scribner shunts, including clotting, skin necrosis, infection and dislodgement; and Cimino realised he could solve these problems by creating an 'under the skin' access point.

His idea of a fistula involved stitching together the radial artery and cephalic vein in the region of the upper wrist. This created a rapid blood flow and distension (arterialisation) of the vein, which could then be used for access with a large-gauge needle. Two sites were selected for the venepuncture: one to take the blood from the body to the dialyser (arterial supply); and the other allowing return of the 'washed' blood (venous). The 'under the skin' fistula revolutionised access, making dialysis easier for everyone, with substantially reduced complications. It is a technique that has become routine for most individuals requiring dialysis even today.

On the morning of Wednesday 26th June, I had 10mg Valium as a pre-med subcutaneously and about an hour later was taken down to the main theatre block for the creation of my fistula by Mr David Dunn, performed under general anaesthetic. It could not be used for several weeks to ensure that the internal ligation between the artery and vein was secure enough to withstand the increased strength of the blood flow. The fistula would be checked extensively, using a stethoscope to listen for a loud 'whooshing' sound. This was quite distinct from the sounds heard when taking blood pressure or listening to a shunt.

The next day I had an exceptionally long dialysis session, starting at 8.30am and finishing at 8.30pm. My legs were still very swollen and during the next week I had three 12-hour dialysis sessions, to try to remove the fluid. My haemoglobin had also dropped to 3.9g/dl, a quarter of what it should have been, and I therefore required an urgent blood transfusion. I had received numerous blood transfusions when I was on dialysis between 1969 to 1970. During the 1980s, the Erythropoietin (EPO) gene was isolated and its function in producing red blood cells was unravelled. However, the human form of EPO did not become routinely available for clinical use for many more years after the gene had been isolated and cloned. Consequently, blood transfusions were regularly needed to combat the appalling anaemia that many patients suffered because of the continual blood loss from haemodialysis and the body's inability to form new red blood cells. In the mid-1970s, it was realised that blood transfusions prior to transplantation improved the acceptance of the kidney by the patient. This was thought to be because the recipient's immune system became 'tolerant' of the 'foreign' HLA antigens. These are referred to as the mismatch tissue type antigens.

Over the following years, patients awaiting a kidney would be routinely transfused with blood. While this worked well for many of those patients who had not already had a transplant, an increasing number of individuals developed anti-HLA antibodies. This was thought to be because they had reacted to the blood transfusion. For instance, this occurred in women who had naturally developed these antibodies after several pregnancies or miscarriages, and those who had rejected the first transplant and developed anti-HLA antibodies. Patients such as these began to appear with increasing frequency on the transplant waiting lists and it became more and more difficult to find suitable kidneys for them. Around the same time, it was found that those who needed multiple blood transfusions were at risk from bovine spongiform encephalopathy (BSE) known as 'mad cow disease', human immunodeficiency virus (HIV) and various types of hepatitis. Fortunately, scientific developments meant that recombinant EPO and changes in new immunosuppressive agents allowed revision of the blood transfusion policy, meaning that fewer people needed to have them.

My 12-hour dialysis sessions continued into the following week until the swelling in my ankles finally reduced. As an example, on Thursday 4th July I was put on dialysis straight after breakfast at 8.30am until 8.30pm. This got rid of 4.3kg fluid, on top of the 4.6kg lost previously, probably 6 to 8 percent of my total body weight. The downside of these extreme sessions was that I always felt completely 'washed out' the following day and unable to do anything. On the upside, my oedema had improved massively and there was also an improvement in my blood pressure. It had started to creep up to around 160/100mm/Hg, even though my transplant kidney had been removed.

I was sufficiently well to go to my friend's house again for the Saturday night. This was a welcome break, following the traumatic events and psychological stresses of the previous two weeks. It allowed me to recharge my emotional batteries by being in a non-clinical environment with his family. We came back to C9 on Sunday evening; and I was back on dialysis the next day, though just for a normal 6-hour session, which removed a modest 1.7kg fluid. Now that all the excess fluid had been removed, I once again faced the hypotension that came with the dialysis. My systolic blood pressure was consistently 100mm/Hg lying down, dropping to 60mm/Hg when I was standing up.

The knock-on effects of this were the numerous clotting episodes with my Scribner shunt. On Tuesday 9th July, the shunt clotted at 3pm but my health-care team managed to unblock it with 2,000 units of heparin by 4pm with the tried and tested pull-and-push on a 20ml-syringe. A further 1,000 units were flushed into the shunt and then again 30 minutes later. The shunt was moni-tored by a nurse every half hour. The doctors had hoped to transfer me back to Exeter on Friday 12th July, but my shunt clotted again in the evening, requiring more painful flushing of both arterial and venous ends with large amounts of heparinised saline. Throughout the night, they continued to check the shunt every thirty minutes and flush it with syringes at both the arterial and venous ends. The syringes had been left attached to the shunt ends and secured in place, but this flushing procedure kept waking me up, so I got hardly any sleep.

A similar attachment of the syringes to the ends of my blocked shunts had been performed when I was first on dialysis. In hindsight, it seems seem rather risky – if I had accidentally pulled on one or the other while asleep or turning over in bed, the clot might have cleared, causing massive blood loss. The syringes were securely fixed to a plaster of Paris back slab, with plenty of Elas-toplast. They were not going anywhere! These problems with my shunt and blood pressure prevented my discharge from Cambridge on Friday 12th July, nearly six weeks after the original plan in May. Meanwhile, my newly created Cimino fistula continued to mature but was still not ready for use.

The dialysis session on the day before saw my blood pressure drop to 80/30mm/Hg when a further 3.1kg fluid was removed. Not surprisingly, I was continuously dizzy and faint. I was now allowed no added salt in my diet, rather than its being salt-free, and I was taking in only 4g salt each day, to try to help with my previous high blood pressure. This meant that I could now eat food with a low or moderate level of sodium, and either no salt, or a sparing amount of salt, could be added to the food. It was not quite as unpalatable as the usual renal diet, and it is still used today, usually to help control hypertension.

As I no longer had a transplanted organ, all my immunosuppressive drugs had been stopped, including prednisolone. Even at this stage, I could not tolerate the low blood pressure that came with stopping the prednisolone. This suggested that the low blood pressure may have been due to secondary adrenal insufficiency due to my adrenal glands having been dormant, or 'switched off', after taking steroids for so many years. I also experienced muscle twitches and aches, another side effect of the steroid withdrawal. While on dialysis on Thursday 11th July, I was given 100mg hydrocortisone directly into the bubble trap of the blood line and I was also started back on 10mg prednisolone. The addition of the steroids helped my hypotension and salt loss and dealt with what might be considered Addisonian crises. This was an issue that was to return with a vengeance some decades later.

Plans were again made for my discharge to Exeter, this time scheduled for Thursday 17th July. In the preceding days, my blood pressure had reverted to reasonable levels. My last dialysis on C9 on Tuesday 15th went well, with the removal of 1.5kg fluid and at the end of the session my blood pressure was an amazing 120/70mm/Hg. The morning of my departure came round, and after a good night's sleep, I was ready to return to Exeter.

Many patients will have fond memories of Douglas House, where I had been in 1970 in Cambridge. At Christmas parties, we recalled various stories and remembered those who were no longer with us or members of staff who had moved on. Few institutions in our current NHS could boast that unique blend of pioneering medical practice with an atmosphere full of empathy, where lifetime friendships were forged. The move to C9 came in the name of progress – a brand-new hospital with all the latest facilities and mod-cons in easy reach. These were all definite improvements but they could replace the special atmosphere at Douglas House.

Nevertheless, there was still a mystique about kidney transplants in 1974 and this meant that C9 was also very special, with its own unique character. Many friendships and close bonds were also formed there, between patients and staff alike. The human survival instinct is very strong among people with kidney failure, and other serious conditions. And this fighting spirit cannot be extinguished just because the physical building and surroundings have changed.

C9 ward had arranged for a female Staff Nurse to accompany me to the railway station and the journey down to King's Cross. There we were met by a London Ambulance Service crew member for the trip across London to Paddington Station to catch the train to Exeter. The Staff Nurse stayed with me all the way back to Exeter. Having made this journey a few times alone, it was strange but reassuring to have a nurse accompany me. In April I had made this same journey on my own, apart from the transfer across London. But now, I was clearly far less mobile and more incapacitated, following the removal of my dad's kidney, and still dealing with massive swings in blood pressure and the rigours of dialysis. The presence of the staff nurse was a firm reminder of my renewed vulnerability. Even though I was now nearing adulthood, it was as if I had stepped back a full four years.

When I first arrived at Cambridge three months before, I had hoped that the problem of hypertension and declining kidney function would be sorted out. The idea of returning to a dialysis machine and having to go back on the transplant list to wait for another kidney, had not entered my head. Now that I have read my hospital notes over the period from December 1973, it was always clear what the outcome would be. Today, a patient would probably be told all this and helped to prepare for the return of kidney failure. Indeed, there are now theoretical models that try to predict the precise time and date when you will be required to return back onto dialysis.

Hindsight is a great thing, but in 1974 the doctors simply had no clinical data to refer to and had to rely on their clinical experience. They also had only limited tools to control the hypertension, while anti-rejection agents (such as monoclonal antibodies and other immunosuppressants) still lay in the distant future. Unfortunately, chronic rejection of transplants is still an area of research with limited resources. A kidney transplant is a treatment, not a cure. Once the decision had been made to remove my dad's kidney and return to dialysis, I simply saw this as another step in my kidney journey. I continued to grasp life with optimism, taking each day as it came.

Chapter 7: Dialysis and a New Kidney

Meeting members of staff and patients at Whipton Hospital on my arrival back from Cambridge on Thursday 17th July 1974 was very emotional. I had been away in Cambridge for around three months and had matured considerably during this time and, no doubt, changed as a person. It was not easy adjusting to being back in Exeter (even though the dialysis unit at Whipton Hospital had an atmosphere not dissimilar to that of Douglas House) and then returning home to Torquay. I was leaving behind some close ties which had seen me through the decline in my health, and I yearned to be with the friends I had made at Addenbrooke's.

Of course, I knew most of the doctors and nurses in Exeter too, but they were now seeing me in a different light. It was going to take time to feel 'at home' again even though everyone was pleased to see me. I dialysed at the unit throughout the next day and finally went home by hospital car to Torquay on the morning of Saturday 19th July. My arrival at home was another emotional roller-coaster. I had not seen my family since early February except for the day when my dad's kidney had been removed in Cambridge. This stay seemed to have had a more profound effect on me than either of my previous long admissions – in Cambridge in autumn 1970 or in Torbay when I broke my femur in early 1972.

During my hospitalisation in 1974, I had to deal with some life-changing events: the failure of my transplant, its removal and my return to dialysis. These events occurred when I was maturing from an adolescent to an adult. Soon I would be a fully grown man, having to make my way through life without any of the safety nets of home life. This was a critical time in my personal and physical development. Whatever my feelings were, they needed to be kept under wraps while I tried to slip back into family life and all that it entailed. Life had to go on and there were still some almost insurmountable obstacles in my path.

The bedroom that had first been equipped for dialysis in 1970 was still intact, and plans were quickly made to restore it for my use for home dialysis. Over the previous couple of years, John had commandeered it for himself and his fiancée, and he was none too pleased when he had to return to the smallest bedroom. It did not take long for the hospital technicians to get the home dialysis up and running again but, while they were working on it, I made three trips a week by hospital car to Whipton for dialysis. Thankfully, these sessions were now only 6 hours long.

While at the unit I was being trained to use a REDY portable dialysis machine, a much smaller machine which was revolutionary at the time. This REDY (**RE**generation of **D**ial**Y**sate) machine used sorbents (substances that can absorb molecules) to remove solutes and toxins from used dialysate, to purify and reconstitute it and send it back through the dialyser. The amount of water needed for each treatment dropped from 6 litres to about 500ml! Malcolm Roberts had first had the idea as far back as 1966 that the fluid leaving the artificial kidney, the dialysate, could be reused or regenerated instead of being discarded after each dialysis. He said: 'Sorbents consisting of zirconium phosphate, hydrated zirconium oxide, and carbon combined with urease were placed in a cartridge and, after completion of animal and human studies, the system was placed on the commercial market in 1973.'

The REDY was, for its time, quite successful, and sustained home haemodialysis for more than a decade. Indeed, in Australia and New Zealand, the REDY was credited with 'saving' home haemodialysis. However, cost was its main Achilles' heel and single-pass systems using Hollow Fibre Artificial Kidney (HFAK) dialysers soon priced the REDY out of the market for maintenance dialysis, although it was still being used into the mid-1990s for inpatient treatment of acute kidney injury. The sorbent concept is currently making a comeback, especially by those attempting to develop a wearable kidney.

Very soon after arriving back in Exeter, my new Cimino fistula was ready to be used for dialysis. There was a 'thrill', quite different from the feel of a pulse, when you put your fingers over the fistula, and it gave a 'burring' noise if you listened with a stethoscope. These were all good signs that it was functioning properly. The nurses at the unit showed me how to insert the large fistula needles into the arterial and venous sides. At first, I injected myself with local anaesthetic at the sites where the needles would be inserted, but it did not take long before I took the nurses' advice, discarded the local anaesthetic and just inserted the needles. Everything was so much easier than my previous experiences in 1970 and, although I still felt 'washed out' post-dialysis, it was nothing like the dreadful side effects I had experienced in the past.

Thankfully, there was also a small relaxation of the salt-free low-protein diet during the first couple of hours, when I could sometimes enjoy a slice of cheese on toast. The training programme had been put together to enable me to do just about everything myself, other than perhaps needing assistance with the initial 'getting on the machine' and 'taking off'. The only help I needed from my family members was ensuring that I had enough pairs of hands when attaching and removing the plastic lines carrying my blood. With practice, it was probably something I could also manage myself, but in these early days it made sense to be cautious.

Summer came and went, and I should have returned to the Grammar School in September 1974. However, although I was feeling much better while on and off dialysis compared to previous times, I was still very tired. I was also dialysing during Monday, Wednesday and Friday afternoons, which left very little time to go to school. Once I was in a routine and my strength and health improved, I managed to attend on the occasional morning or afternoon but not for the entire day.

The teachers were delighted to see me back, although I'm not sure they knew what to make of the situation when I suddenly returned to school, as a sixth former. No doubt they saw a massive change in me since the previous year. They now had a much older student who had been through several more life-changing events, spending months away, essentially living with adults in a hospital environment. By now, although I still couldn't recite any French verb conjugations, I had become quite knowledgeable about many aspects of the life sciences, thanks to the many books I had read and conversations I'd had during the previous months. For example, while at Whipton, I had badgered the Bissons to let me borrow their copies of the *British Medical Journal* and other notable publications. I was determined to try to get my studies back on track after missing nearly another year. One system that seemed to work well was when the taxi organised by the educational authorities picked me up in the morning and brought me home at lunchtime. I would be getting everything ready to put myself on the machine just as my mum arrived home from her housekeeper's job.

My last Scribner shunt, created in Addenbrooke's, finally clotted on Thursday 31st October, and was removed following a trip to Whipton Hospital. There was no need for it now, as the Cimino fistula was working perfectly well. This change, from shunt to fistula to access haemodialysis, was a momentous shift in treating kidney failure and must have saved countless lives. This is in no way intended to dismiss Dr Scribner's achievements, but simply reflects the huge technological advances in the treatment of this condition. It is a testament to these changes, which took place between 1970 and 1974, that life-threatening events (such as those I had undergone in my previous spell hooked up to a machine) no longer occurred. 'The times were certainly a-changing,' to misquote Bob Dylan. With my new routine, I could also socialise by going to a pub with an older neighbour who lived locally and had just gone on dialysis himself. He was in his thirties and had recently been discharged from the Army due to kidney failure. Being a 'newbie', he was still coming to terms with all the rigmarole that dialysis entailed. He needed some guidance and peer support and, as he had a car, we were able to visit one or two local hostelries for a renal diet-compliant drink.

With my newfound desire to socialise and lead a normal life, I accepted an invitation to attend a barn dance in South Molton, North Devon, on Friday 8th November 1974. The event had been organised by the Exeter and District Kidney Patients' Association as a social gathering for patients, families, members of staff and friends. A cheque was also going to be presented to Peter and Peggy Bisson, to pay for a novel kidney perfusion machine. This would help preserve the donor kidney for longer, once it had been removed from the donor, by perfusing it with a saline solution to prevent tissue damage. The kidney would thus stay viable or 'fresher' for longer, from when it was 'harvested' until it was transplanted into the recipient. The theory was correct, but it is only recently that biotechnology and molecular biology have provided suitable systems to enable these machines to be used successfully. It would have been impossible for me to get to this event from my home, so Dr Bisson offered to take me from Whipton, my dialysis centre. So, for that Friday morning, we arranged for the hospital car to pick me up earlier than usual, at around 8am.

As Dr Bisson had organised a hospital bed and cubicle at Whipton Hospital, I brought my overnight bag. The beds were still in separate rooms within the unit, rather like those I had occupied before and after going to Cambridge. Whipton was an old fever hospital and had been built to deal with patients with infectious diseases, so it consisted of several separate buildings. One of these had been refurbished to house the haemodialysis unit as well as in-patient beds.

My dialysis started shortly after I arrived at the unit at around 9.30am – they had scheduled all that day's sessions in daylight hours, to allow everyone to go to the barn dance. After my 6-hour dialysis finished, I went to my room, changed into my smart clothes (including a brown corduroy jacket handed down from Trevor), and I was ready. The Bissons were going to pick me up in their car and I was very excited. This was the first time I was going to a Patients' Association social event on my own as an adult, staying overnight at the hospital. My life had changed dramatically during the past year. In 1974, there were no NHS bed shortages and it was relatively straightforward to arrange to be 'put up on a bed and breakfast' basis in a hospital. This would be unthinkable today, when 'bed managers' spend all their time ringing round wards to find empty beds and asking when, or if, they will be vacated.

The dance was very well attended. Although I was feeling washed out after dialysis, I had been looking forward to the evening for several weeks and had made careful plans for it. Dieticians' understanding of dialysis and renal disease had improved enormously over the previous few years and the renal diet was rather more relaxed than it had been in July 1969. It was still salt-free, so I couldn't eat or drink anything containing sodium or potassium and could still take in only 500ml fluid in 24 hours. But by 1974 there were more choices in the diet because there was a better understanding of the components of food. The Giovannetti low-protein starvation diet was being phased out, as access to dialysis machines improved. Furthermore, at the age of 17, I was still getting taller and fortunately I had gone through puberty. My diet needed to control the renal failure and prevent toxins building up, while still providing enough nutrition, including protein, to ensure that I kept growing. In 1974, this was still not an easy balance to strike.

I now had an overwhelming desire to have control over my body and my medical treatment. I suppose this was partly because I had always been very independent. I had also developed a deep inner strength and resilience which had helped me deal with the life-threatening and life-changing events I'd experienced since I had first become ill as a 12-year-old boy. That evening, I spent a lot of time dancing and seemed to have increased energy for the revelry. At the party, renal diet food was available, and I tried to be sensible with my eating.

However, as the evening went on, I did have one or two glasses of vodka and orange, a popular drink at the time. It was a relatively small fluid volume with only a small amount of potassium from the orange juice; or so I thought! 'Short' alcoholic drinks were clearly preferable for a renal patient because of the fluid restriction.

The portable perfusion machine and the cheque from the Patients' Association were presented to the Bissons, and I had my photograph taken for the local newspaper alongside them, the machine and other patients and relatives. There was more revelry, socialising and barn dancing and by midnight it was time to go back to my overnight accommodation at Whipton with Dr Bisson providing the taxi service. It had been a fabulous night, where I had been able to spread my wings and forge new relationships with a wide range of people.

In the morning, the night nurses brought me my renal diet breakfast – the statutory boiled egg, salt-free bread and butter and 100ml tea. Despite having had my dad's kidney removed and not actually needing any immunosuppression, it had remained impossible for me to stop taking a small dose of prednisolone without being 'Addisonian' with fainting and shakes, and I now took 2.5mg every morning. A few weeks before this, Dr Peter Bisson had asked me to stop taking the prednisolone, but within a few days I developed severe hypotension and rigors and felt totally rotten. The symptoms disappeared once I started taking prednisolone again. These symptoms occurred on top of all the usual ones of being on dialysis. It appeared that my adrenal glands had become dormant during the extensive time I had been taking steroids and I was lacking the effects of the cortisol. Many years later, this was diagnosed as secondary Addison's disease.

It was an early start, despite the partying the night before, and just after 8am the hospital car arrived to take me home to Torquay. The weather was dreadful, a typical British November day with torrential rain and a gale-force wind blowing. The journey didn't take very long at this time of the morning, and I was home just after 9am, being the only patient in the car. My mum was upstairs and I was keen to tell her about the previous evening's barn dance. I dumped my overnight bag on the floor and was just taking off my coat when the telephone rang. We still had one of those avocado-coloured phones (a sign of the times) on a small table at the bottom of the stairs in the hall. The phone call was from Dr Peter Bisson, and he told me he had just received an offer of a cadaver kidney from a young male patient in Cardiff. He was apparently 22 years old, just a little older than me, and had died from a bleed on the brain, a sub-arachnoid haemorrhage from a cerebral angioma. His kidney was an identical tissue type match to my own, although his blood group was 'O' whereas mine was 'A+'. The tissue type match was considered a 'full house', meaning that I had exactly the same HLA-A and –B antigen types as the donor.

Matching the antigens between a donor and a recipient is a critical part of determining whether a kidney is suitable and unlikely to be rejected. In patients who have rejected previous kidney transplants, had multiple blood transfusions, or are mothers with numerous previous pregnancies, anti-HLA antibodies may develop. Therefore, before the transplant operation can go ahead, the recipient's serum must be tested to see if it kills white lymphocyte cells from the donor in a test tube. This is known as the 'cross match'. If the donor cells remain healthy, it is unlikely that the recipient will have a 'hyper-acute' rejection reaction to the kidney.

Since my first transplant in 1970 there had been a revolution in being able to determine the 'tissue type' of recipients and donors. This came about from the pioneering work of Dr Paul Terasaki the father of HLA typing for transplants. After graduating from University of California at Los Angeles (UCLA) he spent time in London working with Sir Peter Medawar on skin grafts. Although he had worked on cellular immunity he was fascinated by antibodies and the B-cells that produce them. On his return to UCLA he became involved in understanding the role of antibodies in matching organs for transplantation and in 1964 invented the micro cytotoxicity assay using the legendary 'Terasaki micro-titre plates. These quickly became the international standard for serum cross matching and later HLA typing. The UCLA tissue typing laboratory was at the forefront in researching the role of antibodies in rejection.

Terasaki was also an uncompromising scientist who always sought the truth. In 1970 he presented the first large study of the role of HLA matching in kidney transplants. He was aided in this work by using computers that allowed statistical analysis of large numbers. The results unexpectedly showed that HLA matching of recipients to donor had no effect on the outcome. His results created a furore amongst established figures and shortly afterwards he was to find all his government grants withdrawn and there was a campaign to tarnish his credibility. However, he had strong support from his peers throughout the world and eventually his funding was restored. His laboratory eventually had as many as 300 people working on HLA typing.

If there *was* a hyper-acute rejection reaction, it would occur within minutes of the patient's own blood supply entering the new kidney. The donor kidney would turn black on the operating table, due to the massive immunological reaction, and this would clearly be catastrophic for the patient. The surgeon would then have to remove the new kidney immediately. Fortunately, this is a rare event; and, with today's new biotechnology, it should never happen. However, in 1974 transplant immunology was still in its infancy. It was not until the beginning of the 1980s that all the serological 'transplant antigens' were identified. Once molecular typing arrived in the 1990s, many new alleles of the HLA proteins were identified and could be used to provide even greater accuracy when matching a donor kidney with a recipient.

Dr Bisson asked if I wanted to accept the offer of this kidney and the answer was obvious. Of course! I never had any doubt that this was the right decision. I don't even remember discussing it with my mum, who was still upstairs tidying up. She would have agreed anyway. Dr Bisson explained that, as previously agreed, my transplant would be carried out at New Addenbrooke's Hospital,

Cambridge. He informed me that I needed to get to Cambridge as soon as possible, as the kidney was already on its way. I now know that ventilation and respiratory arrest of my donor had taken place only an hour earlier, at 8.20am. I was to receive his right kidney and it had already been perfused and put into ice by 8.28am.

At this point, I have to admit I did not really think about how the young man had died or what his parents must be feeling. This might seem cold and lacking in empathy, but my mind was racing with all the things that had to be done. There would be plenty of time later to reflect on what had happened in Cardiff and what a tremendous and generous gift I had been offered by the relatives of my donor. This was a time when kidney transplants from cadavers were still far from common, and there was some resistance to the very idea of using organs from a deceased person. I felt incredibly lucky to be offered this 'full match' kidney so soon after recommencing dialysis, but I have felt over-whelming gratitude ever since to my donor's family.

On putting down the phone, I shouted the news up to my mum; she had already realised that something dramatic was happening and was on her way downstairs. I went over my conversation with Dr Bisson and explained that we needed to get to Cambridge as soon as possible. Fortunately, her fiancé, Alan, was in his workplace as a storeman that morning, rather than out doing deliveries. We managed to contact him (no mobile phones in those days) and explained that he had to come home straight away, as we were going to Cambridge. My brother John was also at work at Renwick's Garage near the town centre. He would stay behind with his wife and look after our dog (Laddie) and cat (Puss). While we were waiting for Alan to come home, I packed my clothes and other essentials for what I knew was likely to be another lengthy stay in Cambridge. Typically, my mum was busy making sandwiches and flasks of coffee for the long journey from Torquay to Cambridge. My own meagre packed lunch was beetroot sandwiches, made with salt-free bread and butter. I was also not allowed to eat or drink anything after midday, as I would be having a general anaesthetic later that day.

Alan was a classic car enthusiast and had a lovely classic Jaguar Mark II, rather like the one owned by Inspector Morse in the TV series of that name. We set off for Cambridge mid-morning and it was still raining heavily, at times torrential, with gale- force winds and poor visibility. By the time we got close to Newton Abbot, about 10 miles from Torquay, I realised that we were never going to make it in time. The approximate distance was 270 miles which, using the roads available in 1974, would take at least 9 hours, possibly too late for me to have the transplant.

We were going to need help to get us to Cambridge in time and I chirped my thoughts from the back seat to my mum and Alan. I thought we should stop at Newton Abbot police station, which we would very soon be passing. Maybe the police could provide a police car or be able to escort us to ensure that we would arrive promptly and safely. Alan parked the car in front, and I walked into the police station and explained our predicament to the desk sergeant. The scene is still fresh in my memory. Of course, in 1974, it was possible to walk into police stations without having to press buttons and talk through intercom systems. There were also many more local police stations then.

After about 15 minutes, the traffic police came out to us, the station commander apologising for the delay. He explained that they had been in contact with all the police forces between Newton Abbot and Cambridge. They needed to confirm our story regarding my transplant, of course, but I am sure that it was such an unusual request that they thought it must be true. With superb efficiency, they very quickly organised a police escort to take us all the way to Addenbrooke's.

They interrogated Alan about the car and his driving experience. As he had recently attained his HGV class I licence allowing him to drive articulated lorries, the police obviously decided that he was a competent driver. However, his car had remoulded tyres and in 1974 these were limited to driving at 55 miles per hour; in the event, our speeds were often more than 90 miles per hour! The police still decided that the best option was to escort us to Cambridge using our own car, given the weather conditions and the need to get there quickly and safely. We were first accompanied by two high-speed police cars from Devon and Cornwall Constabulary. In today's risk-averse society with its fear of litigation, I doubt that any police force would be able to repeat this prompt action. Liability and forms would need to be scrutinised and red tape would prevent it taking place. Fortunately for me, the police acted amazingly efficiently, and so began a journey that enabled me to overcome another massive obstacle in my path.

My memory of the journey is as vivid today as it was on that wet November day, with blue lights flashing and sirens sounding. The M5 section from Bristol to Exeter was still under construction (it was not finished until 1979) and there were many roadwork diversions. The M25 and M11 did not exist at all. We had been told that a new police escort would take over as we crossed each county boundary and became the responsibility of another Constabulary. And they were true to their word. As we drove up the A38, we went through the various roadworks to join the M5 and approached Somerset, and a new police escort was indeed waiting for us on a slip road. As we came up to the border, there was a flashing of headlights from our two police escort cars, while at the same time two new police cars from the Somerset Constabulary came racing down the slipway to join us. Our original police escort cars from Newton Abbot pulled away to make their way back to Devon. These handovers continued all the way up the M5 to Bristol and then along the M4, sometimes with as many as three police cars escorting us.

As we passed Reading, we had to stop at a motorway service station. The police explained that they were going to take us through several towns, such as Watford on the outside of London, to get to the A10 main road to take us to Cambridge. The police again enquired about Alan's driving experience and the car, checked if he was tired and if he still wanted to continue. He was now instructed to stay extremely close to the lead police cars as we would be driving through red lights and busy city centre roads such as Watford.

One of the town centres we went through was St Albans, which was very close to Barnet where I was born. It was breath-taking stuff following the police car through the town centres with tyres screeching, blue lights and sirens going, at speeds sometimes in excess of 70 miles per hour. Eventually, we ended up on the A10 main trunk road to Cambridge with the end of our journey in sight. At just before 5pm, we arrived at New Addenbrooke's Hospital, Hills Road, just as the evening meals were being prepared on C9 Ward. It had finally stopped raining. We heaped praise on the police for their wonderful organisation and the help we had received from all the police forces involved in getting us from Newton Abbot to Cambridge. In the event, we arrived just a few minutes before my new kidney from Cardiff. Alan was exhausted as, unlike the police, he had had to drive all the way and had done a magnificent job of getting us all to Cambridge safely. For him, it was also a unique and memorable experience and a long way from his daily delivery job.

Even today, it gives me goose pimples and makes me slightly tearful when I think about this epic journey. Why did I suggest that we should stop at Newton Abbot Police Station? I had been told that I needed to get to Cambridge quickly and I was aware that the police often provided escorts for those transporting donor kidneys around the country. Perhaps they could escort the recipient as well! One thing I know for sure – we would never have made it to Cambridge in time without that police escort. I believe I made that decision because I was motivated to do what was best for my kidney and my health. In some ways, perhaps you make your own fate and build your own resilience, and your inner strength comes to the fore to ensure that you live another day. Today, of course, patient transfers can be done using helicopters, air ambulances or light planes. However, on that day, with the weather as dreadful as it was, it is unlikely that they would have been able to take off, if they had been available at all. And in today's risk-averse society, escorting civilians at high speeds in the manner we did would no doubt be forbidden.

After we had expressed our huge thanks and said goodbye to the police, it was time to get ready for my transplant. Having left C9 Ward only four months before, many of the nurses and doctors who knew me were on duty that night. They took all my routine and cross match bloods in preparation for the operation, and it wasn't long before the results came back. To my horror, I heard that my potassium level was over 8.3mmol/l, a dangerous level which could have led to a cardiac arrest, and certainly too high to contemplate a general anaesthetic and receiving a kidney transplant. I'm sure this problem was caused by my foolishness in having the orange in my vodka at Friday night's barn dance!

My potassium levels had to be brought down to a safe level urgently and there was no time to use haemodialysis for this purpose. My operation was booked for later that evening, the first of three transplant operations to be carried out that night. The kidney had already been on ice for nearly 12 hours and every extra hour would involve further ischaemic damage to the tissue. In desperation, the doctors decided to use Calcium Resonium, a horrible clay-like paste that removes potassium ions from the bloodstream in exchange for calcium. I sat quietly in a room on the ward, trying to swallow this horrible paste without vomiting, knowing that not doing so would mean losing the opportunity to get this vital transplant. I was determined to swallow as much Resonium as I could, in the shortest possible time. My potassium levels were not going to stop me getting this kidney, which I knew was my only chance of leading a normal life. After what seemed like a lifetime of forcing down and at times gagging on the paste, and with the clock ticking, the doctors repeated my blood tests.

Against all the odds, the Resonium had worked its magic, my potassium levels had dropped sufficiently and my transplant could go ahead. After a quick pre-med, I was taken down to the operating theatre at 8pm. I was really looking forward to receiving my new kidney and not at all worried about having major surgery. I cannot recall the anaesthetist or surgeons bothering to explain all the risks. They must have done so, but we had all been there before and knew that not having this transplant was simply not an option.

It is now over half a century since I developed kidney failure and I have had numerous operations, both minor and major. I try to approach each one pragmatically and with optimism, and I have never once had any doubts about whether to go ahead. I have always been fortunate to have great doctors and healthcare professionals, in whom I have placed my trust. I have employed faith and optimism in everything I have done, from my early school days to the workplace, in family life and elsewhere.

I don't know whether my willingness to trust the medical profession is based on blind faith, or a more deep-seated belief in each case that this is the correct decision and so it will be fine. I have also met many individuals who have turned down opportunities to have surgery, perhaps to correct an arthritic joint with a knee or hip replacement. They often refuse these procedures because they say they are afraid of 'never waking up' from the anaesthetic. These may be otherwise intelligent individuals, often with high-powered jobs, who routinely deal with difficult and stressful situations; yet they still have a primeval fear of losing consciousness which rises to the surface and prevents them making rational and objective decisions.

Mr Maurice 'Taffy' Slapak was the consultant surgeon who would be carrying out my transplant, along with Mr Porter and Dr Andrew Kingsnorth (the senior house officer who assisted with the operation). By a strange coincidence, Andrew Kingsnorth would later become a colleague of mine in the Plymouth Postgraduate Medical School when he became Professor of Surgery. I am certain that he never realised that he had once assisted in my transplant, and I never spoke to anyone in the workplace about my kidney disease and transplant; it was strictly off limits.

It obviously took a little while to prepare my body for the transplant, with the opening of my abdomen and dissection of the vasculature. It was not until 9.45pm that my new kidney was removed from its ice packing and perfused; and it was now nearly 14 hours since it had been removed from my donor. The clamps were taken off the renal artery and vein at 10.10pm and my blood was allowed to circulate into my new kidney. The donor's right kidney was transplanted into the left-hand side of my pelvis. The operation apparently went well, with no technical issues, and I was back on the ward at 1.45 the next morning. It was a busy time for the unit, with two more transplants still to be performed that night and into the early hours of Sunday morning. This was a time when kidney transplant surgeons could gain immediate access to theatres, unlike in today's NHS where the operation does not have the same immediate priority.

In 1974, as in 1970, healthcare professionals were still particularly concerned about infections being acquired by the newly transplanted recipient. Consequently, I was alone in a cubicle with my own toilet facility on C9 Ward, where I was to be reverse barrier-nursed for the next ten days, except when I had to go for specialised investigations including a renogram. This meant that all visitors, nurses, doctors and other healthcare professionals had to put on surgical gowns (or personal protective equipment, or PPE, as we would call it in 2021) before entering my cubicle.

I remember that first day vividly, waking up from the fog of the anaesthetic, with my body attached to a Riches drain and other bits of paraphernalia such as a catheter and drips. Pain relief was provided with 10mg Omnopon given intramuscularly every 4 to 6 hours, rather than pethidine which is often used today. The idea of patient-controlled delivery of analgesic through an intravenous catheter using delivery pumps had yet to be devised. Omnopon is a preparation of papaveretum, containing a mixture of hydrochloride salts of opium alkaloids. Papaveretum is a mixture of 253 parts morphine hydrochloride, 23 parts papaverine hydrochloride and 20 parts codeine hydrochlorides. Although papaveretum is now used relatively rarely, due to the wide availability of single-component opiates and synthetic opioids such as pethidine, it may still be used to relieve moderate to severe pain and for pre-operative sedation.

On the morning of Sunday 10th November, it was all about becoming accustomed to the fact that I had an organ inside my body that had come from another young man. Just over 24 hours earlier, this same kidney had been working perfectly inside my donor's body. His blood had been pumping through its nephrons, and it had been making urine for him. Now we were all hoping it would do the same for me.

Of course, the new kidney had no nerves and so it should not have been possible to experience the same sensations as with my own kidney or other organs. However, there did still appear to be some sensation in my left pelvic area where it had been placed. Not having a nerve supply also meant that there was no early warning system of pain from inflammation that might represent rejection or infection. In addition, the immunosuppressive drugs would dampen down any immune reaction taking place. Consequently, I became overly sensitive to any sign of a dull ache around the area of my new kidney in case it represented something serious. For the first few days, weeks, perhaps even months, I was careful not to move too quickly from side to side, worried in case my new kidney changed position and perhaps developed a kink in one of the blood vessels or in the ureter. If I shifted position too quickly, I would convince myself that the kidney had moved. I doubt that any clinician would have found anything untoward physically, as this was probably all in my mind.

It was difficult to move with all the paraphernalia attached to me, but it wasn't long before the nursing team and physiotherapist started getting me to sit up in bed. The beds in 1974 were still fairly basic, although if you were incredibly lucky you might have one of the newer beds with an electrical hydraulic system that allowed it to move in any direction – up, down, or raised at the foot or head. However, most beds were still limited to pulling out the headboard to raise the head, with the bottom lowered. The nurses made wonderful armchair-like structures with the pillows to support my head and side. With a nurse or a physio on either side of me, their hands placed under my backside, I would take a deep breath, and they would slide me up the bed. If I was lucky, some pain relief might have been administered before this took place, but I often just had to grin and bear it.

The physios were keen to ensure that my lungs expanded fully and did not become congested with secretions that would encourage infection. They would come along and ask me to cough, which is exceedingly difficult when you have a foot-long surgical incision held together with staples. I also had a Riches drain to remove any fluid from the abdominal cavity. One difference from my 1970 transplant operation was the insertion of a Tizzard catheter, placed via a stab incision into my bladder, up the ureter, and out through the transplant incision.

The radiographers would come each morning with their mobile machine to take a chest X-ray. The orange in the vodka from the Friday night must have remained in my system as my potassium level on Sunday was still dangerously high, at 8.6mmol/l! My mum and Alan came to see me that afternoon when I briefly managed to sit out in the armchair. Mum must have been relieved to hear that the transplant operation had been a success from a surgical point of view. It wasn't something we ever discussed; I always felt sure it was going to be a success, so it wasn't an issue for me, but I'm sure it *was* an anxious time for those around me. In the evening I needed another 6-hour dialysis session. Clearly my potassium level was still causing concern for the medical and nursing staff, and my kidney had produced no urine as yet.

This routine continued into the second day when I was also able to sit out again briefly. Everyone said how well I looked, even the day before, with my rosy cheeks. Many people have commented on how quickly the transformation takes place in a person's features following a new kidney, and I was no exception. However, on day two my new kidney still hadn't produced any urine. Sadly, Mum and Alan had to return to Torquay on the morning of Monday 11th November to go back to work.

I was once again alone, this time as a 17-year-old, having to deal with the emotional roller-coaster of a major surgical operation. Everyone around me was nervously waiting for my new kidney to start working and another dialysis session was looming. Indeed, the evening blood results showed my potassium level was little changed despite the previous dialysis; it was 8.2mmol/l. Another overnight dialysis session was arranged, starting that evening and lasting 12 hours, double the normal time. Unfortunately, at 10.30pm that evening a large blood clot blocked the bubble trap and prevented the return of blood through the venous needle. The on-call doctor came to see me and decided to stop dialysis – but I lost a tremendous amount of blood, which had been left behind in the external dialysis lines and artificial kidney.

The following day, Tuesday, was a good one. Though still receiving Omnopon for pain relief, I managed to get out of bed and sit in the armchair. The nurses noted that I was in good spirits even though the kidney had still produced no urine. On Wednesday 13th November, I went for my renogram in the morning and after lunch the Riches drain was removed.

The next day, Thursday 14th November, was the first time that my new kidney produced any measurable amount of urine: the grand total of 50ml. This was an exciting moment, even though I knew the volume was ridiculously small. I had complained of abdominal pain and had been given 30mg Fortral (pentazocine) intravenously, which caused horrendous hallucinations. This was subsequently recorded in my notes as an allergic reaction rather than a 'side effect', which would have been a better description. Fortral is no longer prescribed in many hospitals. I also had another 6-hour dialysis session, using the disposable artificial kidney.

On Friday 15th November, the Tizzard catheter was removed, and the tip sent for bacteriological culture. The day nurses noted that I needed 'encouragement' to move; no doubt the surgical site was still raw. My condition remained stable over the weekend, but I still had no urine output. The medical and nursing team might have been anxious about the possibility of rejection and whether the kidney was going to work, but I never had any doubts. I just knew that everything was going to be fine. This was another time when my deep conviction, inner strength and optimism carried me through. These attributes have clearly been helpful on my kidney journey, and I believe they are essential for dealing with long-term health conditions such as kidney failure.

On Monday 18th November, I went on dialysis during the day and I sensed that the medical team were becoming increasingly concerned about my sparse urine output, and a renal biopsy was being discussed. For the first time, some doubts crept into my mind but these were fleeting thoughts which I quickly 'put in a box' while I regained my former positive, enthusiastic mood.

Even though transplantation in 1974 was not always successful and could be associated with significant morbidity or death, I always believed that my new kidney was going to work.

My urethral catheter was finally removed on Tuesday 19th November. During the previous days, I had scrupulously measured every few drops of urine produced in a 24-hour period. This was done in the 'sluice room', using a small 50- or 100-ml measuring cylinder. I had noticed myself that, from about day five, there had been a slight increase in the urine found in the catheter bag although there was clearly still less than I should have been producing. At the time, taking away the catheter was rather like losing a limb. Measuring the urine output had been my focus for the past ten days and provided a source of optimism, even though the quantities of urine were small. When it was time to measure the urine in the bag, I would ensure that it all travelled from the catheter line, using gravity and squeezing behind it with my thumb and finger. Every drop mattered. I don't know if other patients needed to measure their urine output or were quite as obsessive as me! Alternate suture clips were now removed from the transplant wound.

On Wednesday 20th November, the doctors finally decided they needed to know what was going on and an urgent biopsy was performed by my consultant nephrologist Dr Evans using the large 'potato gun' 14-gauge Tru-Cut needle. At the time, my new kidney was producing only around 30 to 40ml urine over 24 hours – hardly well-functioning! Nevertheless, I was still full of confidence that everything was going to be fine. Some of the healthcare team probably thought I was being overly optimistic or burying my head in the sand, but I always knew that my kidney was working; it was just having a little sleep. The remaining clips were removed from the abdominal wound after the biopsy had been done. Removing sutures and lines has always led to a positive feeling after all the major operations and procedures I have endured. Once the last drain, catheter, intravenous drip or suture has been removed, there is a sense of release, and a feeling that some degree of normality and mobility has returned.

The medical team had clearly suspected rejection and immediately started me on anti-rejection therapy – three days of Actinomycin-D (200mg) as well as high doses of prednisolone (60mg). Actinomycin D was the first new antibiotic to be isolated by Waksman and Woodruff in 1940. It was quickly found not to be particularly useful for antibiotic therapy; but further studies showed it to be a useful chemotherapeutic agent for treating a variety of cancers. Actinomycin was originally isolated from *Streptomyces antibioticus* and is produced by many strains of this bacteria. Actinomycin D is as an inhibitor of cell replication by binding to the DNA helix.

I remained stable during this period, with another daytime dialysis session on Friday 22nd November where I also received 2 pints of blood. This was the first day that my new kidney really started to work, producing 343ml urine, even though I'd had a dialysis session (which usually inhibits urine production).

This was also the last time I would be hooked up to a dialysis machine. A major corner had been turned, as I always knew it would. It was just a case of being patient, believing in yourself and listening to your inner voice. Perhaps it was the biopsy needle that gave my kidney the kick it needed to start working. It certainly felt like it at the time, as I had previously been fastidiously measuring the tiniest trickle of urine in the catheter bag and could now see the volume increase each day. It is hard to capture in words my excitement in those first few days, watching a dribble of urine flow down the catheter tube and into the bag. The doctors and nurses felt likewise. Now that I was producing hundreds of millilitres of urine a day, there was no need to worry about the occasional drop being left behind in a catheter tube, measuring cylinder or similar device. Taking responsibility for measuring the urine in the bag, which I did meticulously, had kept me busy, reporting back to the nurses and doctors. It was as though my whole future depended on it, which of course it did!

The renal biopsy did show that the kidney had suffered a degree of rejection. The histology report concluded that there was a moderate cellular form of allograft rejection of clinical significance present in the kidney. However, there was also some good news, that the kidney was also regenerating satisfactorily after suffering from ischaemic tubular cell necrosis. I was told at the time that this may have been due to the kidney being 'bruised' from the ice in the cardboard box; maybe it had been packed too enthusiastically for its transport from Cardiff to Cambridge. It had also been waiting for me in the ice box for 12 hours! These comments stayed with me in the years to come.

To ensure that I could stay off dialysis, I was given an intravenous injection of the potent diuretic Lasix (Furosemide) on Friday 22nd November, as well as more Calcium Resonium to bring down my potassium level. I was happy to swallow this awful paste if it meant no more dialysis! This, together with my much-improved kidney function, meant that my fluid intake was in balance and dialysis really was a thing of the past. The nursing reports say how much happier I was, now that dialysis was no longer required, and my kidney was starting to work normally.

My kidney function went from strength to strength and very quickly my urine output went from the mere dribble of 50ml to more than 5,000ml. A 24-hour urine collection was carried out every day, for which I took responsibility. I was given a 5,000-ml plastic container with my name and details on, and I would empty the contents of a glass urinal bottle into the container using a plastic funnel. Some days I required two containers! All this measuring activity took place in the ward sluice room. I doubt they would let me do that today; another part of the patient's taking responsibility for their own care has been lost to red tape and 'health and safety' anxiety. Most patients in 1974 took responsibility for measuring their own urine output, another example of what would now be called 'patient empowerment'.

As in 1970, the urine output plus an additional 500ml was the amount that I was allowed to drink the following day. It was quite a challenge to drink 5 litres at that time, as it was ten times the volume I had been used to drinking while fluid restricted! The nurses were rigorous about ensuring that I kept drinking throughout the day and that I was on target with my fluid allowance. Once I could maintain a fluid intake in the range of 3,500 to 5,000ml, the additional 500ml was no longer added to my daily allowance. There is only so much fluid anyone can drink in a day!! Ever since my transplant, maintaining a high fluid intake has remained one of the cornerstones of protecting my kidney and ensuring that it is kept in the best possible condition. Even today, I drink litres of orange squash throughout the day and at night, together with endless cups of tea and coffee.

On Tuesday 26th November, I was taken down to the Old Addenbrooke's Hospital by car for a third renogram. Each renogram used Iodine-131, labelled Hippuran, and on this occasion, it showed good improvement in my kidney function. This improvement continued over the next days and by 1st December I was eating a normal diet. Being released from dietary restrictions is another important milestone for anyone with kidney failure. On 6th December, I had the last of the investigations – an intravenous pyelogram to investigate the structure of my new kidney, ureter and bladder using radioactivity that had been injected through a vein. The results were normal.

As the days went by, a routine developed on C9 Ward. In 1974, the normal length of stay following a kidney transplant was still around six weeks. As my new kidney started to work and I no longer needed dialysis, my strength and health rapidly improved. During these final weeks, Ward Sister Sally Taber once again realised that I needed more mental stimulation. This was partly because the high dose of prednisolone stimulated my brain. While I was able to get off to sleep on the ward at around 10pm, I was often wide awake again in the early hours of the morning, and raring to go. My way of dealing with this was to go and sit with the night nurses at the ward desk. Quite often, the on-call junior doctor would also be around. I suspect I was a bit of a nuisance with my continual chatter and questions about medical matters. But they were very patient and always allowed me to 'hang around', although one had to be quiet for the sake of the other patients. This side-effect of steroids lasted for many weeks. It was a complete reversal of the tiredness and lack of energy that I had experienced while dialysing.

Once my renal function had improved, on Friday 29th November, I was able to take the bus into Cambridge city centre. By now, the city was getting ready for Christmas and I was enjoying the festive ambience and atmosphere. Still only 17 and living hundreds of miles from home, my mind drifted back to thoughts of studying for my A-levels and wanting to be at university. A light had been switched on and I spent hours browsing the numerous bookshops in Cambridge. Cambridge always looks beautiful at Christmas, with its outside market, carol singers and the bustle of all the shoppers. This was a time of escapism for me, in a safe environment, in a place that had provided me with a new kidney that was going to remove the need for dialysis. I desperately wanted to be a young adult like any other, surrounded by people going about their Christmas shopping.

My obsessive personality expressed itself in several ways and I would often visit Heffer's bookshop to buy second-hand undergraduate textbooks on various subjects, from case law to biology. I ended up with quite a collection of second-hand academic books and was running out of space on my bedside locker. My books soon became a topic of conversation on some of the ward rounds, curious doctors picking them up and asking me about them. I still have the books but I'm not sure I could tell you much about their content now.

During my stay in Cambridge for my transplant, I was able to re-establish my close friendship with the staff nurse who had played a key role in helping me through the life-changing events of the summer. We had been corresponding after I had returned home. She had been keeping me up to date with all the hospital gossip and I had done likewise – telling her about events at home. When I was first admitted for my transplant, she was on leave for the first week but on her return to work was thrilled to see I had received a fully HLA-matched kidney.

As the days went by and my recovery accelerated, there was once again time to discuss all those topics we had touched on previously. These included coping with family life, what the future might hold and how I would readjust to normal life. We never repeated the swimming sessions, but we still enjoyed time away from the goldfish bowl of the ward. Once my health had recovered sufficiently, there was always the opportunity to play table tennis. From time to time, I have thought about this relationship and tried to consider what might replace it in today's NHS. Perhaps the nearest would be a counselling session but counselling sessions are a one-way conversation because there is no divulging of personal thoughts and experiences by the counsellor. In today's frantically pressurised NHS system, are healthcare workers such as nurses, given the time and space to really get to know their patients (or service users, as some might call them), let alone encouraged to do so by their line managers? I suspect the answer is no, but this is to the detriment of some patients who would greatly benefit from it.

Another example was a male house-officer doctor, who had also looked after me during my summer hospital stay and again with my new kidney. He invited me to go for a beer with him at The Green Man pub in the nearby village of Grantchester. He had promised to buy me a pint as soon as my kidney started to work normally. True to his word, as soon as I was on a normal diet, he collected me from the ward and we went in his car in the evening for that pint (or perhaps two or three!), which tasted all the better as I was still underage, a situation very unlikely to take place in today's NHS! When he was 'on nights', and had time on his hands, and I was wandering around the corridors high on steroids, we would have long discussions about kidney disease and transplants, among many other topics.

Sister Sally Taber had asked me to help her organise the legendary annual Christmas Transplant patient party, to be held in the Occupational Department at the New Addenbrooke's Hospital on Saturday 14th December. This had become a regular event for me ever since my first party in 1970, and I was kept very busy for a while, sorting out the invitation cards and addressing envelopes. There were also a great many Christmas cards that needed to be dealt with in a similar manner. On the day of the party, there was a lot of carrying of chairs and tables, as well as sorting out the food and drink.

The Christmas party was another great success, with Professor Calne's family providing some of the musical entertainment with seasonal carols. Professor Calne gave an inspirational speech on how transplants were performed, and how much work needed to be done to increase the number of cadaver donors. Dialysis machines were still being rationed at this time and kidney donation was still a relatively taboo subject. These parties were very memorable, emotional occasions, particularly as every one of us was essentially an 'experimental guinea pig'. The medical and nursing teams were learning at an exponential rate each time an operation was carried out. It was a truly inspirational time and we all benefited from this increased knowledge, which paved the way for the excellent results achieved in transplantation today. We also had a sense of pride in having been a small part of something that was unique in those early pioneering days of treating kidney failure.

The next day, Sunday 15th December, it was time to leave Cambridge and say goodbye to the many friends I had made, patients as well as doctors, nurses and housekeeping staff. It was another incredibly emotional moment. C9 had been my home for over five weeks, and I had gone through a range of intense emotions including, at one point, the fear that my new kidney might never work, and I might have to return to dialysis and face an uncertain future. Although my faith in my new kidney rarely wavered, there is no doubt that everyone else had grave concerns about its survival. But I somehow retained my deep belief that my kidney would work, and I would emerge at the other end successfully. This was just another rock to manoeuvre around, in the choppy ocean my kidney and I were sailing across.

After an early breakfast, the taxi came to take me to the railway station with my collection of second-hand books and all my other baggage. Unlike in 1970 (when I had a Red Cross ambulance man to escort me) or in July, following the removal of my dad's kidney (when I was accompanied by a nurse to Exeter), this time the doctors considered me fit enough to travel by myself. However, on arrival at King's Cross Station, I was met by ambulance men from the London Ambulance Service who did provide an escort to Paddington Station to ensure that I was safely on my train back to Exeter. An ambulance met me at Exeter St David's and transferred me to Whipton Hospital.

The doctors in Exeter had wanted me to drop in so that they could check me over before I finally returned home to Torquay. At the time, I really just wanted to go straight home because I knew I was healthy and able to look after myself. I now realise that this attitude was probably rather churlish, as everyone was simply doing their best to ensure that my kidney and I remained in good health. It is also a reflection of how I had once again changed in a short time. I had left home some weeks before, facing a future that would probably have been short-lived without a kidney. I had returned as someone lucky enough to have had a 'full match' kidney from a donor of a similar age. In 1974, there might still have been a great deal of uncertainty among the professionals about how long the transplant would last, but that thought never entered my mind. I knew that I had a bright future ahead of me; I just had to grasp opportunities as they presented themselves.

The staff and patients at Whipton Hospital all wanted to know how the operation had gone, of course, and wished me every success as well as a joyous Christmas! In 1974 the unit in Exeter did perform a few transplants, but – like many around the UK – their success rate was nowhere near as good as at Cambridge. In subsequent years, the transplant programme in Exeter, as in many other small centres, was closed down. Referring patients to regional centres, where larger numbers of similar operations are performed, leads to better outcomes based on good practice and experience.

On Tuesday 17th December, having had a full medical examination and with evidence that my kidney was working well, the hospital car service came to take me home to Warbro Road, Torquay, nearly six weeks after I had left on that stormy Saturday in November. Christmas was just a week away. There was a lot to do. I started to focus on my future and how I was going to cover all the ground I had lost in my education. I had decided that I wanted to apply to medical school, but my academic track record left a lot to be desired. I was determined to do it and knew that I had to be single-minded, with only one objective in my life besides ensuring that my kidney remained in good health. How could I possibly get the A-level grades I needed to make a successful application?

Chapter 8: Return to School and Exams

Christmas 1974 and New Year came and went very quickly, with huge relief in my family that I was able to take part in all the festivities without following that terrible renal diet! I was careful not to overeat though, as I now knew the effect the large doses of steroids (30mg prednisolone and 175mg azathioprine) would have on my shape and weight. I certainly didn't want to return to having a 'moon face'; once was enough! Thankfully, I was disciplined enough to avoid all the steroid side effects I had previously succumbed to.

Once the Christmas holidays were over, in January 1975, it was time to return to Torquay Boys' Grammar School, having barely been there for well over a year. Due to the amount of time I'd lost, the school sensibly suggested that I restart the Lower Sixth year. I had already missed the first term and was, once again, in the position of having to make new friends. But the school put together an academic plan that would make it possible for me to apply to medical school. I now realise how fortunate I was that the teachers believed in me enough to allow me to carry on with my schooling.

It was not compulsory to attend sixth form in the 1970s, and many pupils left after O-levels to take up a job or an apprenticeship. In my spring term report for 1974, my form master Mr Rowe wrote, 'the opinion of staff who have taught Andrew is that he is a capable boy who, as his health improves, should be able to lay the bones for a career'. In the autumn term 1974, Mr Bennett wrote, 'Despite, or perhaps because of, the daunting obstacles he has faced recently, he has wished to make efforts to keep up with his work. In the process he has won the respect and, I may say, admiration, of us all'. I think these comments probably explain why the school was happy to allow me to continue with my studies.

While at Cambridge, following my second transplant, I had written to the Headmaster Mr Smith, keeping him informed of my recovery and how I wished to come back and finish my studies. He replied to me in Cambridge with a lovely letter that still brings tears to my eyes. The last sentence read: 'I do not know whether you will be home for Christmas, but in any case, we all send our good wishes and look forward to seeing you again'. Fortunately, I *was* home before Christmas!

I would never have been able to carry on with my original year group after missing so much school. During the autumn term in 1973, I had taken my teachers' advice and concentrated on passing my remaining O-levels. This meant that I had already missed the first term of the A-level courses in biology, chemistry and physics. There was no time to retake any more subjects in June

1974, as I was still in Cambridge. Physics and English Language O-levels would have to wait until the summer of 1975 to be conquered.

When I returned in January 1975, to restart my A-level courses, all my peers had either left to take up jobs or apprenticeships or were in the Upper Sixth. Once again, I had to join a new class and form new friendships, as had been necessary twice before, in January 1971 and September 1972. This was becoming a recurring theme. It was very hard, both psychologically and emotionally, but it was something I just had to deal with.

Back in 1969, at the beginning of my illness, I had been good friends with two boys who lived close by in Wellswood. However, once we moved to a new house in Warbro Road in 1970, it became increasingly difficult for them to visit me as I was 30 minutes' walk away. They were very loyal though, and still came to see me at weekends, but I didn't always feel up to seeing them. Often, I would still be at the dialysis unit in Exeter until late on Saturday morning and would feel completely 'washed out' when I got home and certainly not up to playing board games with my friends. After going to Cambridge in September 1970, my contact with them ended completely and by the time I came back at Christmas and prepared for school in January 1971, they had naturally moved on to a new circle of friends. This was hardly surprising; since July 1969, I had been an extremely ill child, spending much of my time in hospital and feeling sickly even at home. It had simply been impossible to take part in normal teenage life. At that stage, even kicking a football around in our outside yard was thought to be too dangerous because of the Scribner shunt and my hypotensive state.

Before I had become ill, the three of us had enjoyed playing many games, including pretending to be 'Garrison's Gorillas' (an ITV television series in the late 1960s, based on the film *The Dirty Dozen*). There was a building site close by, in Ashtead Road, where we would spend hours playing in the evenings and weekends when the builders had left for the day. This was long before building sites were boarded up and locked to keep people out. There were no red warning signs then, telling people to wear hard hats. We spent our time there playing tag or Garrison's Gorillas, chasing each other along scaffolding boards, often at a considerable height. Playing tag involved sliding and swinging down the scaffolding poles. It was all very exciting, particularly in the dark with torches!

One of my first tasks now was to find new friends in yet another group of pupils, in the Lower Sixth. The sixth-form environment was completely different from that of the lower years. The school had its own sixth-form block in a run-down detached house across the road from the main campus. There were four forms, and pupils were organised by the A-level subjects they were taking. As I was taking biology, chemistry and physics, I was placed in a science form. There were around 15 other pupils in the group, many of whom were taking extra subjects like further maths. Indeed, the school changed its A-level policy the following year, requiring all pupils to sit four A-levels. There were some very bright boys in my form, and the standard was quite demanding, particularly as most of them went on to Oxford or Cambridge.

I was aware of the massive task that lay ahead – to catch up with my A-level courses, as well as my O-level retakes in physics and English language in five months' time. I had not looked at these subjects for over a year, but I knew these were just further obstacles I needed to negotiate. I approached the challenge with single-minded determination and a complete belief that I had it in myself to do it. Nothing was going to get in my way! Initially, the hardest part was physically adjusting to being in school again and adapting to the classroom routines. My experiences in Exeter, Cambridge and at home on dialysis had given me far greater maturity and I had spent all this time in adult company. I was also a year older than the rest of my classmates, and nearing my eighteenth birthday. I did find one or two of them a little immature – for example, when they were playing classroom games. To begin with, we had little in common, but I tried to close the gap with small-talk, usually about the previous night's television.

During my lengthy hospitalisations, discussions with doctors, nurses and patients, together with my own experiences of kidney disease and transplantation, had solidified my determination to attain the A-level grades I needed for medical school. I had discussed my ambitions at length with medical and nursing professionals at Exeter and Cambridge. While everyone seemed to support me, I'm sure few of them thought it was a realistic objective. The exceptions to this were some of my closest friends among the healthcare professionals at Addenbrooke's who really believed that I could achieve my aim. My mum also believed I could do it if I wanted to, while my brother John brought me down to earth, teasing me and saying I was, 'too thick to pass any exam even if I was given the answers'. The joys of sibling rivalry!

At Torquay Grammar School, the teachers were superb at offering and providing support to enable me to catch up. However, I never fully discussed my ambitions with any of my classmates or teachers, for fear of being laughed at. The other pupils in my form were always nice and accommodating but they had been in the same year since starting school and had obviously formed their own groups, so I was very much an unknown quantity. It would be interesting to know how the teachers prepared the class for my arrival in the weeks before I started. As they were not my original 1968–1969 peer group, there was no reason for them to have even been aware of my illness. Never once during my entire time in the sixth form did I feel comfortable enough to be able to invite any of my fellow pupils to my home to socialise. Likewise, nobody from my class, and none of my friends from previous years, ever invited me back to their homes or suggested going to a social event.

However, there was a silver lining to my relative isolation. New friendships at school would have eaten into my time outside the classroom; instead, I was able to concentrate entirely on my academic work. At the time, I'm not sure the lack of friends bothered me, as I had become very self-sufficient. My outside interests were largely different from theirs, and I was altogether far more mature in my outlook and opinions. I had touched death on many occasions; and that changes your perspective on life.

Over the next 18 months at school, I worked incessantly and was totally single-minded about achieving my goal. I had created a work plan by taking each subject and working through the various topics. On most school days, I studied from the moment I got home until late in the evening, only taking a break for tea and to take my dog Laddie for a walk. Weekends were also mostly taken up with schoolwork. There were times when my mum and Alan would invite me to join them for a day trip, but my response was invariably to say no. I had become entirely content being at home working on my studies. John was still living at home but did not disturb me too much, as he was often out at weekends.

As well as the current science lessons, I had to make up for lost time from the first term. The last textbooks I had read were from 1973, so I could often be found at lunchtime in the laboratory undertaking revision work. I was not the only pupil to do this, and the teachers made someone responsible for opening and locking the lab. A lot of time was spent peering down microscopes looking at slides of plant structures as well as tissues of frogs, dog fish and earthworms. To this day, histology is an area of science that I have never mastered! When I was not in the science lab, I could be found in the school or town library immersed in my studies.

I did have some outside interests, though. During my stay at Cambridge the previous year, I had become aware of the work of Mrs Elizabeth Ward through her daughter who had invited me to their home for weekends. At the time, Mrs Ward was the Chairman of the Silver Lining Appeal for the National Kidney Research Fund. This charity raised money to support renal units by buying equipment or helping patients and their families who needed other types of support. It later became known as the British Kidney Patients' Association and is now known as Kidney Care.

Mrs Ward was passionate about the cause, as her 17-year-old son Timbo suffered from kidney failure in 1970. She was instrumental in persuading Sir Keith Joseph, Health Secretary at the time, to introduce the National Kidney Donor Card Scheme in 1971. This helped raise public awareness of the need for more people to sign the new National Kidney Donor Card and consider becoming donors. The scheme was entirely voluntary and, at the time, covered only the donation of a deceased person's kidneys. If someone carrying the signed donor card became involved in a fatal car accident, the next of kin still had to give their permission before the kidneys could be removed. This remained the law until the opt-out legislation was introduced in England in the spring of 2020.

Through my communications with Mrs Elizabeth Ward, I became actively involved in helping her promote the Donor Card Scheme. At the end of 1974, she invited me to come up to London to help her promote the scheme at

Waterloo Railway Station. She had an exhibition stall there during the week of Monday 17th March 1975, which included a REDY mobile kidney machine, the same type I had used the previous summer. Mrs Ward paid for me to travel up to London and man the stall, talk to the public, give interviews to the national newspapers, and give out donor cards to unsuspecting commuters. The school allowed me to take time off, despite all the time I had already missed. I suspect they thought it was in my interest to go, as I was unlikely to get my desired A-level grades anyway! I set off from Torquay at 8am, arrived at Paddington at 11.35am and returned on the 4.30pm service, arriving home at 8.10 that evening. I was there for two days, with my mum joining me for one of them.

The daughter of the friend whose home I had visited also came and this was an emotional reunion, as her father had recently died of kidney failure. It was very brave of her to meet the public and describe to them what kidney failure means to a family devastated by the sudden death of a parent. There was tremendous interest in the display, and I was interviewed by numerous newspapers, including the *Glasgow Herald*, whose reporter commented on my looks, describing me as 'short, stocky with a pageboy haircut like a medieval page's, highly intelligent and talkative especially on his own subject – kidneys'. The article finished by saying, 'Surprise that he should take so much in his stride is very simply answered, "Well, it's my life". And a brave one'.

The exhibition inspired me to organise similar events closer to home and, on my return, I immediately contacted our Exeter and District Kidney Patients' Association and had discussions with my renal doctors. As part of the publicity surrounding the Donor Card Scheme, I had been contacted by the Chairman of the Southwest Field and Gun Sports Association and was invited to have a free stall at their forthcoming Annual Event at Newton Abbot Racecourse. I knew it wasn't really the right venue to promote a Kidney Donor Card Scheme, but the Chairman was keen for me to come along. I accepted the invitation and decided to use it as a trial for future events, all the time keeping the Patients' Association and doctors abreast of what was being planned.

The event took place on a cold, wet and windy Sunday. My mum, Alan and our family friend Margaret Potter came along to help put up some posters supplied by Mrs Ward. We had boxes of donor cards and car stickers to hand out. The organisers had put us in a dark remote corner where, unfortunately, hardly anyone ventured. In the event, there was little interest in our display, and nobody seemed to want the donor cards that we thrust upon them. Most of the stalls were selling items such as saddles and bridles, air rifles and shot guns. It was a dismal, long day, and a steep learning curve in how to go about delivering a successful event. The next one would be vastly different!

Based on the success of the Waterloo Station display, I realised we needed a venue with a large footfall, which would attract a wider audience. The obvious target was the forthcoming Devon County Show which takes place in early May every year. I formulated my ideas, objectives and plans and put them to the Patients' Association committee, impressing upon them the urgency if we were going to run the event in a few weeks' time. My proposal received an enthusiastic response from everyone, including the doctors and nurses. The County Show was to take place from Thursday 8th through to Saturday 10th May. Once again, this would require me to take time off school, and the event won the school's full blessing.

The Kidney Patients' Association were fortunate in being able to book and pay for one of the last standard tents in the showground, a prime site given to us by the organisers. It helped that many of the members of the committee were from a farming background and were undoubtedly well known to the organisers. There was a lot to do in a few short weeks. We had to send out invitations to all the local dignitaries, including the Mayors of Exeter and Torquay as well as local MPs. The stall would include displays of an artificial kidney and dialysis machines as well as blood pumps. We also had a hospital bed and mannequin. Many of the patients, as well as the Bissons, the renal nurses and technicians, came to offer help and support. It was a very inspiring team effort and in those days there was very little red tape to deal with, even though we were taking clinical equipment off-site to a canvas tent pitched on grass.

There was also a great response from the dignitaries and most, apart from our local MP, accepted the invitation. Journalists from the local and regional newspapers came along and provided excellent reports of the event. As the organiser, I attended all three days, staying in one of the usual 'bedrooms' at Whipton Hospital on Wednesday, Thursday and Friday nights. The hospital had arranged a hospital car to pick me up from home on the Wednesday. It was all for a good cause.

My mum and Alan came along to join in the activities on the Saturday afternoon, including packing everything away and providing a lift home. We had fantastic weather for the entire period, which meant that the County Show was an incredibly popular event with countless visitors. We managed to hand out thousands of donor cards and car stickers. The event took place in subsequent years, but I later had to leave the organisation to the rest of the Committee as it would clash with my A-level exams the following year.

I still have very fond memories of this event and what we were able to achieve. Persuading local dignitaries to attend, organising the press and delegating responsibilities to various members of the Committee were all great skills to gain while I was still a teenager. In today's education system, there is great emphasis on a student's portfolio. Nowadays, organising this event would have been the centrepiece of my portfolio. But, funnily enough, I never discussed it in an interview. Looking back after all these years, I am amazed that all the committee members as well as the doctors and nurses were so easily convinced by my plan. It was not without risks. We might have had bad weather, and we couldn't anticipate the attitudes of the dignitaries, journalists and members of the public. Donor cards were still in their infancy and certain parts of society were still strongly opposed to organ donation.

Apart from all the studying and revising, I still had a passion for the pleasure boats I had worked on since I was a youngster. I was fortunate that I had kept in contact with the owner of the pleasure boats at Meadfoot Beach while on dialysis during the summer of 1974, and he came to visit me while I was on home haemodialysis. He kindly offered to give me back my job working on Meadfoot Beach for the summer of 1975.

At first, I would wander down to his house where he kept the motorboats. In the past, he had paid me to paint the wooden boats, and I also had the job of stripping down and rebuilding the 1.5hp Stuart-Turner two-stroke in-board petrol engines that propelled them. This year he wanted me to take charge of the eight motorboats that were kept overnight in the harbour at Torquay, around 3 to 4 miles by sea from Meadfoot Beach. Each morning, they had to be towed from the harbour to the beach using a lovely wooden clinker work boat. The voyage took around an hour, and the reverse journey would be undertaken in the late afternoon. My job was to tow the motorboats back and forth from the harbour. This required me to have a boatman's licence to allow me to work within the harbour limits.

The days were long, with my boss picking me up around 8 in the morning, along with some of the men working on the beach. He drove an old Ford Consul with a gear change lever on the steering wheel and a bench front seat. He loved to drive fast around the streets, and, with no seat belts, this meant clinging on for dear life, shifting from one side of the car to the other, nearly bumping into him on the driver's side. This would never be allowed now – it definitely went against health and safety and regulations! During the day I was often also put in charge of the ticket desk which included being responsible for collecting the money.

I spent nearly every day that summer working on the pleasure boats at Meadfoot Beach. They were long, hot sunny days with little rain. An exception to this was one day when I towed the boats round from the harbour even though the forecast had warned of increasing wind from the southeast. This was an onshore wind, which would cause very choppy seas around the Daddy Hole headland on the return to the harbour. Just after lunch, it was decided that I should take the boats back early because, if we delayed, it would become impossible, due to the increasing wind and the height of the waves. The boats were towed in two strings of four from the stern of my workboat. When being towed in this way, it was important that they did not 'snatch' and bump into the stern of the boat in front.

Everything went smoothly at first but, once we got to Daddy Hole, the size of the waves increased substantially. I was horrified to see some of the boats start to race over the tops of the waves and crash into the sterns of the boats in front, followed by a snatch on the tow ropes. Anyone with any knowledge of the sea will know that conditions can change very quickly; and my situation was now becoming serious, even though I had slowed to a snail's pace. One of the boats in the middle of the string crashed into the boat in front of it, damaging the wood. When the rope snatched, it had pulled out the cleat that it was attached to, as well as ripping some of the wood away. The boats in the second string were also getting damaged and starting to take on water.

These were the days before VHF radio, but it was clear that I needed urgent assistance – firstly to stop the boats sinking, and secondly for my own safety. Fortunately, the boss's brother was returning to the harbour from Redgate Beach with the *Nomad*. He could see me waving frantically and he immediately understood the gravity of the situation. He manoeuvred close to me, all the time aware of the worsening conditions, and the increasing size of the waves. He was in a much bigger boat and there was a danger of us colliding and putting holes in each other's wooden hulls. I cast off one of the strings of boats and he used a boat hook to pick up the tow line. In exchange, he threw me a long rope, which I used to extend the tow line for the remaining motorboats to try and dampen down the snatch. He did likewise with his string of boats and followed behind me as we slowly made our way to the harbour.

On our arrival, we were met by my boss as well as other boat users who had seen what was going on from the cliff top. Thankfully, the arrival of the *Nomad* meant that the Torbay lifeboat did not need to be launched; it would have had to come over from Brixham. It all ended with an almighty row on the harbourside, with the boss's brother and other commercial boat users giving my boss a dressing-down, firstly for endangering my life and secondly for risking the motorboats. It became apparent that the decision to take the boats back early had been taken too late – because the boss had disappeared for a few lunchtime pints!

At the end of the summer holidays, I returned to school, ready to study in earnest. At the end of the previous school year, I had sat my O-levels in physics and English language and was delighted to receive notification that I had passed both. During the summer I had also managed to save enough money for my first motorcycle, a twin stroke Yamaha 100cc. It cost around £100 and was a few years old, showing some signs of rust and wear and tear. However, it gave me the freedom to get around without relying on public transport or on lifts from other people. The bike was a basic design and, although rusty in places, I loved riding it and maintaining it. Unfortunately, no amount of rubbing with 'rust remover polish' would get rid of the brown marks on the chrome!

With my last two O-levels out of the way, I could now spend all my time focusing on obtaining the all-important A-level grades I needed for medical school. I had no home tutors or mentors. Achieving success would require pure determination and hard graft on my part, together with a large dose of self-belief. The teachers provided wonderful support and were always prepared to help, answering my questions and offering additional reading.

The University and Colleges Admissions Application form (UCCA, now known as UCAS) had to be submitted by the end of October. These were hard-copy application forms, long before the days of computers. I reviewed the UCCA handbook which contained all the universities and courses and selected five that had medical schools: Newcastle, Leeds, Bristol, Manchester and Belfast. There was little guidance on where to apply, so I simply based my choice on whether I liked the prospectus. Neither was there any advice about attending open days. I'm not sure they even had open days then, unlike today's continuous parade of students travelling around in the autumn, spring and summer from one campus to another.

There was no continuous rewriting of the personal statement, either, to ensure that all the correct buzzwords were included, nor indeed any 'professional' writers to write it for you. My application went off through the school and I was never told exactly what support they provided. I had myself written to Professor Roy Calne, asking if he would support my application. He replied saying that, while he couldn't comment on my academic abilities, he would gladly write to my Headmaster Mr Smith stating that there were no medical reasons why I should not be accepted for a place at medical school.

During the Christmas and Easter holidays, I spent a few mornings working in the kitchens of the Gleneagles Hotel where my mum was Housekeeper. This was probably the only time when I wasn't revising for my exams – and much more enjoyable than the hours I spent during school lunchbreaks peering down the microscope at endless histology slides of plant and animal structures.

Finally, it was time to sit my A-level exams, starting with three-hour practicals, which took place during the last week of May, and written papers in June. This time, I looked forward to the exams and felt confident that I would achieve good results. I wrote copious amounts in my answers to the written questions. I have since learned that I have a major problem with answering questions under exam conditions. I tend to go off at a tangent, often in too much detail, rather than addressing what is often just a simple question. And I later had to contend with these problematic characteristics in my professional life.

In late June, the exams had finished and I was able to start my new job as a deckchair attendant for Torbay Council at Oddicombe Beach. Deckchair attendant jobs were highly prized and a big step up from working on the pleasure boats! My job had been secured through the support of my local councillor who I had got to know while on dialysis in the summer of 1974. She lived down the road and she had contacted me following my transplant, asking if there was anything she could help me with – once I had recovered. I immediately asked if she might be able to 'put in a good word for me' and oil the wheels to get me a deckchair attendant's job. This was the only time I can remember using my illness to achieve such an end but working on the deckchairs was a truly cherished prize.

I was thrilled when the official letter came through from Torbay Council. Oddicombe Beach was within walking distance of our house, and I could also use my Yamaha motorbike. As soon as I formally finished school, I started my new employment, working from 8am to 6pm each day. Those working with me included some of my old school colleagues from the first year before I was ill. The others were older, many with alternative 'hippy lifestyles'. My boss, the beachmaster, was a former RN petty officer who I had previously come across while working on the *Nomad*. Everyone accepted me as just another member of the team. This time, there was no need for any explanations or allowances because of my medical background. I was thrilled.

I was a very willing worker and the Area Supervisor in charge of council beaches and car parks soon sounded me out on his daily morning visit as someone he could go to if additional overtime shifts were required. These usually involved working as a car park attendant on the evening shift, for example at the Babbacombe Model Village. It meant staying on at work till 10pm, but I had bags of energy and enthusiasm. Other jobs included having to run the crazy golf and tennis courts in Torquay and sometimes as far away as Paignton.

I was the only person in the workforce at Oddicombe Beach who was planning to go to university. The others were reluctant to take on additional work and for this reason I was selected to work at the left-luggage department at the Council coach station at Lymington Road, close to my school. This meant starting work at 6am and spending the next 16 hours taking in and returning suitcases and other items of luggage. There were no limits on how much weight employees were supposed to lift, as there would be today; some of the suitcases felt as if they contained several kitchen sinks!

In the 1970s, many of the large manufacturing towns in the Midlands and the North had specific fortnights when the factories closed, and everyone went on holiday. These were known as 'Wakes weeks' or 'Trades fortnight' and started in the 18th century as religious holidays. At the beginning of the school holidays, the coach station would be inundated with people travelling overnight on the Friday from towns as far away as Glasgow, arriving any time from early morning to late in the evening. Visitors would return on coaches which travelled overnight to places across the country. Despite the antisocial hours, it could have been worse. It wasn't as bad as sweeping chimneys and sometimes I even got tips from the customers!

The worst possible assignment was to be sent to the bottom station of the Oddicombe Cliff Railway. Thankfully, this didn't happen very often. When it did, my job was to open the metal gates of the railway car when it arrived at the station, let the passengers out, and then allow passengers to enter the car for the return journey uphill. I would close the gates and ring a bell to let the operator at the top station know it was safe to send the car up the railway track. I timed the journey from one station to the other. It took between 90 and 100 seconds, about the time it took me to read three-quarters of a page of a normal-sized paperback. It was an exceedingly boring job.

On one occasion, halfway through a cold, cloudy morning, I found myself being shaken on the arm by one of the other deckchair attendants. I had fallen asleep in my chair, my feet up on a pedestal, with my paperback open on my lap. There were several irate passengers shouting through the glass in the door of the railway car. They were unable to get out but able to see me fast asleep in my chair. The Beach Inspector had received a message from the top station that something was amiss, as I had not responded with the bell to send the car back up. The car had been stationary for about 15 minutes while I was having my beauty sleep. The husband of one of the passengers had earlier spent ages persuading his wife to get into the car at the top of the railway as she suffered from claustrophobia; having travelled to the bottom, she had then found herself trapped inside!

My colleague relieved me, and I was told to report to the Beach Inspector. As I waited outside the Beach Inspector's office, I was certain I would be getting the sack. Eventually, I was asked to enter and found that some of the senior members of the team were also present. The situation with the wife with claustrophobia was explained to me, and I feared the worst. Everyone looked very serious as I tried to give a good account of my actions. Then the atmosphere suddenly changed, laughter broke out and I realised I had been set up. They all thought it hilarious that I had fallen asleep on the worst job we had to do for the Council – and I'm not sure that anyone took much notice of the complaint from the woman's husband. This story always causes great merriment when I tell it at dinner parties.

In the middle of August, I was anxiously waiting for the postman to deliver my A-level results. As I was working, I was unable to go to the school to collect them. In the 1970s, there was less media frenzy about results day and pupils either picked them up from school or waited for the postman to deliver them. I had chosen the latter. The results were also published in the local newspaper, the *Herald Express*. It turned out that I had achieved a B grade in chemistry and Cs in physics and biology. I was a little disappointed, as I had thought I would achieve three Bs. Still, in 1976 the entry requirements for medical school were often B, C, C or even three Cs, so I still had my qualifications.

I now had A-level grades to get me into medical school. However, none of the medical schools I'd applied to had made me an offer so I would either have to apply for medicine through the UCCA clearing scheme, or take a biological sciences subject and try to change course once I got there. The option of delaying for a year and reapplying never entered my head and I did not seek guidance at this stage, nor was it offered. Going through UCCA clearing wasn't an option, as they did not consider medicine. I therefore opted to get a place through clearing to study biochemistry or a similar subject, in a university with a medical school. The UCCA clearing system had automatically sent my application to the University of Surrey, as the system had suggested that there were still places available there to read medical biochemistry. But I was not keen on Surrey as it did not have a medical school.

There was nothing for it but to take the bull by the horns, rather than waiting for the clearing process to finish. It was time for drastic, but affirmative, action! I decided to phone up the admissions officers of biochemistry departments of universities with a medical school, excluding those to which I had applied first time round. I suspect it was highly unusual, and probably frowned upon, for an applicant to make direct contact with admissions tutors, but I was determined. My first phone call was to the admissions tutor in the Biochemistry Department at the University of Leeds. This choice was based on looking at the prospectus and the fact that they took only 24 students per year. I had accumulated many of the prospectuses of universities with medical schools the previous autumn; and I knew that some universities had large intakes of students, with a fairly generic first-year course attended by students studying many different biological sciences. Entry into the second year would then depend on success in the first-year examinations, and often students would not be accepted into the second year.

The morning after I had received the letter from UCCA informing me that my application had been sent to Surrey, I phoned up Leeds and was extremely fortunate to get hold of the admissions tutor at my first attempt. Explaining that I really wanted to come to Leeds, but clearing had sent my application to Surrey, he told me they had a spare place as someone had failed to get the required entry grades. He took my word that I had achieved the entry requirements for the course and immediately offered me this place without seeing my application. This was before the days of computers, when everything was done in hard copy and by making telephone calls.

Even so, it was still extraordinary that he accepted me on to the course without any prior knowledge of who I was, what I had achieved or my academic references. He said he would contact UCCA and request my application and confirm with them the offer of a place to read biochemistry. I was to inform Surrey and UCCA of this decision. Interestingly, by the time my application had arrived at Surrey, all the places had been filled. Had I not rung Leeds, I would have ended up without a university place at all. Once again, my inner voice had told me I needed to take action – and I made that telephone call to Leeds. I did, however, have a backup offer to read Pharmacy at Portsmouth Polytechnic. My grades had easily passed their entrance criteria so I also had to inform them that I would not be coming.

With only a few weeks left before the start of term at Leeds, I had a lot to do, including getting myself a room in the halls of residence. The University of Leeds ensured that every first-year student had a place in university accommodation, so it was back to the prospectus to look at the various options for places to live. The new accommodation complex at Boddington Hall appealed to me. It comprised six individual halls, each accommodating around 100 students. The halls were 5 miles north of the main campus in the city centre on the Otley Road, and the university playing fields were situated on the same site. After phoning the accommodation office, I secured a place in Barbier House.

There was still a lot of organising to do at home, and I was working on the deckchairs until the very last day before going to Leeds. I had to buy a trunk that would be sent up by train a few days before my own journey. In the 1970s, there were no couriers. Most large items were sent using the Rail Express Parcels service, which collected the goods from the recipient and took them to the local railway station, where they were transported to the station at the other end. A lorry would then take the goods to the actual destination. Most importantly, I had to discuss my imminent departure from Torquay to Leeds with Dr Peter Bisson at Whipton Hospital. He was thrilled that I had finally achieved one of my goals and secured a place in read biochemistry on one of the best courses outside Oxbridge. He kindly offered to write to the Renal Consultant at St James Hospital Leeds as well as the University Health Centre, informing them of my imminent arrival and medical history.

On Sunday morning, 19th September 1976, I left home with my mum and Alan to catch the train from Torquay to Leeds to start a new chapter in my life. The journey was long with a train packed full of passengers, many of them students, and the weather was miserable and drizzly. My mum had prepared me well for the journey with a packed lunch and flask of coffee. On arrival at Leeds, I was met by two third-year students who were organising transportation to the halls of residence.

This was to be the start of a new leg in my kidney voyage that would no doubt throw up more rocks for me to steer around. I had already surmounted some significant obstacles, having obtained a place on a highly competitive degree course at a top university. This had been achieved against all the odds, by relying on my inner strength, dogged determination, resilience, and belief that you can do anything if you try hard enough. Out of eight years (I had taken an extra Lower Sixth year) since starting school in 1968, I had attended the equivalent of only three full academic years. I was present for only 15 out of 24 terms, and even then I was often absent for various reasons.

My initial O-level results in summer 1973 had been an annoying setback, but at that time I had been unsure of where my future lay. This all changed with the rejection and loss of my dad's kidney, the return to dialysis and receiving my second transplant. From that point on, I had only one goal, which was to obtain good enough A-levels to be accepted into medical school. In hindsight, on receiving my A-level results I wonder if I should have sought advice from my school. Should I have retaken my A-levels and reapplied for medical school the following year? Or could I have reapplied with the grades I achieved? At the time, I felt the offer to read Biochemistry at the University of Leeds was an excellent option. When we make decisions, we must stick by them and not look backwards. And that is what I did.

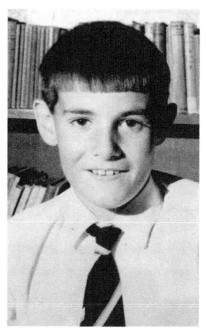

TOP LEFT: The last family holiday at Caister, Norfolk in the summer of 1965. From left to right is Trevor, John, my dad and me standing in front of him. TOP RIGHT: My official school photograph in the library at Ilsham School, Torquay, summer of 1968 (final year at primary school, Year 6 today). BOTTOM: The Northcott family not long after moving to Torquay at the end of 1966.

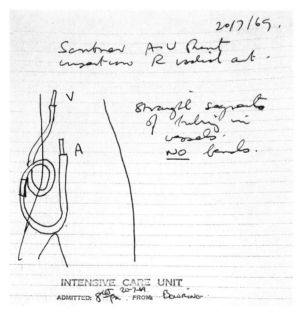

TOP: A copy of my medical notes, July 1969. This is the first page showing a debate over my diagnosis, originally Henoch-Schonlein Purpura then Thrombotic Thrombocytopenic Purpura and finally Haemolytic Uraemic Syndrome. BOTTOM: A hand written diagram of my first Scribner shunt, inserted into my right arm whilst I was in a coma on 20th July 1969.

Modified Giovannetti Diet

Containing 2,000 calories, 3.0 g of nitrogen.

Breakfast:
Grapefruit.
Fried apple rings.
Toasted P.K.N. bread with butter from day's allowance and marmalade.

Mid-morning:
Tea with milk from day's allowance.
P.K.N. biscuits.

Lunch:
3 oz. boiled rice and savoury fried vegetables (excluding peas, beans or lentils).
Pudding made of wheat starch and fruit with vegetable margarine in the pastry.

Mid-afternoon:
Tea with milk from allowance.
P.K.N. bread and jam or honey.

Evening meal:
Clear broth and vegetables. Vegetable salad.
P.K.N. bread and butter.
Fruit if desired.

Notes on diet:
Take a whole egg during the day, plus a half egg per 3 g of protein lost in the urine daily.
Add Methionine 0.5 g, Multivite tablets (N.F.) 2 t.d.s. and oral iron to the diet each day.

Daily allowances of: Butter 1½ oz.
Egg 1.
Milk 6½ oz.
Bread: Phenylketonuric bread (P.K.N.) loaves, biscuits and flour (P.K.N. Drymix) obtainable from Birkett and Bostock Ltd., Coronation Bakery, Stockport, Cheshire (England).
Vegetable margarine *only* must be used.
Sugar or glucose can be taken freely.

Foods forbidden:
Ordinary flour and bread made from it, meat, chicken, fish and cheese.

This diet was invented by the Italian doctor Giovannetti in the 1960s as a means of keeping people with kidney failure alive for up to 6 months if they had no access to dialysis. It was effectively a non-protein starvation diet. This was my diet during the first episode on dialysis in 1969-1970.

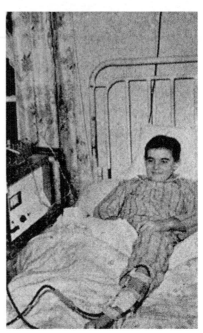

C.	M per c.mm.	C.I.		W.B.C.		per c.mm.	
20 % 8 8 8 % Hypochromasia				Differential Count	%		**Date Received** 8/8/69
ocytosis	Poikilocytosis			Polymorphs. Neut.			
ocytosis	Microcytosis			" Eos			
chromasia	Punct. basophilia			" Bas			
eated R.B.C.	per 100 leucs			Lymphocytes			
ulocytes	%	per c.mm.		Monocytes			
lets 148,000 per c.mm.				Metamyelocytes			
26 %	M.C.D.	μ		Myelocytes			
cμ	M.C.H.C. 34	%					-JMH
mm./hr.:	mm./hr.:(corrected)						

Sodium	134	mE/l. (132-144)	Protein		g/100ml(6.1-8.0)
Potassium	4.2	mE/l. (3.5-5.5)	Albumin		g/100ml(3.0-4.5)
Chloride	98	mE/l. (96-106)	Electrophoresis		
Bicarbonate	25	mE/l. (22-30)	Thymol Turb.		u. (0-4)
Urea	113	mg/100ml(15-40)	Bilirubin Total		mg/100ml(0.2-1.0)
Sugar. Time-		mg/100ml(F60-105)	Conjugated		mg/100 ml.
As.A.T.(G.O.T.)		u./ml. (5-28)	Alk. Phosph.		u./100ml.(3-13)
Al.A.T.(G.P.T.)		u./ml. (8-35)	Calcium		mg/100ml.(9-11)
L.D.H.		u./ml.(160-400)	Phosphorus		mg/100ml.(2-5)
Amylase		u./100ml.(0-200)	Uric acid		mg/100ml.(3-6.5)
Acid Phos.(F.S)		u./100ml.(0-3)	Cholesterol		mg/100ml(140-250)

TOP LEFT: Home in Dunolly, Wellswood, Torquay, late 1969 protecting the Scribner shunt in my right arm. TOP RIGHT: Home dialysis began on my birthday 11th March 1970. The rear bedroom of our house in Warbro Road was now a clinical area. The Scribner shunt was now in my leg as all access sites in my arms had been used up. BOTTOM My medical notes are a unique record of how medicine was practised at this time. This is one of many chemical pathology reports often hand written including the calculations.

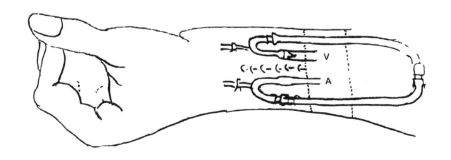

The Artificial Kidney — and the will to live

TOP: The Scribner shunt is created by inserting a plastic tube into an artery in the arm or leg whilst another tube is inserted into a nearby vein. Both tubes exit the body through a punch hole and are then joined together with a rubber connector. During dialysis blood is pumped from the artery to the machine and returned through the vein. BOTTOM: My dog Chum gave me the will to live during difficult times.

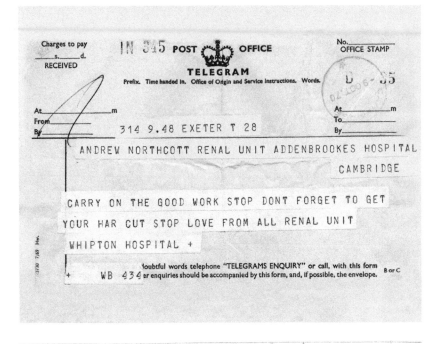

TOP: On lst October 1970 I received a kidney from my dad in a life saving operation performed by Professor Roy Caine at old Addenbrooke's Hospital, Cambridge. This is a telegram I received from my doctors and nurses at Exeter. BOTTOM: By day 5 I had developed a life-threatening pneumonia and my newly transplanted kidney had started to reject. The graveness of my condition only became apparent to me after researching my medical notes over half a century later.

TOP: Professor Roy Caine made major contributions to transplantations. In September 1969 his advice to my doctors saved my life, by removing my kidneys. A year later he transplanted my dad's kidney to me. BOTTOM: This photograph shows how quickly I developed 'Cushing-noid' symptoms in 1970 with 'moon face' and severe obesity due to the very large doses of steroids. The horrendous changes to my body made me a target for bullying.

ROYAL DEVON AND EXETER HOSPITAL

1000 CALORIE WEIGHT REDUCTION DIET   (D 39)

		Approximate Calories
BREAKFAST	Tea or coffee with milk from allowance. No sugar	
	½ Grapefruit	15
	1 Egg or grilled bacon (1 oz.) or Haddock (3 oz.) Kipper or Herring	90
	Tomato or Mushrooms - not fried	10
	1 Slice bread from large cut loaf (1 oz.)) Scraping of butter from allowance)	100
MID-MORNING	Tea or coffee with milk from allowance or Bovril or Oxo or Dietetic fruit squash	
DINNER	Clear soup or unthickened vegetable soup.	
	Average helping of lean meat (2 oz.) offal, poultry, rabbit or fish (5 oz.) roast, boiled, stewed, grilled, baked - NOT FRIED	130
	Unthickened gravy	
	Green vegetables - brussel sprouts, cabbage, celery, cauliflower, leeks, marrow boiled onions, runner beans, tomatoes, and spinach as desired	10
	Small helping of carrots ~~~	
	~~ e oil, salad cream, nuts.	
	Average helping of stewed fruit, sweetened with saccharine OR one piece of fresh fruit (i.e. medium sized apple, orange, pear OR small banana).	50
TEA	Tea with milk from allowance	
	1 Slice of bread (1 oz.) or 2 plain biscuits) Scraping of butter from allowance) Tomatoes, lettuce, cucumber, marmite)	100
EVENING MEAL	Meat (2 oz.), fish (5 oz.), ham, cheese (1 oz.) or large egg	130
	Green vegetables or salad	10
	1 Slice of bread (1 oz.) or 2 plain biscuits) (i.e. Ryvita, cream cracker or Vitawheat) Scraping of butter)	100
	Stewed or fresh fruit as at Dinner	50
BEDTIME	The remainder of milk in tea or coffee	
	MILK ALLOWANCE - ½ pint daily	
	BUTTER OR MARGARINE - ¼ to ½ oz. daily	190
	TOTAL CALORIES	1000

At the end of 1971 my doctors challenged me to go on a 1000 kcal diet, This is my original diet sheet kept on the door on the fridge at home, I stuck to it and over the next year returned to a normal weight for my height.

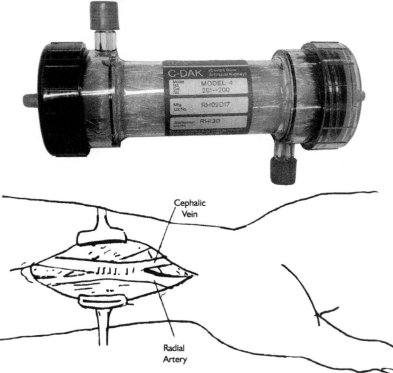

TOP: I returned to home dialysis using a REDY dialysis machine. MIDDLE: This shows my disposable dialyser that revolutionised treatment. BOTTOM: Dr Cimino designed an internal shunt, where the artery and vein are joined together under the skin. After a few weeks the pressure in the artery causes the vein to swell. For dialysis, two wide bore needles are inserted into the vein. One needle takes the blood to the machine whilst the other returns it back to the patient.

EXETER & DISTRICT KIDNEY PATIENTS' ASSN.

4th Annual Ball

AT

THE ASSEMBY ROOMS, SOUTH MOLTON

FRIDAY NOVEMBER 8TH.   9 - 1.30

Dance to The Cy Eastman Band

£1.50 INCUDING BUFFET

LICENCE APPLIED FOR

TOP: Since July 1974 I was back on dialysis. On November 8th I attended the 4th Annual Ball organised by the Exeter and District kidney patients association. I was dialysing at home so my doctors had organised for me to dialyse at the unit and stay the night. BOTTOM: Although only 17 years old I was enjoying myself having the odd vodka and orange and dancing with members of the nursing staff.

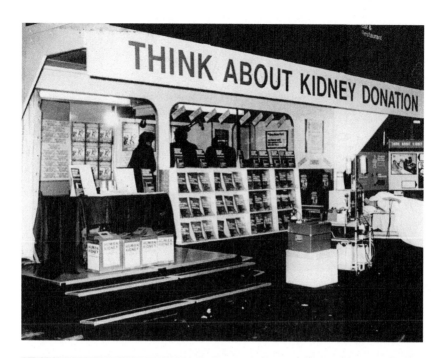

TOP: I had become passionate at increasing awareness of the newly introduced National Kidney donor card scheme. Mrs Elizabeth Ward the founder of the British Kidney Patient's Association invited me to London Waterloo for a week to hand out donor cards to commuters. BOTTOM: In 1979 I represented Exeter in swimming and field events at the second Kidney Transplant Olympic games in Portsmouth.

TOP LEFT: 24: My first job was as a Tissue Typist at Guy's Hospital, London matching kidneys between recipients and donors. Dr Ken Welsh's arrival created the opportunity for me to undertake a PhD and start my research career. TOP RIGHT: In 1993 we moved to the University of Plymouth to set up a new research group and establish the postgraduate and then undergraduate medical schools. BOTTOM: In 2004 my family supported me to deliver my inaugural professorial lecture. It was the first time I had spoken in public about my kidney failure. Left to right - Ann, Andy, Oliver. Thomas & Lucy.

Chapter 9: A New Life at University

In September 1976, I started my new life as an undergraduate student reading biochemistry at the University of Leeds. It was a completely new experience for me to be able to mingle with other people in my peer group who had no idea of my medical condition. People in the transplant community always feel that it's a truly successful treatment if we are able to fit into a normal social group – in my case, this was a group of university students. I was determined that my condition would not stop me taking a full part in university life. I longed just to be a normal guy attending university, able to participate in everything it had to offer.

My new home in my first year was in Barbier House, Bodington Hall, around 4 miles north of Leeds city centre on the Otley Road. It was the largest hall of residence, with eight separate buildings, each housing at least 80 single rooms, and a main building with a central refectory where breakfast and evening meals were served. It had been opened in 1961 and the architect, Denis Mason-Jones, won the Leeds Gold Medal for its design. The hall was named after the first Vice Chancellor of the University, Sir Nathan Bodington.

My room was on the ground floor, with four other rooms coming off the communal corridor. On one side there was a lovely third-year overseas engineering student from Kuwait. This was the first time I had met someone from the Middle East, and he was great to talk to about politics and other matters. My other neighbour was a chap from Leicester who was reading microbiology and who we nicknamed 'Kip'. He was a very laid-back hippy type, with long tangled hair, who often wore sandals or went barefoot. The fire door for my corridor was located opposite the Warden's house, and he happened to be one of the biochemistry lecturers. He lived in the house with his wife and children and, within hours of my arrival, he made himself known to me, explaining that he was available nearly 24/7 were I to have a medical emergency, or feel unwell. This was very kind of him, and the admissions team had clearly put a lot of thought into accommodating my medical needs, even though I was not aware of telling them anything about my condition. I imagine that my school must have contacted the university once I had received my place through UCCA.

I had specifically applied to read biochemistry at Leeds because of my desire to switch to medicine. Accordingly, within a few days, I made an appointment with the admissions tutor in the medical school as well as the one in the biochemistry department. While they both seemed willing to listen to my request, I received a resounding 'no'. They said it was not possible to transfer courses immediately, although I could apply for medicine once I had finished my biochemistry degree in three years' time. Interestingly, they never mentioned the option of taking a year out and perhaps retaking my A-levels and re-applying for medicine. I was not surprised by this response, having already talked to several students about it. It still came as a blow, after working so hard for 18 or more months, but I knew I had to take it on the chin and, for the time being, get on with reading biochemistry.

I had no idea what to expect, never having met any recent university graduates, but it didn't take long for me to get into the swing of things. Within a few days, I had my introduction to Freshers' Week. In 1976 this was nothing like the razzmatazz that takes place today, which is no doubt heavily commercialised. My Freshers' Week took place in the Students' Union. It was a very impressive building, which boasted the longest bar in the country and a phenomenal range of beers. It was also a famous music venue where many rock bands appeared, such as The Who, Cream and Black Sabbath.

Being rather naïve, I didn't know where to start with the many student societies who were touting for freshers to join them. I'd expected to find a Model Railway Society but was instead confronted with groups like the Socialist Workers' Party and the Campaign for Nuclear Disarmament. The only advice I'd had from my family was to make sure I joined the Ballroom Dance Society, as they thought it would be useful for me to be able to dance the Foxtrot or Waltz if I were invited to a social event involving formal dancing. I duly headed for the Ballroom Dancing Society stall and paid for a term's membership, which included weekly lessons. I was partnered with a girl who wasn't very talkative and seemed to think I was some kind of alien being. Nevertheless, I persevered, but things came to a head (or I should I say foot?) when my size 11 boots kept getting in the way during a slow recital of Strauss's 'Blue Danube'. She vanished to the ladies' powder room and never reappeared! I can't say I blamed, her as I wasn't enjoying it much either. So, after just a few weeks, my ballroom dancing adventures came to an ignominious end. My new circle of friends at Bodington Hall thought it highly amusing and, for reasons I've never understood, all seemed to sympathise with my disappearing partner. I never did find the Model Railway Society.

At the first meeting of my fellow biochemistry students with our Professor and other academic staff, it was impressed upon us that we were a select group of 24, as other life sciences courses had lower entry requirements and many more students. A certain amount of pride welled up in me that I had achieved as much as I had. There were also a number of students doing combined subjects, but they were considered 'lesser beings' as their course content was so diluted!

Combined honours degrees began to be introduced around this time and people reading the pure subject always had contempt for the combined ones. We were told that combined degrees were out of favour with employers at the time, and unemployment was rife in the mid to late 1970s. The entry requirements for reading biochemistry at the University of Leeds were among the highest of all UK universities outside Oxbridge. As we were of such high calibre, we were expected to achieve high academic standards. That said, there were several first-year lectures in common with other subjects, such as microbiology, pharmacology and physiology, which took place in the main lecture theatre with 200 or more students attending.

The people not studying straight biochemistry really hated the biochemistry lectures, and this created considerable rivalry and banter between the groups. We biochemists also had to attend first-year lectures in their subjects. However, there was similar intense rivalry between the Biochemistry and Chemistry Departments in how to teach us 'the chemistry of life'. I am sure we were the Chemistry Department's playthings, as our lectures took place from 5 to 7pm on Mondays and this was the only department in the university that took a student register. Having a rebellious nature, I and many other students refused to sign a register and be treated as if we were back at school. Our rebellion caused great consternation but the Chemistry Department still insisted that we had to sign the register.

This was repeated in the second year when, once again, we had weeks of two-hour lectures on physical and organic chemistry. Try staying awake during an explanation of Boyle's Law that includes the derivation of formulas from first principles! In contrast, learning about the history of key discoveries in modern chemistry by scientists such as Berzelius, Dalton and Wöhler fascinated me.

Notwithstanding my failure to engage with my partner in ballroom dancing, I quickly made friends among the students in Barbier House and elsewhere. There were only a few people reading biochemistry, so my new circle of friends studied a range of subjects, from French to food science to medicine. As the weeks went by, our group became particularly adept at playing student pranks, such as kidnapping the fairy from the top of the Christmas tree in the refectory, an achievement that required ingenuity and teamwork, given the enormous height of the tree. At Christmas, I returned home and finally read *The Hobbit*, which Dr Bisson had given me when I'd had my fractured leg. One of my Christmas presents was a paperback copy of Tolkien's *Lord of the Rings*, which I also read from cover to cover, and was barely able to put down. I was also in receipt of the 'Old Grammarians' Prize' for outstanding all-round achievement from my old school. I decided to use the prize money to purchase a book on statistics in biochemistry.

For the rest of the year, I worked reasonably hard and was pleased when the exam results came out in June 1977, and I was graded an upper second in biochemistry. I had worked diligently for the exams, despite being distracted by endless social activities. However, the same could not be said of chemistry where I was pleased to get through with a pass. Nearly all my peers received similarly poor results in chemistry. This was my first introduction to petty inter-departmental university politics, although at this stage of my life I was seeing it from a student's perspective.

While waiting for the exam papers to be marked, I invited my close friends to visit my home in Torquay and spend a weekend there. Everyone thought this was a great idea and we decided to make it a hitch-hiking race. Hitch-hiking was a popular way for impoverished students and others to move around the country back then. We would stand in places where passing cars and lorries could easily pull over, such as laybys and service stations, and just stick our thumbs out, hoping they would stop and give us a lift. It was popular with people of both sexes and not considered dangerous if you were sensible.

We decided to hitch-hike from the beginning of the M62 westbound motorway slip road in Leeds to my home, with everyone doing the journey alone, starting at around 8am on the Friday morning. We hoped to get to Torquay that evening. Some members of the group had great success, including getting lifts in a Rolls Royce, while others made do with slow-moving articulated lorries. My trip was not so good. Having got to the Burtonwood services on the M62 (just west of the junction with the M6 and close to Liverpool) by late morning, I realised it was going to be difficult to get a lift going south down the M6 towards Birmingham. I was on the wrong side of the M62, and few cars and lorries stopped at the service station when travelling south. I managed to get over to the east-bound service station and patiently waited for a lift, but to no avail. As darkness fell, it became clear that I was going to have a long, uncomfortable night, sleeping on hard chairs in the service area.

After grabbing some breakfast and chatting to other hitch-hikers, I realised I had made a dreadful mistake in coming to Burtonwood at all. Fortunately, wandering around the lorry park, I met an HGV driver who was going to Glasgow. He said there were hardly any cars or lorries that stopped at the services to go south, as it was too close to Liverpool from where they had only just begun their trip. He advised me to travel north and start again at another service station. Alternatively, he offered to take me to Preston railway station from where I could catch a train home. My friends were going to be leaving Torquay on Monday or Tuesday and at this rate I would hardly see them. I made the decision to give up hitch-hiking and the driver took me to catch the train. I was lucky, as there was only one more train that day that could get me home.

I had just enough cash to pay for my ticket. When I got home, late that afternoon, I had to face a lot of teasing and banter. Nearly all my friends had made it to Torquay by the previous evening as planned, and had received great hospitality from my mum, with tea the previous night and a full English breakfast in the morning. They had already seen many of Torquay's fabulous sights; but I was not alone in having problems hitch-hiking and two of my friends apparently went only a few miles before deciding to give up and return to Leeds. It was all good fun and that weekend at 'Wolfie's house' in Torquay is still fondly recalled by those who made it. 'Wolfie' was the nickname affectionately bestowed upon me at the beginning of the year, on account of my thick beard and hairy body.

By now, I had sold my 100cc Yamaha twin-cylinder motorbike. Once at Leeds, I was very keen to purchase some 'new wheels' and one of my new friends had a Triumph Bonneville 750, a motorbike that was a classic even then and is certainly a classic now. He persuaded me (without much difficulty) to buy a second-hand Triumph Cub that had a single-cylinder 250cc engine. It was a disaster, and certainly couldn't have been described as 'new wheels'.

My plan had been to join the University Motorcycle Club in order to attend functions around Yorkshire as well as commuting to university. However, the bike spent most of the time in bits, often in the corridor outside my room, much to the horror of the warden and the cleaners. Araldite and a hammer came in useful to stop the perpetual oil leaks! At the end of my first year, I managed to get it to Leeds City Railway Station, just about freewheeling there, where it was put onto a freight wagon along with my trunk, and despatched home, care of Red Star parcels. This was a real disappointment as I had planned to use it to make the trip home. Back in Torquay, I managed to sell it to a man who was setting up a motorcycle museum – an apt destination!

Once I was home for the summer vacation, I went back to working on the deckchairs for Torbay Council. The previous Easter, I had contacted the Council to ask if my job could be kept open for when I returned. During the summer, working tax-free as a student, I quickly earned enough money to buy an almost new Honda 250 twin-cylinder motorbike to replace my 'museum piece'. It was painted a lovely yellow, and I spent around £500 on it. In 1976, you could still ride motorcycles up to 250cc with 'L' plates, although I planned to take my driving test once I got back to university. In the wrong hands, these machines could cause many fatalities as they could travel at more than 100 miles per hour.

At this time, it was only four years since a law had enforced the wearing of safety helmets while riding motorcycles. The introduction of this legislation had been fiercely opposed by many MPs, who considered it a 'gross infringement of personal liberty'. There were sizeable protests, including among the Sikh community who at first were not exempt. A retired schoolteacher called Fred Hill became famous for leading these protests well into the 1980s. He was imprisoned 31 times for non-payment of fines for refusing to wear a helmet. There are still memorial rides to honour his campaign – and it shows how much our society has changed since the 1970s that something we now consider perfectly normal and sensible was once such a cause célèbre. It is also an interesting contrast to most people's willingness to comply with the removal of numerous freedoms during the Covid pandemic.

The summer came and went very quickly, and I was able to continue working on the deckchairs until late into September 1977. I can't say I missed university over the summer, as I was busy earning money and immersed in my job. However, I now had to think about accommodation for when I returned. I had missed out on all the arrangements for house and flat shares that had taken place at the end of the first year. But it wasn't a problem, as I was offered a first-floor bedroom at 5 Brudenell Grove, Hyde Park, Leeds, in a house-share with five student nurses working at St James's Hospital.

We had all been friendly with the nurses in our first year, as one of them was the sister of one of my friends. The house was very rundown but had the advantage of being close to the university. It was a far cry from the accommodation some students live in today, with Sky TV, fitted kitchens and laundry facilities. The house I moved into in 1977 had a black and white TV in a cold basement, with threadbare carpets and damp seeping through the walls. There was no communal spirit. The nurses came and went like ships in the night, usually leaving plates of leftover food for the 'house fairies' to tidy up.

I was quite ambivalent starting my second year, compared to my previous year, and found it hard to adapt to being back at university. Nearly all my friends lived in the north and they had been able to get together quite often during the summer while I was busy working in Torquay. Two of my closest friends had also had to drop out and repeat the year because of glandular fever. I had 9am core biochemistry lectures in the main lecture theatre nearly every day, as well as intense small group tutorials for six to eight students. Even though I lived within walking distance of the university campus, I struggled to make it to the lectures and was relying on obtaining notes from other students and copying the few handouts provided by the lecturer.

We still had two-hour chemistry lectures starting at 5pm, which sent everybody to sleep, and my enthusiasm for university academic work simply evaporated. Many people say, 'Oh the second year is the worst, and everyone gets a low...', but it should not have been this way for me, having worked so hard to get a place on an outstanding course studying the 'chemistry of life'. I think one problem was the fact that so many lectures focused on nothing but bacteria or plants. I had no interest in learning about these 'micro-beasties' or how chloroplasts worked. I was only interested in studying material related to human beings. This was probably rather immature on my part – I failed to see the bigger picture, in the sense of relating the science of these organisms to mammalian cells. But I think I was also feeling 'a bit at sea'.

In my second year, I was finally able to adjust to being a normal person, without all the baggage of my medical history. I could let my hair down and enjoy myself for the first time for many years, just like many other students who were also living away from home and finding their feet. Of course, I had already become independent in a different way earlier in my life, having spent months at a time in hospitals surrounded by adults. But I had never previously been able to socialise with peers who were not involved in any way with hospitals. I was growing up in a different way.

The euphoria of getting to Leeds had died down and I now found myself in the real world. The protective cloak, which had previously been wrapped round me by doctors and nurses, some of whom had provided a great deal of emotional input, was absent. I had achieved my aim, which was to be independent and live as a normal person, but it was a lot harder than I had anticipated. A great many mundane tasks that went with living alone had to be dealt with, such as shopping for food, cooking meals and doing my own laundry. All these jobs had been done for me during my lengthy stays in hospital. Once again, I needed to dig into my inner reserves, my determination and self-belief, to cope with these new pressures.

With respect to my renal care, Dr Bisson had kindly written to Dr Alex Davison at St James's Hospital, Leeds, as well as the University Student Health Clinic. During the first year, I visited the out-patient renal clinic at 'Jimmy's' and was met by a very fierce Sister who appeared to have zero sympathy. This came as quite a shock. She demanded to know where my 24-hour urine collection was, and I politely informed her that this was my first visit to the clinic and so I was unaware of the need to collect my urine and had no bottle anyway. My answer did not impress her, and she took it upon herself to thrust a bottle into my hand for next time.

My consultation with Dr Davison was similarly awkward. My understanding had been that I would contact him if I felt unwell or had any concerns while in Leeds. However, Dr Davison seemed to be under the impression that my renal care had been permanently transferred to Leeds. I really don't know how he came to that conclusion, as I have now been able to read the correspondence between the two units. My hackles were well and truly raised. I had spent seven years being cared for by Exeter and Cambridge with no issues. The clinic visits in Exeter were always marked by a warm engagement between me and the doctors, so this was quite an alien experience.

Perhaps it was my appearance the Sister objected to, as I had gone to the hospital on my motorcycle and was wearing my Belstaff jacket. I came away from the clinic with the 5,000ml plastic bottle hidden under my jacket, determined to resist future visits. I did attend again at the beginning of the second year, in November 1977, after having seen Dr Bisson in Exeter before I left for Leeds. Dr Bisson politely asked me to give it another go. True to my word, I did indeed go back, but was again scolded by the fierce Sister who demanded to know where my 24-hour collection was (I had not learned from my previous encounter!)

It might seem a minor objection, and perhaps arrogant on my part, but carrying a 5,000 ml 24-hour urine bottle around during the week does not fit well with attending lectures and having a social life at university. I found it incredibly embarrassing. I had kept my transplant secret from everyone, although those doing medicine had probably guessed that I had a medical history based on the numerous scars on show when we went swimming. Nevertheless, I was not at all keen to waltz around with a massive urine bottle and funnel in a plastic carrier bag. On top of this, Exeter and Cambridge had given up doing these collections many years earlier, unless the patient was on a ward where collections could be carried out accurately and were required for a specific reason. I felt I was taking good care of myself, as I was still seeing my doctors in Exeter during the vacations and travelling to Cambridge for a check-up during the Christmas party weekend. Indeed, while researching this book I came across several studies showing that 24-hour urine collections are invariably incorrect and invalid unless they are carried out in a clinical setting. Many decades later, I have been vindicated.

I only went to two more clinics while in Leeds and that was in my final year, following more pleas from Dr Peter Bisson. My failure to attend on numerous consecutive occasions had obviously caused a great deal of consternation and correspondence between Exeter and Leeds. At the time I had not appreciated the extent of Dr Davison's concern for my wellbeing. However, we now know that young adults with chronic kidney disease can have major psychological and other issues during their transition from paediatric to adult clinics or when they move hospital units for further education or employment. These issues can lead to their losing contact with their medical team altogether, non-compliance with their drug regimen and the risk of rejection of their transplant. This loss of contact is one of the single biggest identifiable causes of transplant rejection. It also happens in other chronic diseases, such as type I diabetes, when the person moves clinics and reappears in the health system, often turning up in a crisis or at an ante-natal clinic. However, in my case, I was still having regular check-ups at Exeter and had ample supplies of my immunosuppressant drugs, which I took without fail – even when I knew I was going out for a typical rowdy student party.

The second year brought with it my 21st birthday on 11th March 1978. I decided I was going to celebrate it in style – and hired a smart nightclub at the Merrion Centre, in Leeds, close to the university. This grand event was booked to take place on Monday 13th March, and I was also planning a separate house party on my real birthday the previous Saturday.

I paid £22 to hire the venue, which could hold around 200 people, and organised the printing of tickets with WH Smith. The party was fantastic, with all the members of my large social circle attending. It meant a great deal to me to be able to celebrate this important milestone in my life. The entire weekend was probably partly an over-reaction to the many years of illness I'd endured as a child and teenager, surviving on low-protein, salt-free diets, and spending so many birthdays in hospital. I had planned the entire weekend meticulously, with the help of my close friends. The house party was an equally great success, typical of most student social events!

For the first time, I was able to celebrate a notable event without being mired by my medical condition. I was just a normal guy having a 21st birthday party. Considering I'd had my second transplant just over three years before, I had a lot to be happy about! Most people who came to the party at the Merrion Centre were there because I was a friend. There was no food or drink provided by the venue to entice them to come, although they did lay on a disco. People had attended because of genuine friendship and a desire to help me celebrate my birthday. I don't know how many of them were aware of my medical condition and perhaps I am being naïve in assuming my transplant was 'a secret'. Certainly, my close friends just accepted me as their mate 'Wolfie' – and by now most of them were aware of my condition.

At the beginning of the second year, I had ridden from Torquay to Leeds on my newly acquired Yamaha 250 motorbike, sticking to 'A' roads as I had not yet passed my driving test. It was quite an achievement on what was a very wet Saturday. A few weeks later, I passed my test at the first attempt and threw away my 'L-plates'. It was now time to buy another motorbike. I couldn't afford the one I really wanted, which was a four-cylinder Honda 750cc, now a sought-after classic. Instead, I was able to buy a Honda 500cc twin-cylinder with double overhead camshafts. It wasn't a popular bike because of the complex engine arrangement but I didn't realise this at the time, as customer reviews were not as accessible as they are today.

There were more exams to get through as I neared the end of my second year. I hoped I might get a reasonable mark, but it was not to be. The truth was that I was still struggling to make progress with my studies, even though I revised extensively, using the fantastic library we had at Leeds. I also found it hard to revise from my lecture notes, and handouts were rarely given out. This long before PowerPoint, and other media tools. The lecturers would stand at the lectern and recite the topic, sometimes using the enormous blackboards that rotated by pulling up or down. Writing legibly and quickly was vital in order to obtain coherent notes – and this was a task I failed at miserably. I finished the second year feeling rather low and annoyed with myself for not working harder. I knew I should have done better and I had let myself down. On the other hand, I had revelled in the social side of being a second-year student. The social and academic sides of university were two sides of the same coin, and I desperately wanted to excel at both. This was a great challenge and I knew I would have to correct the balance in my final year.

I rode my motorcycle home as soon the examination period was over at the end of the second year, with my faithful trunk coming by train. I then used the bike to commute to Oddicombe Beach where I returned to working as a deckchair attendant. The fact that I had my own transport and was a very keen worker meant that I was often sent to many other Council sites across the Borough for evening car park and leisure facility duties.

After working all summer for the Council, mid-September came around quickly and once again it was time to leave for Leeds. I had to delay my departure for a few days because my motorbike cam belt, part of the bike's complex engine structure, had broken. As it was an unusual model, it took longer to repair than anticipated and term had already begun before it was fixed. I had a phone call at home from a very anxious third-year tutor who was concerned that I had not registered with the university and might not be returning to complete the course. I had not appreciated that they were probably concerned for my welfare, while I was simply trying to sort out the repairs for my bike. On reflection, I can see I should of course have informed them that I had needed to delay my return to Leeds and why. It simply hadn't occurred to me, particularly as the first few days tended to be mainly socialising.

For the final year, I had a house-share with two of my friends who had had to take a year out. One was back doing his second-year medical course, having suffered from glandular fever, and the other was reading French and Business Studies with a year out working for a company. We decided not to live in Headingley, where most of the students tended to rent properties, but instead chose a more residential part of the city. One of my friends had found a two-bedroom terrace house in the Harehills district, in the eastern part of Leeds. This was much better than the house I had shared the previous year. It was a traditional two-up, two-down, with a cellar and reasonable-size rooms and nice décor. It was close to a large pub, which was a favourite with the Afro-Caribbean community as well as other locals and we would all play pool on the tables in the bar. We had been told the atmosphere was particularly lively in the pre-Christmas period.

I finally packed up my side saddles, top box and tank bag and set off for the north in the afternoon, when the repairs to my bike had been completed. I made very good progress, travelling up the M5, M6 and then the M62, with almost empty motorways. At around 1am I had just got past Rochdale, and was close to Saddleworth Moor (site of the infamous Moors Murders in the 1960s). Travelling at a reasonable speed, I was thinking I would be in Leeds within the hour. But then, having overtaken a lorry on the outside lane, the bike started to weave uncontrollably. I managed to steer it closer to the inside, where it went from underneath me, and I found myself sliding and hurtling along the tarmac. In 1978, in the early hours, traffic was considerably lighter than it is now, and thankfully there were few vehicles behind me. A lorry driver stopped on the hard shoulder and together we managed to remove my bike from the carriageway. Fortunately, at first glance I seemed to have avoided any major injuries, despite the speed at which I'd been travelling. I had come to a halt under an overbridge, and it was now beginning to rain. After thanking the lorry driver for his help, I contacted the RAC, which I had luckily joined a couple of years earlier.

Although I had all the usual protective motorcycle gear, it wasn't long before the freezing cold weather started to have an undesirable effect on my body and shock started to kick in. When the recovery vehicle finally arrived, we looked at the bike and realised the rear wheel had collapsed, with many broken spokes, and so it was put on the back of the truck, I jumped into the passenger seat in the lovely warm cab, and we headed for Harehills and my new home. After a few hours' sleep in my new bed, I recounted my adventures to my housemates while using cold towels to try to reduce the pain in my right wrist which by now had swollen up like a balloon.

My medical student friend used his immense first-year knowledge to diagnose a possible fractured wrist. It had never occurred to me that it could be broken, and the cold wet Pennine weather had obviously dulled the pain! It was time to take a trip to St James's Hospital ('Jimmy's') which was located close by. There, an X-ray confirmed that I had suffered a Colle's fracture of the distal radius bone. This is a common fracture that occurs when you put out your hand to break a fall. I had clearly done exactly that when falling from my bike. My right arm was put in Plaster of Paris and back to university I went. My injury meant that I could not do any biochemistry practicals with my arm in plaster. I think the Head of Department took a dim view of me turning up for the course a week late, although – once he realised that I had broken my arm – he was more sympathetic.

It didn't take me too long to settle into the course, which this year was just biochemistry, with no evening chemistry lectures. I was by now fully aware that I had not worked hard enough during my second year, with poor attendance at lectures (particularly the early morning ones) and not getting to grips with the extra work and revision required in addition to the teaching. I worked reasonably hard during my last year and the subjects covered were much more to my liking – biochemistry of humans and health and disease, rather than the generic bacterial, fungi and plant topics that had dominated previous years.

I was determined to try and get back on track. I had always found it difficult to concentrate during lectures, my mind drifting off to other things. I had never been one to sit near the front, but I now realised this was precisely what I should have been doing. My lecture notes often failed to reflect what the speaker had said, and usually consisted of incoherent scribble. Some of the students in my year had formed small study groups and were sharing materials. This was something I really should have made more of an effort to do. Instead, I tended to work on my own, immersing myself in the library facilities. I was still overwhelmed by the sight of rows of academic books and particularly the scientific journals. I now taught myself to use Index Medicus to access these journals, which formed a large part of my learning materials.

The fact that I found it difficult to interact academically with my fellow students was probably down to my own lack of confidence. Right from the beginning of the first year, I had been in awe of some of the students who were extremely knowledgeable and had communication skills to match. Consequently, in their presence I tended to clam up, even though I was more than capable of engaging in the discussions. Looking back, it probably took the whole of my time at university to overcome my lack of confidence and decide that I would no longer let it hold me back.

The next district to the north from where we were living was the infamous Chapeltown red light district. Our stay in Harehills coincided with the time when the Yorkshire Ripper was preying on women who lived and worked in Chapeltown. On one occasion, the three of us were walking back from the city centre during the early hours of the morning, unaware (until we put on the radio later that day) that he had murdered another young woman not far from where we had been walking. Even though, as men, we were unlikely to be his victims, it made us very wary of going through that area late at night.

This period (1978–1979) was also notorious for mass strikes of public service workers that sometimes went on for months at a time. Rubbish was left uncollected and striking gravediggers left corpses in makeshift morgues. 'Green Goddess' fire engines (the colloquial name for the RLHZ self-propelled pump, manufactured by Bedford Vehicles), held in reserve by the Government to be used in times of emergency, came to the rescue when firefighters went on strike during this 'Winter of Discontent'.

The ambulance crews were also on strike and their place was also taken by the Armed Forces. We would wander past the striking firefighters sitting around their lit braziers to keep warm. In addition, this winter was extremely cold, with snow on the ground at our house in Harehills from November right through to the end of March. We would often wake in the mornings to find frost on the inside of our bedroom windows. Our house was on a steep hill that joined the main road. The road was iced over nearly all winter and I had fun steering the bike down the hill, avoiding the parked cars and trying to ensure that I could stop when I got to the junction!

In the final weeks of term before Christmas, my housemates and I enjoyed all the merriment our local pub had to offer and then it was time to head home. The weather was atrocious, with freezing temperatures and heavy snow, but I saw it as a challenge. The weather forecasts predicted no end to the cold spell so I could have been stuck in Leeds for some time. I gingerly rode on the inside lane of the motorways, unable to see far with the snowflakes getting into my eyes. This meant keeping to a low speed with articulated lorries passing me in the middle lanes, their tyres continually churning up wet slush that left me drenched. Even my waxed cotton Belstaff jacket was soon damp. And my fingers and toes quickly grew numb from the cold, despite my thick gloves and leather boots.

The weather also had a detrimental effect on my final-year project. I had elected to do some research at a psychiatric hospital out towards Leeds-Bradford airport and some miles from the city centre. The project was interesting and involved collecting urine samples from patients with manic depression (now better known as bipolar syndrome) who were being treated with lithium. Blood samples had also been taken and, looking at them together with the urine samples, it was possible to measure the rate at which lithium was absorbed into the body and how much of it was excreted. The samples had to be collected and brought back to the Biochemistry Department where flame spectroscopy was used to measure the lithium. Unfortunately, the weather was so bad in the weeks before Christmas that at times it was impossible to get to the hospital. My project suffered due to lack of samples and I had to plead mitigating circumstances. I wondered if I should have stuck with bacteria!

Christmas and New Year came and went, and it was back to university for my final two terms. My third year also saw the arrival of Professor W.I.P. Mainwaring from the Imperial Cancer Research Fund Institute (now part of Cancer Research) in London. Professor Mainwaring's expertise was in the workings of sex hormones in health and disease. His lectures on testosterone and oestrogen pathways were the best I had listened to in three years at Leeds.

I was also in his tutorial group and totally mesmerised by his delivery of the subject. In contrast to my other subjects, I ended up with superb lecture notes and spent ages in the library reading around the topic. Professor Mainwaring somehow brought it all to life. Consequently, I became quite confident in the tutorials, making a full and active contribution to the discussions.

I had a similar experience with a module focusing on the biochemistry of teeth and dental decay that was delivered jointly with the Dental School. Many of my fellow students found the topic boring and had opted not to do it. In the event, there was only a small handful of students and the teaching was superb. I very quickly became one of the 'more engaged' students and felt able to fulfil my academic potential. The module was one of the last we did before we broke up for revision for the final exams in May and June 1979. I was so enthralled by of fluorination of teeth, and how it protects them from decay, that I approached the Academic Lead to discuss the possibility of doing a PhD on the subject. They were very enthusiastic about this possibility at the time.

As the teaching part of the year came to an end, I had to think about revising for the final exams. Universities in 1979 invariably held 'finals' at the end of the third year. The final degree grade was based solely on these exams, together with your project mark. There was no such thing as continuous assessment, with marks accumulated in the previous year contributing towards your final result. It was all down to how you performed in around half a dozen exam papers. So it was time to get my head down for some serious revision. During this period, I also had a crazy idea that I should work at night and sleep during the day. I thought it would be easier to concentrate at night, but it was a disaster. Nevertheless, I felt reasonably confident when the time came to sit the exams and thought they had gone well. With the exams finished, it was time to enjoy my final weeks in Leeds.

While we waited for our results, we went a few camping trips to places such as Windermere, Scarborough and the Yorkshire Dales. My circle of friends always had to make these trips a challenge, just as we had with the hitch-hiking race at the end of the first year. We made it a rule to find sites to pitch our tents that were essentially in the middle of nowhere. Most of the time we managed to do this without any issues, and we found some beautiful sites overlooking Lake Windermere or on coastal paths with views over the North Sea, 'far from the madding crowds'.

However, our trip to the North Yorkshire Moors wasn't quite so successful. It was an extremely hot day in early May, and we had found an idyllic spot where the moorland sheep were grazing by a river that looked ideal for pitching our tents. We set up camp well away from prying eyes and headed to a nearby pub for beer and food. When we came back some hours later, it was dark, and we were aghast to find both the outside and inside of our tents covered with black sheep flukes. It was like a scene from a horror movie! We quickly sobered up and set about trying to remove these nasty parasites. Once the insides of the tents were clear of the flukes, we got inside and zipped up our tents, hoping they could not crawl in, and had a somewhat fretful night. In the morning, thankfully there was no sign of the monstrous parasites as we tucked into our fry-up, cooked on the campfire.

With the exams out of the way, I was also thinking about my future and what type of job I was going to apply for. More than a third of my year had decided to apply to do PhDs, either in our department or at other universities. I never followed up the possibility of researching the 'biochemistry of teeth', having decided by this time that I wanted to work as a Medical Laboratory Scientific Officer (MLSO) in the NHS. I suspect there was quite a lot of careers advice and the usual 'milk round' graduate recruitment fairs had been to Leeds, though I had given them all a miss.

I think it was probably my lack of confidence and my desire to avoid revealing my medical history that also prevented me from discussing future employment options with any academic staff. It now seems bizarre that I never approached anyone, and it is reminiscent of how I approached my UCCA application. It might also have been a deep-seated fear of being rejected and simply considered not good enough for whatever reason. While I was clearly more than capable of expressing myself with people involved with my medical care, this did not extend to other professionals in my life. I had somehow unwittingly compartmentalised these feelings and abilities.

For similar reasons, it never crossed my mind to stay in Leeds or look for a job in the local hospitals or with local employers. I had that 'calling' to be back by the sea in Torquay and working on the deckchairs. The exam results were finally pinned on the noticeboard in the corridor of the Biochemistry Department in Hyde Park Terrace. This was a converted house, and the corridor wasn't very wide. The results were posted in alphabetical order. Struggling through the scrum, I saw my name and the grade 'III' alongside it. I was bitterly disappointed and made a quick getaway. These were the days before 'degree grade inflation' and there was a normal distribution around the upper and lower second-class degrees. My fellow students had planned to have a celebratory drink at The Faversham, a pub that was close to the department. I wasn't really in the mood but went along anyway. My sense of deflation at these results was reminiscent of the feelings I'd had when I'd first sat my O-levels. Where and how had I gone wrong?

With the completion of my degree course, I made a radical decision – to change my surname by deed poll to my mother's maiden name, Demaine. I've often been asked why I decided to change my surname and the answer is somewhat complicated. Mum had always said she would change back to her maiden name after she and my dad divorced. Trevor and John had also claimed that they would follow suit, though I suspect this might just have been to humour Mum. I had a deeper and different reason for doing it. At the time, I felt I would always associate the surname 'Northcott' with being ill, and it would remind me of all the trauma I had gone through since the age of 12. Having come through all that, despite coming close to death many times, I had survived. I had managed to obtain good A-level grades, despite only being able to spend less than half my time at school, with some of that being disrupted by ill-health. Finally, I had been accepted and completed a biochemistry honours degree at the best department outside Oxbridge.

In my new life I wanted to be a 'normal person' and leave the past behind, once and for all. I wanted to be able to compete for employment and socialise on equal terms, without any special favours or anyone 'pitying' me. These were my overwhelming reasons for changing my surname. A major part of life where I had previously struggled was in forming meaningful relationships. My lack of confidence had been removed and I had become adept at forming friendships with 'mates', but I was acutely aware, as I came away from Leeds, that this was not true of more personal relationships. I doubt that I was very different from countless other students who go through university just having a good social life with mates. For me, however, there were always a great many insecurities at the back of my mind. I was quite different from everyone else. I had to take tablets every day just to stay alive, which had horrendous physical side effects. My shoe size was out of proportion to my height (as I had stopped growing due to my illness), my body was covered with scars – and how could I explain what I'd been doing for the past ten years of my life? These were topics that would undoubtedly be raised on any romantic date or shortly thereafter. It was time to face the real world, with no cotton wool surrounding me. University had been a 'dry run' and had worked to a certain extent, but when I finally moved on and gained my first employment it had to be on an equal footing with my peers.

I left Leeds for the final time, having changed my name to Demaine. Before I left, I went to the Registrar's Office with a copy of my deed poll to ensure that my degree certificate would arrive with my new name on it. I still had my job on the deckchairs, this time with my new surname. Most of the other people working there were new, and the others asked no questions. The summer of 1979 went by very quickly, as I was spending every possible hour working. Indeed, by the time the summer was over, I had earned just enough to start paying income tax at the basic rate.

The highlight of my summer was the second Kidney Transplant Olympics, held in Southsea on the weekend of Saturday 19th–20th August 1979. These were established by Mr 'Taffy' Slapak, who had performed my transplant in 1974 when he was at Addenbrooke's, and Professor Lee, who was the Consultant Nephrologist at Portsmouth Renal Unit. Although only in its second year, the Transplant Olympics had already attracted entries from across Europe. Dr Peter Bisson and Staff Nurse Pauline Woodhams were very keen that I should take part and represent the Exeter Unit. I was therefore entered for the 33m and 100m freestyle swimming and 1,500m running events. Trevor was still in the Royal Navy and based in Gosport, close to where the Games were being held, where he was living with his wife Judith and my nephew and niece Philip and Victoria. It was decided that my mum, her fiancé and I would come and stay with Trevor and Judith for the weekend while I competed in the events. We drove up from Torquay early on the Saturday morning, with the first events not taking place till in the evening.

I hadn't done any training and just assumed I was quite fit and healthy and able to compete. After getting settled in, I went off to the Victoria Park Swimming Pool for the races. I was in for a shock. The standard was a lot higher than I had expected, but even so I came away with a silver medal in each of the freestyle events. It was exhausting and I needed all my resilience to get to the finishing line. By now I sincerely wished I had done some training during the summer!

The following day was the showcase. It was a beautiful sunny day and ridiculously hot – but I wasn't able to repeat my previous aquatic success in the 1,500m track event. I started off far too fast and collapsed with heat exhaustion close to the finishing line, despite all my family and the crowds cheering me on. My legs were like jelly and cramping up badly. I was bitterly disappointed at not finishing. With hindsight, I realise I should have done a lot more preparation and should have thought ahead about hydration and taking water on board before the race. It is also true to say that running has never been one of my strong points and I am much more at home in the water. Incredibly (given that we now know he was a serial predatory paedophile), Jimmy Savile had been invited to give a speech at the final ceremony. He also handed out the medals to the successful competitors, including me. I even had my photograph taken with him, as well as my niece, who at the time was just a toddler.

The Kidney Transplant Olympics went from strength to strength; and in subsequent years, patients with liver, heart and other organ transplants took part. It is now known as the British Transplant Olympic Games and has become one of the largest events promoting organ donation in the UK. Winning participants are nominated to take part in the World Transplant Games. In 2019, Team Great Britain and Northern Ireland came out on top, winning 205 gold, 152 silver and 127 bronze medals. In second place was the team from the USA, with 67 gold, 51 silver and 38 bronze medals. The Islamic Republic of Iran came third, Canada fourth and South Africa fifth. In the same year, almost 1,500 athletes competed in 16 sporting events across 13 venues in the region. All competitors were transplant recipients, donor families, living donors or those whose lives had been touched in some way by organ donation. Through these inspirational stories, the Games highlight the lifesaving and transformational impact of organ donation, and the second chance of life that competing athletes are given.

While working in Torquay that summer, I had started to look seriously for a job as an MLSO in the NHS, buying a copy of the *New Scientist* weekly magazine which carried adverts for most of the available NHS jobs. I didn't really have any idea of where I wanted to work at that time, or in which area of laboratory-based clinical sciences. I simply applied for whatever was advertised that week; and having a biochemistry degree meant I had plenty of choices. I had applied for only a few jobs when I received my first interview at Queen Charlotte's Maternity Hospital, West London. I was excited by the idea of working in London, at such a famous hospital. The job was for an MLSO who would move around the various departments before specialising.

For the interview, I bought myself a new outfit, including a tweed jacket, trousers, shirt and shoes. The hospital paid my travel expenses, which was a good thing as I didn't get the job. The next interview, in mid-August, was to work as a trainee histopathologist MLSO in Wexham Park Hospital, Slough. It was a small district hospital and I can't say I was thrilled at the prospect of working there. Even so, my train fare was covered and the next day they rang me to offer me the job. I accepted and we agreed a start date at the beginning of September. However, I didn't tell them I had another interview the following week, to work as an MLSO in the Tissue Typing Laboratory at Guy's Hospital. This job would involve learning to do the HLA tissue typing for kidney transplant matching, and screening for antibodies.

I turned up late morning for a lunchtime interview on the 18th floor of Guy's Tower, itself a very modern 30-storey building. I was completely overawed by Guy's Hospital and immediately fell in love with the place. There were a few other candidates, so I had no idea what my chances were of getting the job. I had to declare my transplant as part of the medical questionnaire. I tried my best and then I just had to wait to find out whether I had managed to secure what for me was the 'job of a lifetime'. Yet again, my train expenses were paid so at the very least I had the joy of being on a journey to London and back, using my favourite mode of transport.

The next day, before I went to work at Oddicombe Beach, the telephone rang. It was Lesley Kennedy who, at the time, was running the laboratory, to say that they would like to offer me the job, subject to my having an Australia Antigen (hepatitis) test. In a calm voice, I told Lesley I would be happy to accept the job, while inside I was feeling overwhelmed and thrilled at the thought of going to work in such a prestigious hospital. Fate had been kind to me, and a few of my prayers had again been answered.

I now had the unenviable task of phoning the Head of Histopathology at Wexham Park Hospital to inform him that I would not be turning up for work. He was not pleased and, to be honest, I never understood the etiquette of accepting job offers at that time. However, the two jobs were like chalk and cheese and there was no way I was not going to Guy's. When I think about these events some decades later, I see the pattern – I was rejected for the first jobs I applied for, and then accepted a mediocre one, but kept going until I had my dream post. Those 'monkeys on my shoulders' that had sapped my self-confidence and held me back during the past three years were finally gone. I was back to my usual self, brimming with confidence and self-belief. My Torquay GP organised my Australia Antigen test, which came back negative, and the Personnel Department at Guy's wrote to me, giving a start date of Monday 10th September, together with a Contract of Employment, with an annual starting salary of £3,357.

Thankfully, I didn't have to worry about organising a place to live in London, as the Hospital provided me with a room in the Guy's Nurses' Home, located in Bolton Garden's, Earl's Court. I had many things to organise and planned to work at home for as long as possible. Towards the last week at work, my Honda 500cc motorbike finally gave up the ghost, with a connecting rod in one of the cylinders breaking and destroying the engine. The engine was a write-off and I decided to sell the bike for spare parts. However, I had made enough money by working for the Council, together with what I received for my old bike, to buy a brand new one. I had researched the motorcycle market through the monthly magazines and had opted for a new model – a Yamaha 750 three-cylinder, costing in the region of £800. It was based on the Triumph Trident motorbike that was the last model to be produced at Meriden, England, before they went bankrupt. Yamaha had taken the engine and built it horizontally to stop oil leaks, which had always been a running joke among British motorcyclists. They had also replaced the large chain from the engine gear box to the rear wheel with a shaft drive, as you would find in a car. The result was a superb motorbike, with a top speed of around 120mph.

I ordered my new bike from Motor Cycle City, based at the time on the A4 trunk road in Hounslow, close to Heathrow Airport, and specialising in discount bikes. Mum and Alan had dropped me off at the station and I caught the train to London, Paddington, leaving my home in Torquay for what would be the last time on Sunday 9th September. It is only now, over a half century since I'd been 'at death's door', that I realise what a proud moment this must have been for Mum. She had seen her youngest son wake up from a coma in July 1969 and survive numerous near-death events, and she was now saying goodbye as he embarked on a new life in 'The Smoke' working in one of the world's top-rated hospitals in the field of kidney transplantation.

I wasn't sure what to expect from my temporary home in the Guy's Hospital student nurse accommodation. My room was in the basement and was not particularly welcoming, with no windows and an extremely uncomfortable hospital bed with a mattress that seemed to have springs popping out all over the place. Still, I was grateful for the room and my accommodation included access to the large dining room with breakfast, lunch and dinner provided if required. I had a meal alone in the dining room that first evening and went for a walk around Earl's Court before returning for an uneasy night's sleep, waiting with trepidation to see what my new job at Guy's Hospital would bring. I still couldn't believe that I would be catching the Tube the next day to work at Guy's Hospital. I had to keep pinching myself!

My three years at university had been my first substantial period of normal life since the age of 12. I had no health problems there, other than a broken arm from a motorcycle accident. Although it wasn't the first time I'd lived away from home, this time I was fully in charge of my own affairs. I was able to turn up at Leeds just like all the other freshers, with no labels or comments from people, such as 'he's had a transplant', 'he's a freak', 'be careful you don't knock his kidney' or 'look at all his scars'. I was no different to the next person sitting in the lecture theatre or pub. It gave me immense satisfaction that I had come through all the illness, life-and-death situations, and difficulties in my home life, and had somehow gained the A-levels I needed to be enrolled on a degree course with high academic standards. Looking back, there is no doubt that I could and should have achieved a higher grade in my degree. However, I had needed this time to be myself finally, without all the baggage and labels. Now I could look forward to starting my professional life.

Chapter 10: Thrills and Spills

On Monday 10th September 1979, I had my cooked breakfast at the nurses' home in Earl's Court and headed for the London Underground to catch a train to Guy's Hospital at London Bridge. Most of my previous journeys on the Underground had been outside rush hour so being pushed and shoved in a congested train carriage was a new experience! I had already planned my journey and took a copy of the London A-Z in case I got lost. After alighting at Bank Station, I duly followed the signs for London Bridge, swept along by the many thousands of commuters walking across the River Thames. This was a million miles away from my life in Torquay or my time at university in Leeds. As I walked south to London Bridge, I could see Guy's Tower across the river in the distance. It was fantastic to think I would soon be working on the 18th floor and be part of one of the greatest medical institutions in Britain, perhaps even the world. This sense of 'floating on cloud nine' persisted for several weeks. I felt a bit like a country mouse coming to the big city!

Having arrived at Guy's Tower, I took the lift to the 18th floor where the tissue typing laboratories were located. Lesley Kennedy would be my direct line manager, although Mr Mick Bewick, the Consultant Transplant Surgeon, was in overall charge. Bob Vaughan, who was a few years older than me, would be involved as the other NHS tissue typist. There were other research scientists working on many projects, ranging from rejection of transplanted kidneys to isolating the insulin-producing cells of the pancreas for possible transplantation to people with type 1 diabetes. There were no other new or recent graduates but there was a wide age range and a good mix of genders and nationalities. Lesley Kennedy, originally from Canada, was probably in her late thirties or early forties. She was a very tall woman and quite dominant, both physically and personality-wise, and interacted with people in a forceful way. I soon realised that having Lesley as my line manager was going to be an interesting experience.

I now needed to pick up my new Yamaha motorcycle and on Friday 14th September Lesley allowed me to leave work early so I could get to Hounslow before closing time. It was exciting to finally take ownership of a brand-new bike that I had saved up for over so many months. It was certainly my most prized possession. I had no experience of riding in London and, while the traffic in 1979 was nothing like it is today, it was still daunting. I made my way very carefully back to Bolton Gardens in time for the evening meal.

The previous evening, I had struck up conversation with some of the student nurses and on the Friday evening we all went out to visit some of the local hostelries. At the time, Earl's Court was full of Australians, and this created a fun and vibrant atmosphere. I was flattered to be invited, but also rather apprehensive. I was not at all prepared for socialising with mostly female student nurses. For a moment, that troublesome inner voice (telling me I wasn't a normal individual) came to the surface but, unlike in previous years, I was quickly able to ignore it. I told myself that I was now a much stronger person and could handle this part of my social life.

It was also quite different from when I had been a second-year student living with the nurses in Leeds. My new friends in the nurses' home would also be work colleagues and this changed the dynamics of our interactions. Nevertheless, I had little experience of socialising with young women of a similar age. Throughout my teenage years, and to some extent at university, I had missed out on learning how to form friendships with people of the opposite sex. These social skills had effectively passed me by, and I was extremely conscious of my personal deficiencies. Until this point, my experience of women was largely confined to meeting nurses from my medical healthcare team or the wives, daughters or sisters of fellow kidney patients.

This evening in Earl's Court was another milestone on my journey towards becoming a 'normal' person without any 'baggage' and being accepted into a mixed-gender social group. In my last year at university, many of my friends had had girlfriends and I was increasingly self-conscious about the fact that I had not yet formed such a relationship, other than going out for an occasional drink and a disastrous date when I had taken a girl to see *Call of the Wild*, a film about animals!

I had an overwhelming fear of rejection; and I desperately hoped that my deep insecurities wouldn't prevent me forming a lasting relationship. Of course, the fact that I had been outwardly a rather rowdy student at university, with attire to match, probably hadn't helped! These worries continued over the summer while I was working on the deckchairs. The other guys at work seemed to find it so easy to strike up a conversation with girls (which soon led to a relationship), whereas I simply didn't know where to start. This first evening out in Earl's Court, and other subsequent evenings, gave me an enormous confidence boost and I began to learn the ropes and pick up the 'social cues' even though the friendships I formed were only 'brief encounters'. Nevertheless, I very quickly became more confident and was surprised to discover that, despite all my concerns about my body image, someone might actually be interested in going out with me on a date. The ice had been broken and now it was simply a matter of waiting for the right person to come along.

Although Lesley Kennedy was a firm line manager, she also had a very caring side. She went above and beyond to ensure that I settled into my job and life in London. She was aware of my transplant, as this had been declared at my interview, and was very keen for me to engage with other social groups as I had mentioned to her that I enjoyed sport, particularly rugby. She introduced me to someone from the clinical pathology laboratories who played Rugby Union for Guy's Hospital Medical School. He invited me to come along to one of the Tuesday-night training sessions at Honor Oak Park, a few miles south of the hospital. The rugby club at Guy's was formed in 1843 and is accepted, by both the Rugby Football Union and the *Guinness Book of Records*, as the oldest rugby club in the world.

I had been a keen follower of English rugby for some time. While at university, some of my closest friends were medics who played rugby and we were all very keen on following the sport. We once travelled to Twickenham for a weekend to watch England scrape a win over France, 7-6, in the Five Nations Championship. On 17th November 1979, I made a trip back to Leeds to watch the English Northern Division playing the All-Blacks at Otley. They had a historic 21-9 victory against the All Blacks that is still recalled in rugby clubs in the north to this day. The following Saturday, it was off to Twickenham to watch the All Blacks just beat England in a 10-9 win. However, although my mates and I had often mucked around with a rugby ball, I had never joined the student rugby club at Leeds. My doctors had made me aware of the potential danger of being knocked in the abdomen, which could lead to my new kidney getting bruised or even ruptured. Consequently, I had shied away from participating in the sport. However, this was all about to change, thanks to Lesley.

Having been so reticent at university, I'm not sure what made me change my mind, but I soon joined the Guy's Hospital Rugby Club. Perhaps it was because it came with Lesley's 'blessing' as she had persuaded me to go along, but I think it was more to do with my newfound confidence about being accepted as a normal person. It was just another obstacle to be overcome. I was so happy to be doing something I'd never thought I'd be able to do – playing contact rugby! There was a beautiful old-fashioned sports outfitter's shop between St Thomas Street and Tooley Street, where I bought my first rugby kit – boots, socks, shorts and rugby shirts in Guy's yellow and dark navy colours. I came away feeling immensely proud that I would soon be part of the team.

After a couple of weeks at the nurses' home, the Matron started to quiz me about when I would be moving out, which came as a bit of a disappointment, having only just found my new circle of friends. London is an enormous urban sprawl so it was difficult, if you didn't already know the city, to get a feel for which areas to look at for accommodation. Although Lesley joked about how life must be easy living in the nurses' home, with all meals and laundry provided, she helpfully told me about the Capital Radio accommodation list. In 1979, Capital Radio had a scheme whereby people with rooms to rent would send in their details. Every Thursday morning at 11am the list was made available for would-be tenants to collect from their offices on Euston Road. Lesley gave me time off so I could get to Euston Road on my motorbike early enough to collect the list and start telephoning people with rooms available.

This was an extremely competitive process, the photocopied list being pages long but not sorted according to area or the type of person who could apply, let alone the rent. By the time I had sifted through the pages, many of the rooms had already been taken. It took a week or so before there was a property for me to view, but I finally found a flat-share at 28 Park Court, Park Hall Road, West Dulwich, with two chaps, older than me, who both worked for the former British UK electronics giant Marconi. It was on the top floor of a purpose-built three-storey block of private flats, with the living room converted for use as a bedroom. I bought a self-assembly MFI chest of drawers which came in a flat pack. This was convenient, as it fitted on the back of my motorbike, but the quality was dubious and assembling it required some engineering ingenuity, together with a hammer, extra screws and a screwdriver!

Over the first couple of months at work, I was acquiring basic laboratory skills, such as handling and using micropipettes, learning the scientific vocabulary and recognising the difference between Eppendorf and Falcon test tubes. I had picked up a rudimentary knowledge of the Human Leucocyte Antigen (HLA) system at university and knew that these were important molecules that had to be matched up between a recipient and a donor. Indeed, I was aware that I had received a 'full house' kidney transplant, but at that stage I didn't understand what that meant at the cellular level.

Now I had a chance to get into this field in much greater depth, including getting to grips with the complicated nomenclature composed of lists of numbers that could easily have been taken from a train-spotter's logbook. It was my idea of heaven to immerse myself in the various HLA Workshop reference books which contained many pages of numbers and tables of data. This was a time before desktop computers so everything was recorded by hand on little cards and sheets of paper. However, I soon realised that laboratory work was not all glamorous, and at least 95% of it was repetitive and boring. My many tasks included pouring mineral oil into small plastic plates invented by Paul Terasaki in the 1960s. They were about 6 by 4cm in size and you had to ensure that none of the oil spilled on to the table or elsewhere. Around 200 or 300 of these had to be prepared each time; getting them ready was a great task for a Friday afternoon.

Every day the laboratory received blood samples from South London hospitals, as well as from far-flung parts of the country, and occasionally even from other countries. These samples needed to reach the lab as quickly as possible because the white cells (lymphocytes), which were used in the tissue typing test, were fragile and had to be fresh, particularly if the patient was seriously ill or taking drugs that might damage the cells. There were no couriers, such as DHL or FEDEX, then. Instead, most samples were sent by British Rail Red Star Parcels to London Bridge Station, then picked up by a hospital taxi; while other, more local, ones were delivered by taxi. The occasional sample coming from overseas needed to be collected from the airport. Patients on the wards had their samples delivered by hospital porters.

Once the samples had been delivered, they had to be logged and processed. From the sample of whole blood, the white cell lymphocytes had to be harvested, using a centrifuge. A serum sample was taken from the sample of blood after it had clotted. After 30 minutes of centrifugation, the white cells could be removed, washed in a saline solution, checked under a microscope and then carefully divided into the quantities needed to be pipetted into the oil-filled Terasaki plates containing the serum. Within the serum were antibodies that would kill the white lymphocytes if they recognised a particular HLA antigen on their surface. After adding some clotting factors called complement, any dead white lymphocytes that had been killed by the antibodies would turn blue, using a dye that could only enter dead cells.

Once I had become competent in performing the HLA test, I was expected to participate in the 'on-call' rota. When I joined in September, Lesley and Bob were the only scientists at Guy's with sufficient experience to take part in the rota. The laboratory at Guy's Hospital was a central hub in South-East England for the retrieval of kidneys from people who had been declared 'brain dead' due to a road traffic accident, brain haemorrhage or other catastrophic event, and Guy's hosted one of the busiest transplant programmes in the UK. The transplant surgeon, who at this time was invariably Mr Mick Bewick, could be called to retrieve kidneys from a donor at any time of the day or night. Once removed, the kidneys were stored on ice in an insulated box and brought back to the laboratory where we would perform the HLA test.

Once we had the HLA result, we would use the donor's own white lymphocytes, usually harvested from their lymph nodes or spleen that had been brought back in the same ice box as the kidney, to see if the cells would be killed by the serum of the patient awaiting a transplant, who had already been selected as a possible recipient. This is still known as 'the Cross-Match'. This all took around 4 to 5 hours and it was obviously critical to do it carefully. If a patient had antibodies to the donor kidney, the result would be a medical emergency. This is a rare event but, if it occurs, the donated kidney turns black within minutes, as soon as the recipient's blood starts to flow into it. The surgeon would need to remove the new kidney immediately, before the patient died of shock from the massive inflammatory response and release of cytokines.

At first, I found it strange being 'on the other side of the fence', having been a kidney patient myself. I would now be expected to play a part in deciding whether or not a kidney would be suitable for a particular patient. It was only five years since I had been a recipient myself; and here I was, working in a tissue typing laboratory. Interestingly, when I was working as a tissue typist no one ever mentioned my own situation or asked how it felt to be involved in making these decisions. Everyone was very professional; I was just another member of the team.

I soon learned the techniques Lesley taught me but I was also curious to find out what other people in the laboratory were working on. However, I began to realise that I had become a pawn in some small-scale laboratory politics. I discovered that Lesley had previously been unsuccessful in retaining an assistant. Her overpowering character, and reluctance to allow anyone any independence, apparently meant that people soon sought work elsewhere.

On Fridays, it was customary for lab staff to go for lunch and a drink at one of the many pubs surrounding Guy's. Although I was invariably invited along, Lesley would always suddenly find minor tasks for me that had to be completed before five o'clock, thus preventing me from going. Though irritating, this experience taught me a lot about how to manage, and work with, my peers in the laboratory. Unfortunately at the time I was not fully aware of what was happening, and occasionally I wondered what I had let myself in for. Thankfully, I soon got a chance to see the bigger picture. When Lesley went to Saudi Arabia for a few weeks to do some private tissue typing work, Bob Vaughan took me under his wing. He seemed to think I was quite capable, and we worked very well together, dealing with the daily samples. He also gave me the opportunity to get involved in running the HLA assays on donors during the daytime and let Mr Bewick know that I was ready to be part of the on-call rota.

By the end of November, I had settled into to my new day job and, despite some issues involving Lesley's management style, I was thoroughly enjoying the work. People in the laboratory privately commented to me that I seemed to be managing Lesley quite well. I had by now developed a relaxed though assertive manner with her, as well as charming her into giving me more opportunities and responsibilities. I was learning how to cope in the workplace.

At this point, I had also had my first outpatient appointment with Professor Stewart Cameron in the renal clinic at Guy's. Dr Bisson had kindly sent him a potted version of my medical history and had formally transferred my care so that it could continue under the auspices of Guy's Hospital. He must have completed this task with mixed emotions. He and Peggy, and all the other doctors and nurses at Exeter, had taken care of me for over ten years. They had seen me through numerous near-death experiences, from their first decision to take me on as a desperately ill 12-year-old. They had followed my progress and seen me mature from childhood, through my teenage years, to become an adult working in the field of kidney transplantation. This journey would not have been possible without them, and I shall always be eternally grateful for their dedication. They had been called into the hospital in the middle of the night on numerous occasions when I had a clotted shunt or severely water-logged lungs requiring emergency dialysis. I'm sure they had a great sense of pride on seeing me move on into a 'near normal' life. Fortunately, there were no fierce Sisters in the Guy's clinic demanding 24-hour urine collections and I was thankful that all my blood results came back normal.

Rugby training was on Tuesday and Friday evenings, and I was regularly turning out for the third or fourth team on Saturdays. Rugby quickly became a big part of my social life and I revelled in the fact that I was competing in a sport that was meant to be out of bounds and enjoying the physicality of the game. The other players were either medical or dental students, together with a smattering of graduates and people from the laboratories who accepted me just like anyone else. This was another big obstacle I had circumnavigated on my kidney journey. My physical fitness levels were already quite good but started improving massively with the twice-weekly training sessions. Lesley was always interested in hearing about my attendance at training and she ensured that I could leave work on time to ride my motorbike down to Honor Oak Park. Although I had never played any rugby since my first year at grammar school, during the early training sessions I was spotted as being a possible prop forward. This put me in the front row of the scrum, in among the most physical part of the game. I loved it.

Before my illness, I had been extremely strong, and I had regained much of this strength along with my health. Although my height was reasonable, at around 5 foot 8 inches, it was nowhere near what it would have been without my illness. Ever since the first year at grammar school, I had worn size 11 shoes so I had clearly been destined to be a tall man. My dad was well over 6 foot tall, as were my brothers, and it was rumoured that my maternal grandfather took a size 14 shoe! My solid frame and long arms made me a perfect candidate for the front row of the scrum. (My arms seemed to have grown in proportion to my size 11 feet, unlike the rest of my body.) During matches, I loved the one-to-one competition in the scrum. There is no other team sport where this close-contact duelling takes place in quite the same way, offering opportunities for players of all shapes and sizes to excel.

I soon mastered the rudiments of the sport and on occasions my opinion was even sought by other players during training and matches. Having been unable to play team sports since my first year at school, this was a very new and welcome experience. As expected, the rugby club often had post-match social events, including invitations to parties later. At these events, I finally felt relaxed and confident enough to engage with women of my own age. It was at one of these parties that I met Brenda, my first real girlfriend, and our liaison developed quickly, within a couple of weeks, from a casual to a serious relationship.

London at Christmas has always been a magical time, and 1979 was no different. There was now also all the fun of work parties to look forward to. The Department of Medicine was responsible for organising a very special party in the Banqueting Suite at Guy's Tower, which was officially the world's tallest hospital building, from its opening in 1974 until 1990 when the O'Quinn Medical Tower in Houston took the title. The Department of Medicine's Christmas party was by far the classiest in the hospital, with wonderful food and musical entertainment. The rooms had floor-to-ceiling glass panels, providing spectacular views west over to St Paul's Cathedral; while those to the north and east gave views of London and Tower Bridge. It was magical! For the first time, I could take part in a social gathering with a partner on my arm. For those who have never had to experience all the traumas and problems of growing up as a child with kidney failure, these are normal parts of life. For me, it felt like another huge milestone in my kidney journey.

On Friday 21st December, the laboratory closed for Christmas and New Year, and Lesley and Bob had to provide the on-call cover. Sadly, the festive period always generates many donors, due to the number of fatal road traffic accidents. Trevor and Judith invited me to stay with them for the weekend at their home in Gosport, so I rode down the A3 that afternoon, the Friday before Christmas, feeling very festive, accompanied by snow flurries blowing across the road from time to time. So many parts of my life were coming together, and I was very happy and looking forward to the future. I had never had it so good!

This was the only occasion I had ever spent any time alone with Trevor and his family and it was a very special weekend. Trevor took me to several navy hostelries on the Saturday and we developed a real brotherly understanding. I had never really seen much of Trevor while growing up, as he was often away for extensive periods on the Polaris nuclear submarines or on other engagements and when he was at home he had always teamed up with John. Tragically, John was now suffering from a severe form of multiple sclerosis that had developed when I was nearing the end of my first year at university. He had quickly become very disabled, having to give up work as a foreman at the Dutton-Forshaw Motor Company in Torquay. By this time, he was confined to a wheelchair and needed a lot of care.

I rode back to Torquay late on the Sunday afternoon, enjoying the exhilaration of riding a motorbike on the relatively empty A303 trunk road. I was already prepared for Christmas, having bought my presents and packed them in London. However, Christmas ended up being quieter than expected. John and his wife Gill came over for the day from their bungalow, and it was sad to see John in such a disabled condition at such a young age. I was also restless, having established a new life and relationships in London, so there seemed little to keep me in Torquay, other than seeing my mum. She had gone to great trouble as usual cooking a fantastic Christmas dinner with all the trimmings, including sausage rolls and mince pies.

For me, this visit closed a chapter of my life, and it would be my last ever Christmas at home in Torquay. Indeed, I would only return to the place that had housed my kidney machine room on a few occasions in later years. On reflection, this house contained a great many memories of the pain and suffering I had gone through as a patient on dialysis; and I was now putting these memories and emotions into black boxes that would remain sealed for a long time, until I started writing this book. Seeing John so severely disabled with another chronic disease, but no prospect of treatment, also took its toll. The burden of living with a chronic condition had clearly given me my own issues to deal with, and I perhaps struggled to take on the significance of his at the time. I returned to London the weekend before New Year's Eve in plenty of time to celebrate with Brenda, looking forward to everything the coming year had to offer.

Once back at work, I continued to be Lesley's 'right-hand man', patiently waiting for opportunities to learn new techniques and skills, until I was finally considered competent to participate in the on-call rota. I was also really looking forward to starting to play rugby, with the matches recommencing just after New Year. However, another abrupt detour in my kidney journey took place on Saturday 26th January 1980. It was a very bright sunny morning and our rugby match was scheduled to be played in Esher, in South-West London. I was now effectively living with Brenda at her flat in Acton, as it was more spacious than my room in West Dulwich. I had stayed over, and I was planning to drop her off at Kingston Shopping Centre while I went and played rugby. We were riding down a residential street near the shopping centre around midday, at around 25 miles per hour, when a car pulled out without warning from my right-hand side. As I swerved to avoid the car, it hit my bike on the left side and shunted us into another parked car. Brenda, who was riding pillion, thankfully suffered only minor bruises, but I was not so lucky.

My left lower leg took the full force of the collision with the car, which was then hit in the rear by a second vehicle. I remember being in extreme pain. Thankfully, it didn't take long for the ambulance crew to arrive this time. In sharp contrast to my car accident in 1971 the paramedics immediately gave me Entonox to relieve the pain and set about immobilising my broken leg with splints. My left foot appeared to be at a very strange angle! We were both taken to nearby Kingston General Hospital where I was very keen to let the staff know that I was a kidney transplant recipient taking steroids. Despite the Entonox and additional opioid pain relief, I was alert enough to persuade the A & E doctors to contact Mr Mick Bewick at Guy's Hospital. My remonstrations worked and he arrived in the Casualty Department in a short space of time. He was superb at explaining my medical and transplant history to the doctors, and he told them that my life-saving steroids must be continued at all costs. He wanted to transfer me to Guy's that evening to manage my care, but this was clearly going to be impossible, so instead I was promptly taken to theatre to have my leg operated on.

From the X-rays, it became clear that I had sustained serious midshaft fractures of both my left tibia and fibula. On top of that, my ankle was in a bad way. Several of the bones, including the medial malleolus, were fractured and the orthopaedic surgeons needed to wire them together in order to stabilise them. The arterial and venous blood supply to the ankle were badly obstructed, reducing the circulation to my foot. There was concern that urgent major vascular surgery would be needed to prevent amputation of my ankle. On the Sunday, Trevor and Judith and their children came up from Gosport, along with my mum, to see me in traction once again. My niece Victoria, being an inquisitive child, was intrigued by the weights and pulleys at the end of my bed and decided to lift them up. The pain was excruciating!

A few days later, my leg was placed in a plaster cast and the fractures were manipulated under anaesthesia (MUA) to further stabilise them, to prepare for my transfer to the Astley-Cooper renal ward at Guy's on Friday 1st February. This transfer came as a massive relief, as I had genuine concerns about my care at Kingston Hospital regarding my transplant; I'm sure I'm not the only patient to feel this way when being looked after in unfamiliar hospitals. This was an era when patients with transplants were still so rare that district hospitals had little or no experience of handling immunosuppressed patients after trauma. Perhaps my bad experience on Boxing Day 1971 in Torbay Hospital underlay my lack of confidence; I certainly did not want to relive that experience.

Mr Alfred Franklin my surgeon at Guy's Hospital, was the spitting image of a slimmed-down Eric Morecambe and looked old enough to retire. However, I trusted him – after all he was a 'Guy's doctor' – and on the Saturday my leg was X-rayed again. Based on the X-ray, he decided I needed another MUA, followed by an above-the-knee plaster cast. The aim was for me to start mobilising on non-weight-bearing crutches. After a further two weeks on Astley-Cooper Ward recovering from the trauma, I was discharged home with crutches on Tuesday 19th February. I obviously needed care at home, being unable to do any shopping or laundry, so we decided I should move in permanently with my girlfriend Brenda in Acton as my care was transferred to nearby Charing Cross Hospital. I was extremely concerned about my job, having only just started work at Guy's. However, although I hadn't worked there very long, the NHS came up trumps and my sick pay allowed me full pay for two months, followed by two more on half-pay. My income was a serious concern, as I still had to pay rent for a short time on my room in West Dulwich.

My first out-patient clinic appointment at Charing Cross was due on the morning of Tuesday 4th March; and I began to realise that things would be a bit different as a working adult, with none of the 'special privileges' I had been used to receiving as a child or teenager with kidney failure. Previously, I had always relied on the Hospital Car Service for my trips to and from hospital. I naively assumed that, as I was on non-weight-bearing crutches, this would be provided again, but London was not the South-West and times had clearly moved on, with the NHS changing fast. However, the hospital did provide a free minibus, although this meant arriving at the hospital well before the time of my appointment and waiting again at the end for everyone to complete their consultations. I attended the clinic alone, expecting everything to be fine; but once the X-rays had been taken, I was in for a shock.

My Consultant Orthopaedic Surgeon at Charing Cross, Mr Strachan, explained that the ends of my tibia and fibula were misaligned and, if left like that, would be unlikely to heal properly and would cause me severe disabilities (requiring the use of a walking stick) for the rest of my life. In his opinion, trying to keep four ends of bones in place over many weeks to heal in the right alignment was not feasible unless I was placed in traction again for numerous weeks. 'No thank you!' was my response. Thankfully, orthopaedic surgery had progressed considerably during the previous decade and there was another option. A '16 x 34 Kuntscher-nail' (K-nail) could be inserted down the shaft of my tibia to keep the ends of the bones aligned and this would allow healing to take place correctly. Although I was at first rather depressed that I had wasted weeks in a plaster cast, this seemed a sensible way forward.

At this stage I didn't ask why the surgeon at Guy's had not used this procedure in the first place, instead of messing about with plaster casts and MUAs. In hindsight, I can only assume that he was trying to avoid subjecting me to another major operation. The outpatient orthopaedic nurses organised my admission directly from the clinic to Elizabeth Ward that afternoon. Once on the ward, the plaster cast was replaced by a 'back-slab' and I had to remain on bed rest until I was reviewed by the Consultant on the Thursday. I was then transferred to Ward 7 South. My sudden admission also came as a shock to Brenda, providing an early introduction to what life might be like with someone who had kidney failure. Even though I had a well-functioning transplant, she would have to get used to unexpected telephone calls from hospitals and the need to put together a bag of belongings for a lengthy stay.

The use of the K-nail system for the treatment of long bone fractures has been one of the most important advances in trauma surgery in recent history. Since it was first used in a German hospital in the late 1930s, it has been the mainstay of treatment for most femoral and tibial shaft fractures. However, while removing the nail is usually trouble-free, it can sometimes be really challenging. This is because new bone can grow around or even into the K-nail; while mechanical problems, such as damage to the proximal threads of the nail, a broken nail or locking screw, may complicate its removal. There are therefore many techniques for removing it. The biggest challenge is knowing what to do when all the described methods *fail* to remove the nail. I didn't know it then, but this was something I would have to deal with the following year.

The bed rest continued, and I was occasionally allowed to sit out, with my leg elevated. Having been in a cast for the previous month, several open sores had developed around the back of my calf and heel, which needed to be dressed every day using 'Blue Spirit'. This brought back unwelcome memories of using EUSOL to clean the access points of my Scribner shunts. Someone obviously thought it would be a good idea to use the same fluid but add blue dye! It was not a pleasant experience.

On Thursday 6th March, I had an unexpected visit from Professor Hugh de Wardener, then Professor of Medicine at the hospital. I later found out that he was an eminent clinician and scientist who had contributed enormously to our understanding of various renal diseases, having established the dialysis unit at Charing Cross. However, for reasons I never quite understood at the time, he was under the impression that I had sustained several fractures since my transplant. One of his research interests was bone metabolism and he had clearly reached the conclusion that my fractures were spontaneous and that I must have some abnormal calcium metabolism.

Mr Strachan was operating on me later that evening to insert the K-nail, and Professor de Wardener wanted me to have a bone biopsy at the same time. I was very taken aback at this suggestion and argued strongly that there was nothing wrong with my bones, as all my fractures had in fact been due to road traffic accidents. As far as I was aware, my calcium metabolism had not contributed to my brother driving a car too fast, or the rear wheel of a motorbike collapsing, or a car pulling out in front of me! I was quite firm with him about all this (not knowing at the time what high esteem he was held in), as he held court in his white coat, surrounded by junior doctors. Refusing point blank to have the bone biopsy, I reiterated that there was nothing wrong with my bones and he would be subjecting me to an unnecessary procedure. He clearly wanted to have me wrapped in cotton wool and prevent me from ever venturing out on to the roads.

I made it crystal clear that my clinical transplant care was under Guy's and strongly suggested that he contact Mr Mick Bewick. My hospital notes of Wednesday 10th March show that he took my advice and immediately made the required phone call. Mick confirmed that my fractures had all been due to road traffic accidents and a bone biopsy would be an 'excessive investigation'. The notes state that 'a bone biopsy would not contribute much to my clinical care and would inconvenience me greatly'. I never saw Professor de Wardener again on the ward. During my entire stay in hospital, I continued to have excellent kidney function with a serum creatinine of around 107mmol/l.

This episode had been very stressful in my compromised situation, and I had surprised myself by how successfully I had argued my case with this eminent professor, with all his years of experience of renal disease. I felt very angry that he should appear out of nowhere with his entourage and assume that he could take over my care. Looking at my notes, it is hard to see how he ever became involved at all. I was certainly never asked whether I wanted him to review my case, and there is no formal request in my notes from the orthopaedic team for him to see me. It probably originated with an overly enthusiastic junior doctor innocently passing comment to a colleague, perhaps in the dining room. This sort of exchange of information would have been common at the time, though it would be frowned upon today. Looking back, it was probably the first time during my decades of medical treatment that I stood up to an overbearing, paternalistic doctor. Luckily, my previous experiences of doctors had been very different. But this is a good example of what we now refer to as 'patient empowerment'. Patients (and their relatives and carers) need to feel confident about expressing their thoughts openly, irrespective of the status of the healthcare professional they are dealing with. Eminent consultants and professors can make mistakes, just like anyone else!

By chance, the insertion of the K-nail that evening was to be carried out on my birthday, Thursday 11th March. This would be yet another birthday spent undergoing some form of medical or surgical treatment! As theatre was planned for the evening, I was at least able have a proper breakfast. These were still the days when hospitals had catering departments and the nurses would dish out the food from heated trolleys, with a large menu for patients to choose from. I was going to be 'nil by mouth' from noon so I opted for the 'full English'. Professor de Wardener did make one useful contribution to my care, which was to write in my notes that I must receive hydrocortisone during the operation, although I had already informed the surgical team and I'm confident that the orthopaedic team would have done it anyway.

At 6.40pm I was prepared for theatre with a pre-med. Pre-meds were still commonly given in those days, though they have since been found to provide little patient benefit and have been phased out. Soon afterwards, I was taken down for the two-hour operation. My notes record that I was back in theatre recovery at 10pm, though still not conscious. During the operation the surgeon, Senior Registrar Mr Stallard, removed the new bone callus that had formed around the fracture site and inserted the 16 x 34 K-nail. His operation notes suggest that this was a difficult procedure. It required significantly more force than usual to get the K-nail through my tibia to reduce the fracture. He also removed the wires around my ankle bones, except for one piece that proved impossible to untangle from the newly formed callus and is still with me today. Until I reviewed my medical notes decades later, I was always under the impression that the Consultant, Mr Strachan, had done my operation, rather than the Senior Registrar. Perhaps this helps to explain some of the issues that occurred further the line.

I was back on the ward just after midnight and in the early hours of the morning the nurses became concerned about considerable bleeding from the wounds. The on-call surgeon was bleeped, and he prescribed 2 units of blood. My bed end was elevated to try to slow down the oozing from the operation site and a Braun's Frame was put in place to keep the bed sheets off my leg. The doctors continued administering regular 100mg hydrocortisone as well as four-hourly 20mg Omnopon for pain relief. Throughout the day, my temperature had been giving concern, with worries about potential infection and the lack of effective pain relief.

On Thursday 13th March, Mr Strachan came to see me and became concerned about the inability to control my pain adequately, the bleeding and the temperature spikes. Thankfully, over the next couple of days, my condition seemed to improve and I started to make a good recovery. Though I was still in considerable pain, at least my condition had finally stabilised. Following another X-ray the previous day, Thursday 20th March, it was back down to the operating theatre for another MUA with Mr Stallard to try to get the fibula into a better position. According to the operation notes, this went exceedingly well.

I was now definitely on the mend and on Monday 24th March was able to get about the ward on non-weight-bearing crutches. Finally, on Thursday 26th March I was discharged from hospital and Brenda collected me and we returned to Acton with only a below-the-knee plaster cast. The plan was for the K-nail to be removed in 18 months' time. Over the coming weeks, I went from strength to strength; after a month the cast was replaced by a back-slab and, by the beginning of June, I was finally free of any support to my leg. At the beginning of May, I had made a visit to the Tissue Typing Laboratory to meet up with Mr Mick Bewick and my colleagues, all of whom were very keen for me to get back to work as soon as possible. I started back shortly after getting the nod from my Consultant on Monday 9th June.

For the first few weeks, I was still using my crutches, although I was able to weight-bear on my legs. This was essential as I had to travel to and from work on the Tube; although, to begin with, I was allowed to travel outside the rush hour. It was fantastic to get back to work after such a long and unexpected break. Nothing much had changed in my absence. Within a few weeks, I was able to get an identical replacement motorcycle through my insurance, which helped considerably with commuting. This was also important because it meant that I was finally able to participate in the on-call rota. Of course, when the day came, Lesley would not allow me to be in the laboratory on my own; she came in as well, to make sure I was competent! But it all went well, and I am sure that she was only looking out for me.

As this accident had occurred through no fault of my own, I had decided to put in an insurance claim. I wasn't going to make the same mistake as my mum had, in 1971. On that occasion, I kept telling her to see a solicitor to make a compensation claim for both of us, even though John had been the driver. To my disappointment, she listened to John who said it wasn't worth it and it would increase his insurance premiums. He simply walked away from the accident, while I had nearly five months of hospital care, not to mention the long-term physical and emotional effects to deal with. This time I contacted the RAC Legal Department and instigated a claim for damages against the car driver who had caused my accident. I would have to wait a couple of years before it was settled but it was certainly worth it and the RAC provided very good service. Today, of course the motor insurance industry is inundated with claims for damages, some of which are spurious – to the extent that the government is taking action to clamp down on insurance fraud. However, my claim was certainly justified, and I later found out that the driver had been prosecuted.

Chapter 11: Tissue Typing and Affairs of the Heart

Over the next few months, life settled back into a blissful harmonious rhythm and on 17th August 1980 Brenda and I rode down on my motorbike to Warminster to look after her parents' house and dog. On Wednesday 20th August, we went into the town centre early and – on the spur of the moment – I said, 'Why don't we get married?' She had already accepted my offer of marriage some months before, and the Registry Office had a vacant slot in an hour or so. We went away to prepare ourselves and, on our way back, asked two builders, who were working on a house nearby, to be our witnesses. To our amazement they agreed, and after the ceremony we had a celebratory lunch in a nearby pub. When we announced our marriage to our parents, the responses were quite different. Brenda's were delighted but my mum was terribly angry. Apparently, she had been discussing my wedding arrangements with Trevor's wife Judith and thinking about what to wear and all the other paraphernalia.

There was a great deal of banter from my friends regarding the hasty way we got married. Having had several decades to reflect on it, I have some thoughts on these events. The first and most obvious question is why I got married so quickly after meeting my girlfriend. Most people have their first serious, long-term relationships during their school and university years, but this part of life had completely passed me by, other than a short experience on my first arrival in London. There is no doubt that I was very insecure and seriously doubted that I would ever find a soulmate with whom I could have a lasting relationship.

In our short time together, Brenda had been forced to cope with me being in hospital for weeks at a time, with all the emotion that entails, and then the rehabilitation that followed. My deep fear of personal rejection had no doubt risen to the surface – and proposing marriage was perhaps my way of dealing with it. This leads me to consider another poignant question: why would any normal young woman want to enter a long-term relationship with someone who had such poor prospects of living a long life, let alone fathering a child? I had revealed my transplant and medical history the morning after we first met and had joked about my scars and disfigurements. This was my way of dealing with the worries I had about my body image.

Despite all these issues, she accepted me for who I was. It was certainly a loving relationship with many fun times, including holidays spent travelling round Greek islands and camping holidays taken on my motorbike. But over the next few years, the flames of passion were gradually extinguished, and I found myself 'falling out of love'. From the outside, it probably appeared (to friends and family) that we were happily married. However, I suspect that over the years I became more confident in myself and no longer so insecure about personal relationships. This made me realise that my marriage was not all that it should be. In addition, my passion for research was taking centre stage and I was spending more and more time working in the laboratory and away from home.

By the end of 1980, I had started to take a full part in the on-call rota and I decided on a new strategy to make working with Lesley easier. I reckoned that if I got into the laboratory very early, I would be able to take control of the day's work before she came in. This succeeded and I gradually I ended up doing more and more of the work, while Lesley was able to put her feet up. Towards the end of the year, we learned that major changes were afoot and a new Director of Tissue Typing was to be appointed. This developing science needed a forward-looking scientist, and it was absolutely the right decision for Guy's to make this appointment. It was also music to my ears as I was getting towards the end of my tether having Lesley as my line manager.

Soon the news broke that Dr Ken Welsh would be taking over. Ken came over to introduce himself before Christmas and he was a breath of fresh air. He arranged a one-to-one meeting with every staff member, and I felt I had met a kindred spirit. All my prayers seemed to have been answered! Ken was leaving the Immunology Department at the Royal Postgraduate Medical School (Hammersmith Hospital) where he had run the Tissue Typing Laboratory as well as carrying out research projects into the cause of kidney transplant rejection. He had previously worked at the highly esteemed Karolinska Institute in Sweden and was a protégé of Professor Richard Batchelor, one of the pioneers of transplant immunology who worked at the famous Blond-McIndoe Research Centre at East Grinstead.

Sir Archibald McIndoe was born in New Zealand in 1900 and had a great interest in surgery from an early age, but it was after moving to London in his thirties that his career really took off. He worked closely with his cousin, the highly regarded plastic surgeon Sir Harold Gillies, buying into his practice, until the outbreak of the Second World War. As one of only four experienced plastic surgeons in Britain, McIndoe was posted to the recently rebuilt Queen Victoria Hospital in East Grinstead, where he founded a Centre for Plastic and Jaw Surgery, patching up wounded RAF casualties.

It soon became clear that this was the start of an important new chapter in medical treatment, as the hospital saw numerous injuries of unprecedented severity. With the help of Canadian plastic surgeon Ross Tilley, Sir Archibald devised new ways to treat the wounds and evolved plastic surgery techniques, and ideas around rehabilitation and reintegration of burns survivors into society. During this time, he formed the Guinea Pig Club for his recovering patients. His friends Neville and Elaine Blond took a particular interest in the welfare of the injured airmen and opened up their house to 'the Guinea Pigs'. After the war, the three of them began planning a new research institute at the Queen Victoria Hospital to carry on this pioneering work, but sadly McIndoe died in his sleep in 1960, at just 59 years old, so he never saw the institute open in 1961.

Professor Batchelor had moved to Hammersmith, along with Ken Welsh. From January 1981, Ken split his time between his old place of work and Guy's. He wanted to make dramatic changes to the organisation of the Tissue Typing Laboratory, ensuring that every member of staff (including Lesley) spent part of their working week taking part in a research project. My project would be to develop a laboratory assay for identifying genetic markers (called allotypes) that are present on the end of the immunoglobulin G (IgG) molecule, away from where it binds antigens. These are heritable markers designated Gm, which behave like HLA and blood groups.

Ken provided me with a laboratory bench in a small room on the 17th floor of Guy's Tower, the floor below the routine laboratory, where I was able to establish the assays. This opportunity was nothing short of fantastic. I quickly became completely obsessed with the project and was continually meeting up with Ken to ask his advice and show him my results. This was a world away from anything I had ever experienced before. Being in a different venue, away from the routine tissue typing area, was also a blessing. The room was available to anyone who wanted to use it for research, but at first I was the only one to show any real interest in the research opportunity. Consequently, I spent more time downstairs on the 17th floor and less time involved with the routine tissue typing work on the 18th floor.

At this time, only a few researchers in the world were working on these genetic markers. The research agents and chemicals required to carry out the assay were simple, except for the antibodies that recognised these allotypes. These came from commercial sources, using rabbits that had been immunised with the human IgG allotypes to produce the required antibodies. Although the assay used 'haem-agglutination', a technique in use for many years, it could be extremely temperamental. Factors such as the laboratory temperature all affected its success. Trying to get the assay to work consistently became quite addictive and I was spending increasing amounts of time during the day working on it, as well as long evenings and entire weekends. Ken gave me his blessing even though, as well as discussing the research with me, he was having to cope with Lesley who was not happy that she had effectively lost her assistant.

As I became more engrossed in immunology and science, I started to think about how I was going to progress my career. After much background reading, I asked Ken if I could register for a PhD. He was very supportive and suggested that I should speak to Professor Stewart Cameron, the first Professor of Renal Medicine in the UK. His office was also situated on the 17th floor, very close to what had become 'my lab'. My main problem was that I only had a third-class degree. Unfortunately, Guy's Hospital Medical School had just changed their registration criteria for PhDs and would now only accept a first or upper second honours degree. Stewart kindly went to see the University Registrar on my behalf to see if there was any way I could be registered. One option was for me to complete and pass the pathology content of the medical course. This would be a mammoth undertaking, requiring two years of study, and still with no certainty that I could register for a PhD.

While my research endeavours were ongoing, I started to have problems with the fracture sites in my left leg. This started towards the end of 1980 with a loss of movement and considerable pain in the ankle that became quite debilitating. I was referred for physiotherapy at Guy's. The physiotherapist explained that there was some new technology available that generated ultra-sound waves, which could pass through the skin and tissue to break down any scarring that might be hindering the movement of the joint and causing pain. It seemed to work well, together with some additional physiotherapy exercises such as standing on a balance board. Ultrasound technology is commonly used now but at that time many people were worried about the safety of the 'sonic waves' and there was quite a lobby against it.

The significant pain that I was experiencing around the fracture site on my left leg led Mr Strachan to decide that the K-nail should be removed earlier than planned, after 15 rather than 18 months. On Wednesday 5th August 1981, I was duly admitted to Charing Cross Hospital. The next day I had routine bloods taken, my leg was shaved and my skin checked for allergic reaction to plasters. At 10.30am on Friday 7th August, I was given my usual pre-med and hydrocortisone and waited to be wheeled down to the theatre at midday. As before, I had been under the impression that my operation would be carried out by my Consultant but instead it was performed by Mr Marshall, someone I had never heard of before. I wonder if this was a recurring feature of the ortho-paedic department at this hospital. Unfortunately, I cannot recall any of the conversations that took place, and the ethics form is of no help. In today's NHS, the consent form would make clear who would be carrying out the operation and who would be assisting.

I went into the recovery room at 1.50pm, following a two-hour operation to remove the K-nail, and finally returned to the ward at 3.15pm. Later that day, when I had recovered sufficiently from the anaesthetic, I started to get tremendous pain in my left leg. The extent of the pain was something I had never before experienced, and I hope never to experience it again. The Ward Sister was extremely concerned and there was a heated discussion between her and the surgeon. In true Sisterly fashion, I heard her remonstrate with him, demanding to know what he had done to her patient. Although there was nothing in the surgeon's operation notes to suggest there had been problems removing the nail, subsequent clinic letters confirm that it had been 'techni-cally difficult'.

Apart from the excruciating pain over the first couple of days and a slight temperature, I made a speedy recovery and was discharged to my marital home in Walthamstow on Wednesday 12th August, with weight-bearing crutches and a long list of physiotherapy exercises to carry out. We had been able to jointly purchase our three-bedroom end-of-terrace house with a repayment mortgage, despite my having had a kidney transplant. People with kidney transplants often have major problems obtaining a mortgage, and life insurance is completely out of the question. At this time, endowment mortgages were popular, whereby applicants took out life insurance that only repaid the mortgage at the end of the term. I wasn't eligible for this type of mortgage; and this turned out to be a blessing in disguise, as there were subsequent scandals where many of these life insurance policies failed to cover the cost of the mortgage, leaving homeowners in debt.

Everything seemed to be going well until the end of August when I developed a large hard lump on my left thigh. To me it looked like an enormous boil. It was painful to touch but it disappeared after a week. Things then started to go downhill on Friday 11th September when I began to feel unwell with flu-like symptoms. Two days later, I spoke to the doctors on Astley-Cooper Ward at Guy's and was advised to come into hospital immediately, causing more anxiety for Brenda. By the time I arrived at the hospital, I had what appeared to be full-blown septicaemia with rigors, a racing pulse and a high temperature. I was quickly prescribed ampicillin and flucloxacillin intravenously. The blood test results in my notes showed that I had a neutrophilia with white cell count of 18,000 per microlitre. My creatinine level had also risen sharply, from 107 to 157umol/l, another indication of septicaemia. As all this happened around a month after the K-nail removal, an initial diagnosis of osteomyelitis was made.

Even I could tell that my left leg felt hot to touch compared to the right. My doctors organised a radioactive bone scan to see if any areas of inflammation could be identified. The scan showed that my tibia glowed glaringly white down the track where the nail had been inserted. They suspected a *Staphylococcus Aureus* infection, but all the blood cultures came back negative. After a few days, my temperature came down to normal, together with much improved blood results. Two weeks later I was able to return home, on Monday 28th September, having switched from intravenous to oral antibiotics to ensure that my symptoms didn't return.

Meanwhile, I was still pondering about doing a PhD. Having further searched the regulations, I found it would be possible to register if I was a Fellow of the Institute of Biomedical Sciences (FIMLS). This qualification could be undertaken as a part-time evening course over a year in a subject such as immunology. Following discussions with Ken, I registered in autumn 1982 at what is now the City of Westminster College, Paddington, close to Edgware Road. The course was predominantly for hospital MLSOs who needed the FIMLS qualification for promotion. By the time I started, I already knew quite a lot about immunology, particularly in diseases as well as in transplantation and genetics. All this meant that I was probably one of the more able students and really pushed the speakers in the Q&A sessions. Part of the course involved carrying out a research project and I found this relatively easy as my research on Gm markers was going from strength to strength and Ken Welsh was now suggesting that we should publish my results in a scientific journal. The written exams were all performed at the end of the year and consisted of long essays and short-answer multiple-choice questions.

In late spring 1983 I waited for the results, feeling confident that I had passed and would now be able to pursue my real ambition, to undertake a PhD. When the post arrived, I was astounded to find that I had failed! I was bitterly disappointed and simply could not believe what was in the letter at first. But after checking with the College, I had to accept the fact that I had failed. I was filled with all kinds of emotions, ranging from anger to despair and intense embarrassment. How was I to tell Ken that I had failed, let alone everyone else? It had been assumed that I would pass the course with flying colours. My life had been turned upside down by this one letter.

I've now had many years to reflect on my poor performance in written examinations. I suspect it is an innate issue and I may have some kind of specific learning disability that puts me somewhere 'on the autistic spectrum'. When I took my A-levels, I was very careful to follow my teachers' advice, such as putting together a plan, 'brainstorming' the question and making sure my answer directly addressed it, rather than drifting off into what I preferred to write about. I had not used this approach in my O-levels as I was sure my knowledge base then was good enough to pass the exams and this was certainly borne out in the mock exams. Similarly, when I sat my finals for my degree, I suspect that I did not spend sufficient time studying how I should answer specific questions but instead got carried away with writing down my own ideas. With the FIMLS, it seemed incomprehensible that my research project would have failed, given that it was based on an article that was about to be sent for peer review (and was subsequently published). However, I suspect that once again I went off on a tangent with my own ideas, rather than answering the questions as the examiners expected me to. I now know I tend to overthink answers in multiple-choice questions. It causes great merriment among family and friends when I find 'grey' answers even when doing family fun quizzes!

Despite this setback, Ken was still incredibly supportive of my registering for a PhD. Over the next few days, he concluded that the examiners simply did not understand my answers or my research project because they were on a higher level than they were used to. I'm sure this comment was partly 'tongue in cheek' but I was starting to reach the same conclusion, and his support gave me the confidence to 'get back in the saddle' and come up with a solution.

In 1983, there were two forms of higher education institutes that bestowed degrees on students. The older universities operate under a Royal Charter, and some of these charters go back many centuries. The Universities of Oxford and Cambridge received theirs in the 13th century, and in Scotland the Universities of St Andrews, Glasgow and Aberdeen were granted theirs in the 15th century. Some newer universities, such as Keele, were created in the 1960s, and once again in 1992, following two Acts of Parliament. Before 1992, polytechnics such as Portsmouth, where I had received an offer to read Pharmacy in 1976, usually provided this training. Their degrees were awarded by the Council for National Academic Awards (CNAA), the national degree-awarding authority in the United Kingdom from 1965 until its dissolution in 1993. Fortunately, the CNAA also awarded postgraduate degrees such as PhDs, which were particularly suitable for people conducting research projects outside universities.

This seemed a distinct possibility, so I got hold of the application forms and presented Ken with my plan of action. Once again, he was supportive, advising me that it would be beneficial for my future career to have one research supervisor from another academic institute. With his links to Hammersmith Hospital, he was aware of the arrival of Professor Lucio Luzzatto, from the International Institute of Genetics in Naples, as Head of Haematology. Professor Luzzatto was a highly respected clinical scientist who was embarking upon a research programme to clone the red cell G6PD gene found on the X chromosome, using some of the first recombinant DNA techniques. He also supported research projects studying various types of leukaemia involving immunoglobulin (Ig) and T-cell receptor (TCR) genes.

My own research project was already moving away from using the haem-agglutination assays towards using the newly discovered recombinant DNA techniques. Ken showed great foresight in seeing the massive advantage of having Luzzatto as my supervisor. This would give me access to a laboratory already using assays that could be used back at Guy's. My only problem was how to persuade him that I was a worthy candidate for him to devote, not just his own time, but also the commitment of others working in his laboratory.

I arranged to meet Professor Luzzatto, armed with my research plans and the necessary forms. I was exceptionally lucky that he had only recently arrived at the Hammersmith and was still 'finding his feet'. He had taken over Ken's old laboratory which had been newly refurbished. In the days leading up to the meeting, I was somewhat nervous! He had a reputation as a very serious scientist who did not 'suffer fools gladly'. Fortunately, the meeting in autumn 1983 went extremely well and he agreed to be my second supervisor, with Ken as my Director of Studies. More importantly, when I asked about the possibility of spending time in his laboratory learning the new DNA techniques, he agreed. He also introduced me to Dr Letizia Foroni, who had joined him from Naples and was working to develop this technology.

The registration forms duly went off and I was finally registered as an MPhil/PhD student on 1st January 1984. It is hard to describe my euphoria at having achieved this vital stage in my research career, albeit via a circuitous route. I had overcome some enormous obstacles since 1969. Even at Guy's, I'd had to demonstrate my determination to Ken and others, including Luzzatto, in order to be allowed to do a PhD. It was hard work, but I always believed I would eventually achieve my objective. It just required perseverance, self-belief and the patience to wait for the right door to open.

Over the previous year, Ken had able been able to acquire tissue typing laboratory space on the ground floor of Nuffield House, the hospital's former private patients' wing. He had also teamed up with Professor Panayi (Rheumatology) to gain additional space by turning the 18th-floor laboratories into research labs. I was delighted when Ken gave me the task of organising the new research facilities. I suggested that we should give this laboratory a new name, acknowledging our work at the cutting edge of emerging new techniques, from molecular biology to immunogenetics. The laboratory duly became 'the Department of Molecular Immunogenetics'. Lesley Kennedy and most of the tissue typing team would work in Nuffield House, leaving me in charge of the new labs.

We planned to share the space with Professor Panayi's researchers, but they hadn't yet moved in. I spent an entire weekend with my toolbox from home, moving benches around, putting up shelving and shifting equipment. It was exhausting work, but Ken had essentially given me the green light to create my own laboratory. It therefore fell to me to sort out all the health and safety issues and administrative tasks. I applied for a 'Use and disposal of radioactive isotopes licence' from the Environment Agency, as the new techniques utilised radioactivity. There were many risk assessments and reams of paperwork to complete. In 1983, researchers had begun to employ 'cloned' pieces of DNA that had been inserted into artificial viral vectors and then into disabled *E. coli* bacteria, and there was a need to regulate their use. At the time, no one could imagine the potential risks to human health so the government's Medical Research Council was scrambling to catch up with regulating all this activity. This required more paperwork and the establishment of a committee to oversee research using 'recombinant DNA'. Again, at the time simply extracting DNA from cells was classed as a 'regulated activity'.

Today, recombinant DNA technology has become a household term and, since the Covid pandemic, familiar to almost everyone. But in the early to mid-1980s, it really was a revolutionary scientific development, which has since had an impact on many aspects of our lives, from producing medicines to diagnosing disease, to producing the food we eat. A milestone meeting was held on a Saturday in autumn 1983 at the Laboratory of Molecular Biology (LMB), in Cambridge. At the time I had a personal subscription to the scientific journal *Nature* and just happened to see the advert. I booked places for Ken, Gabriel Panayi and myself. The speakers included numerous clinicians and scientists who had either received, or were later to receive, Nobel Prizes, such as Frederick Sanger and César Milstein. Many of the others were Fellows of the Royal Society (FRS). It was here that I met Professor Terry Rabbitts FRS and introduced myself and he generously helped me in these pioneering days by sharing important laboratory reagents. As well as Professor Rabbitts, I set up links with other international researchers. Ken heard that one such investigator, Professor Honjo from Japan, was visiting Paris and arranged to fly me there so that I could meet Professor Honjo, pick up the molecular biology reagents and return to London the next day.

While all this was going on, I was also busy writing my first research grants with Ken. Raising funds for research is vital to keep the work alive. These applications were based on my first peer-reviewed research paper, later published in the journal *Transplantation* in 1982, looking at Gm allotype markers in chronic renal disease. This had formed the basis for the research project for my disastrous FMLS examination. Not long after that paper, I was lucky enough to publish another with Ken and Gabriel Panayi, studying giant cell arteritis and polymyalgia rheumatica. By now, Ken was allowing me to work full time on research while also taking part in the 'on-call' tissue typing rota. Understandably, this was not to everyone's liking and we agreed that the next successful grant application should pay for a replacement assistant to support Lesley. Consequently, we applied for a project grant from what was then the National Kidney Research Fund (NKRF, now known as Kidney Research UK).

At this time, word processors and computers were only just appearing, and most people still used typewriters. Ken, again ahead of his time, had invested a substantial amount in buying a computer from Research Machines (later known as RM). It was an enormous heavy contraption that filled a whole desk. It used 8-inch 'floppy disks' and each disk held a meagre 64 or 250 kilobytes. Fortunately, the first Microsoft word-processing packages, such as Wordstar, were incredibly basic and therefore used little memory.

It was on this machine that we wrote our first grant application. As well as writing the main description of the project, there were many administrative pages that needed to be completed. We probably could have done it with a typewriter but we were determined to conquer the computer! We spent ages carefully lining up completed boxes on the screen with what came out of the printer. It was time well spent, as these techniques became essential for form-filling in the years before the advent of desktop publishing and powerful computers. The thrill of sending off your first grant application is similar to the excitement of getting your first research paper accepted for publication. There is an enormous sense of satisfaction in knowing that your work will appear in a scientific journal. After the publication of your research, the next major goal is to get the next stage of your research funded by a grant-giving body. Of course, there was such a long time lag between research data being gathered and the paper being written, submitted, peer reviewed and published, that most scientific research was at least six months out of date by the time it appeared for the world to see. Even today with electronic publications, there is still a time lag between obtaining the research results and getting them published.

As well as using typewriters or primitive Microsoft word-processing packages, we had to submit our manuscripts in the post, often to distant places, relying on air mail. The manuscript would then be sent out to appropriate referees for their comments and their reports returned to the editorial office. It could take months to complete this process. If the Editor decided that the journal would accept the paper but asked for some changes to the manuscript or even additional results, the entire process would then be repeated. It was important to be able to cope with rejection and not give up. It could be very frustrating, particularly reading a referee's critique of your manuscript when it had been rejected. This sometimes led to very heated debate, with some terse views being expressed. Electronic publishing has overcome much of this, and during the Covid crisis many articles have appeared as pre-publishing e-publications which have not been peer reviewed. It will be interesting to see if this practice continues after the crisis is over.

As well as publishing results in journals and applying for research grants, presenting the work at scientific meetings was a major way of communicating in science. My first opportunity to attend such a meeting came out of the blue. One Monday lunchtime in spring 1983 Ken returned from a meeting with tissue typing colleagues at the Hammersmith Hospital and told me that I had to join them at an HLA and transplantation conference being held in the Palais de Congrès, Strasbourg. This was the first conference organised by the Council of Europe for scientists working in tissue typing and immunogenetics and Ken was an invited speaker. I was instructed to contact the people who were going from the Hammersmith to get all the details. The conference was on the Friday.

I was tremendously excited. I had hardly ever travelled outside Britain and there was much to organise. First, I had to find my passport; then I had to buy traveller's cheques, remember my tablets and acquire some French francs, before finally thinking about packing some clothes. Thankfully, the people at the Hammersmith Hospital had already arranged accommodation. We met up on Thursday morning at Victoria Station to buy our train tickets to Strasbourg. We were due to get to Strasbourg in the early evening, with a direct train connection from Calais. Between us, we took over an entire train compartment. Being a train enthusiast, I was enthralled by the novelty of travelling on the French SNCF railway, though I wasn't about to mention my previous life as a train-spotter to my new companions! Around mid-afternoon, the train came to an abrupt halt, spilling all our coffee. There was a lot of to-ing and fro-ing up and down the corridor by the guards. None of us spoke French but after around four hours we found out that the goods train in front of us had derailed. We eventually got to Strasbourg close to midnight and fortunately our hotel was almost adjacent to the station.

I had no idea what to expect from a scientific conference. After my first experience of a continental breakfast with my colleagues, we walked to the Palais de Congrès. My colleagues were far more used to all this than I was, and they led the way, getting registered at the desk, and picking up the 'goody bags' with badge, notepad, abstract book and pens. I was completely bowled over by the whole experience; the talks were nothing like university lectures. As this was my own research area, of course I had a personal interest in understanding the numerous aspects of transplant immunology and why kidneys do or don't get rejected. Subsequently, I have always enjoyed taking new students to scientific meetings. If their sheer naive excitement mimics my own, I know they are hooked.

My return to work the following Monday was rather anti-climactic. I soon realised that there was a big gulf between the conference buzz and the reality of what could be achieved. There were so many ideas in my head about work that could be carried out after excited conversations with other researchers at the conference, but I was forced to realise that only a few of them would realistically be possible. Nevertheless, certain things *could* be put into practice. Since then, I've found that all the ideas developed at conferences during intense conversations stay with you, help your thought processes and, ideally, confirm that your direction of travel is correct.

Over the next few months, my research went from strength to strength. This was partly due to luck, though I also worked hard. We were successful in our grant application to the National Kidney Research Fund and we then received further funding from the Wellcome Trust. Bob Vaughan joined me in the research lab from the routine laboratory and I was able to help him set up molecular assays to carry out HLA-DR and DQ typing (the HLA-DR and –DQ alleles are the most important in matching for transplants). We also now know, from the work that we and others carried out, that people with certain auto-immune diseases (such as type 1 diabetes and systemic lupus erythematosus) often have more of one particular allele, compared to people who do not have that disease. This may increase their risk of getting the disease, though it's not the direct cause. This area of immunology is now called 'HLA and disease'; my own research at the time was closely related but could have been better described as 'non-HLA and disease'.

I often went to work in the laboratory from early morning until late at night and all through the weekends. It became very addictive and probably suited my personality, even though most of the practical work was repetitive and far from glamorous, once the assays had been established. One thing I quickly learned, which is also one of the first pieces of advice I would give to new students, is that research is more than 95% repetitive and it helps to treat it as a hobby that you love. Research scientists in most countries are relatively poorly paid, bearing in mind the qualifications they hold, and they are often employed on short-term contracts of two to three years. So why do so many people want to do research?

For me, it was the passionate desire to understand my original medical condition, treatment and transplantation. This went hand in hand with wanting to 'give something back' to all those people afflicted by kidney disease, which has such a devastating effect on the lives of those who have it, and their family members. I know I have been extremely fortunate to have a well-functioning kidney and to have been in the privileged position of being able to work in tissue typing and perform this research. It was this that drove me on through the dark times when nothing worked for days on end, as researchers so often find. Then one morning you go in and repeat the same experiment, perhaps after tinkering a little with the methodology, and 'bingo' – it works! You look back and try to rationalise why you succeeded this time when you had previously failed. And you learn that tiny details matter a great deal. This is just the way it is, and there are no short cuts. Patience, persistence and determination are key – and luck sometimes also plays a part.

I was to learn that research also brings together scientists at different levels of seniority, in a less hierarchical manner than in many professions, even medicine, with the scientific subject binding them together. Despite being only a PhD student employed as an MLSO, I was thrilled that my research attracted the attention of several eminent researchers from across the world, who were keen to collaborate with me. For example, in March 1985 one of the world's most acclaimed nephrologists, Professor Eberhard Ritz, came as a visiting fellow to Guy's renal unit from Heidelberg. At the last minute I was asked to present my results to him during an afternoon session of talks from researchers at Guy's. As soon as I had finished my presentation, Professor Ritz jumped up from his chair and came over to congratulate me on the work. We had an intense discussion about the results while his hosts, Professor Cameron and others, were trying to move him on to his next event.

The result of our exchange of ideas was a plan to collaborate and an invitation to me to present my work in Heidelberg, Germany. Of course, I went – and it was a great honour to present to such an esteemed department. Throughout my stay I was treated like a visiting professor, with sumptuous dining, while Professor Ritz himself took me on a sightseeing tour of the River Rhine region. Our collaboration proved extremely fruitful, leading to publication in a highly prestigious clinical research journal.

He later tried to persuade me to move to Heidelberg to work on renal disease, with a fellowship from the internationally renowned European Molecular Biology Organisation (EMBO) but I turned down the offer. The main reason for my decision was my old problem of insecurity. How would I cope with being a transplant patient in a foreign country without the security blanket of Guy's renal unit? I only briefly discussed the offer with Brenda and quickly dismissed it, although I am sure she would have supported the move. I don't suppose Professor Ritz realised that I was a renal transplant recipient, and I am now quite sure that the hospital care would have been superb in Heidelberg. However, at that time I didn't want to disclose my condition or take the risk of leaving Guy's. My deep-rooted anxiety about not being 'normal' had surfaced again and would continue to do so for years to come. It didn't always dictate my decisions but sometimes, as in this case, it did.

I had a similar dilemma some months later when I was invited to consider a post-doctoral position with Professor John Newsom-Davis who at the time was one of the world's leading authorities on the autoimmune disease myasthenia gravis. I had collaborated and published papers with him. He was based in the newly renovated Molecular Medicine Laboratories at the John Radcliffe Hospital, Oxford, which is now considered to be a world-class centre for understanding health and disease, including Covid-19. After a few meetings I declined his kind offer, mainly because I would only be able to work on myasthenia gravis in Oxford. At Guy's, I enjoyed being free to study whatever came my way, particularly kidney disease and transplant rejection. I realise now that it was Ken who gave me the freedom to do this work, as well as allowing me to take credit for all the work I did. Not all supervisors are so generous, but Ken had worked out what made me tick.

The period when I first registered for a PhD was an extremely exciting time in the world of immunology. Until then, there were some big gaps in our understanding of how T-cells recognised foreign antigens entering our bodies. Again, the enormous technological revolution that was taking place in molecular biology allowed assays to be used to identify was what called the 'antigen receptor' of T-cells (lymphocytes). We now know this to be the T-cell antigen receptor (TCR) which is similar in structure and function to immunoglobulins (antibodies).

In recognition of the enormous progress made in our field in a short space of time, the EMBO organised a week-long scientific meeting at Marseille-Luminy, France. They restricted the number of 'students' to 25 but included 50 speakers, all from leading laboratories around the world. These were scientists who had competed with each other to be the first to publish experiments about the nature of the TCR in renowned journals such as *Science* and *Nature*. Again, some of them later went on to share Nobel Prizes for medicine. The identification of this molecule and reaching an understanding of its function have had massive benefits for understanding and treating many diseases.

Having applied to go to the meeting, I succeeded in obtaining one of the highly sought-after 'student' places. All the participants stayed in the same building, which was also where the meeting was being held. It really was an amazing experience to share your breakfast table with such distinguished people who were prepared to include you in discussions even though you were just a 'lowly student'. The lectures started at 8am and sometimes finished close to midnight. I came away absolutely buzzing and felt honoured to have been able to take part. I was also accepted to participate in a similar, though slightly less prestigious, two-week meeting on immunoglobulins in Genoa, Italy, organised by NATO later that year.

By the end of 1985, I was nearly two years into my PhD and essentially also operating as Head of the Department of Molecular Immunogenetics. Ken and I were pretty inseparable and spent hours discussing research projects as well as the politics of the scientific community. These discussions were often carried out in the numerous pubs around Guy's, starting in the afternoon and continuing well into the evening. As Ken did not live in London, this sometimes meant that he stayed over at our new house at 139 Antill Road, Bow, with both of us feeling rather the worse for wear after that extra pint and a curry!

The beginning of 1986 saw the start of big changes in my personal and work life. I was now working incessantly to finish the practical part of my PhD while at the same time writing and submitting papers and grants. My home life started to deteriorate and felt like a distraction from my obsessive research – a marked work-life imbalance! During this time, the laboratory was rapidly filling, with more and more people wanting to work there. These new staff members included a research medical registrar who was working on her MD degree project investigating the immunology of identical twins who developed type 1 diabetes. I was already working on the same autoimmune disease with collaborators at St Bartholomew's (Barts) Hospital and Ken suggested that she came to the laboratory to learn some molecular biology techniques and carry out similar research.

Once I'd shown her the rudiments of molecular biology, we quickly developed a strong rapport and spent time discussing future experiments and how to develop the research. Soon she was able to present the early results at various national and international meetings. Although her research was on type 1 diabetes, there was a strong overlap with my own research as I was now working on diabetic kidney disease.

By early 1987, I had finished writing up my PhD thesis and, following the viva examination, I was awarded my doctorate in July 1987 with no corrections. Now that I had my PhD under my belt, I began to feel the need to spread my wings. An opportunity came my way to set up a new laboratory with Professor Alan McGregor, the newly appointed Professor of Medicine at King's College School of Medicine and Dentistry (KCMD) in Camberwell. I had just been promoted to Senior Biochemist at Guy's and Ken had planned to help me secure a 'new blood lectureship'. These would both be tenured permanent posts. But, despite Ken's huge support over the previous few years, I really felt I needed to leave the safe, secure position at Guy's, and I opted for a three-month contract with Professor Alan McGregor.

I also applied for a prestigious RD Lawrence Senior Fellowship to work on the genetics of diabetic kidney disease from the British Diabetic Association (now called Diabetes UK). If this was successful, it would start immediately after the short-term contract finished. If I failed to win the Fellowship, I would be without any employment at all. In hindsight I realise this was a massive risk, but I was extremely confident that I would be successful, and I trusted Alan. Fortunately, I was awarded the Fellowship, despite certain senior members of the diabetes research community, also based at King's, trying to block my appointment. This was my first exposure to personal political attacks by other researchers and academics. It was a rude awakening, as Ken had always shielded me from the petty politics and in-fighting which is rampant in academia and the NHS. Consequently, I made the move down the road to King's.

Ken Welsh had been desperate to keep me at Guy's and my leaving led to a fracturing of our friendship which lasted a few years. People who were close to both of us described our relationship as like that of a father and son; and my leaving caused him to go through something akin to a grieving process. At the same time, Brenda and I agreed to have an amicable separation and I moved out of our marital home in Bow to live in a rented flat in Camberwell Grove, just a short walk from KCMD. It would not be long before my first marriage came to an end. There is no doubt that our relationship had started as a respectful and a loving one but over time my feelings had gradually changed and with it the dimming of the lights on my marriage.

I was now on my own as an independent researcher without the security of a permanent position. I was responsible for applying for research funding in my own right without any senior scientists to add 'weight' to my applications. Ann Millward was the registrar who had come to the laboratory at Guy's to complete her MD, whom I had offered to take under my wing. With my PhD finished, we started to collaborate in earnest and wrote grant applications and papers together, with some of our activities causing ripples in the upper echelons of the KCMD hierarchy. The academic partnership that started over the test tubes at Guy's laboratory was to last until we retired together many years later. We also became romantically involved and lived together in our maisonette at 106 Denmark Hill, in walking distance of the hospital and laboratories. Our research gathered pace, with several successful grant applications and research papers. It was a young scientist's dream.

At KCMD I had moved up a step and become involved in finding funding for scientific meetings. Alan McGregor asked me to join him in organising a NATO scientific meeting on 'The Molecular Biology of Autoimmune Disease' in Athens in spring 1989. I suggested that we use the model I had seen working so well in Marseille and Genoa. To obtain funding from NATO, at least 50% of the speakers had to come from the USA. I felt there should be one speaker for every two students to allow time for quality discussion between seniors and juniors. This would make it quite different from conventional scientific meetings where there are fewer speakers and just a few minutes for questions. Enormous strides were being made at this time in our understanding of how the body's immune system attacks itself, and these developments had been possible due to the elucidation and characterisation of the TCR and Ig genes and proteins.

Although Alan had numerous scientific contacts of his own, these were predominantly in his speciality of Graves' disease of the thyroid. Meanwhile, I had been able to maintain contacts with many of the world's leading scientists working in immunology and autoimmune disease after my trip to Marseille. Together, we wrote and successfully obtained a large grant from NATO to cover the travel expenses of over 50 international speakers. The meeting was planned to start on a Friday evening, lasting until Monday. At the very last minute we were faced with a Thursday-night baggage handlers' strike, boycotting all non-Greek airlines. Fortunately, most of our speakers from the USA and Japan had already arrived, but those coming from Europe had major problems. A few days later, when the speakers were departing, the baggage handlers had another strike, this time affecting only Olympus Airlines. The meeting itself was still a great success, even though it took a phenomenal amount of time and effort to organise.

In spring 1991, Ann and I moved into 30 Gaynesford Road, Forest Hill, London, a beautiful semi-detached four-bedroomed house built around 1900. Earlier in the year, I had been invited to chair a scientific session at the forthcoming International Diabetes Foundation meeting in Washington DC in June. This is a huge scientific event held every four years with many thousands of participants. We quickly decided to organise our wedding around the meeting dates and extended our visit to the east coast of America to include our honeymoon.

Following our wedding, on 22nd June 1991, we said goodbye to friends and family at our home and headed to a hotel at Heathrow Airport, flying to Washington the next day. We hadn't realised that many of our research students were booked into the same hotel in Washington. Once we had registered, we wandered down to the bar in the evening and were congratulated very touchingly by members of our group who had arrived the previous day. As they were presenting their work at the meeting, they had been unable to make the wedding itself. Once the meeting was over, we finally said farewell to our group and started our honeymoon – this time on our own! This included highlights such as undertaking a road trip through the Blue Ridge Mountains and visiting American Civil War historic trails.

Many people (including members of our family) have since remarked on how strange it was that we met our colleagues on our honeymoon. 'How can you have a romantic honeymoon at a scientific meeting with your students in tow?' they ask. 'Why not wait for a lovely beach honeymoon somewhere? How romantic to go on an American Civil War Trail!' Strange though it may seem to others, we were delighted and thought nothing of it at the time. For each of us, it was (and still is) the most perfect way to spend time with your spouse, friend and lifelong soulmate.

We didn't have to wait long to welcome our first child - a healthy baby daughter was born the following year, in April 1992, and we called her Lucy. Before finding out that Ann was pregnant, we had discussed the issue of my fertility and researched the topic as well as asking about it in the outpatient clinic. As we expected, little was known about azathioprine and male fertility at that time, but it was known that certain immunosuppressive drugs (such as cyclophosphamide) should be avoided as they could cause neonatal defects.

At the time, the advice for women with a kidney transplant was to avoid getting pregnant at all, as it was thought the pregnancy might cause irreparable damage to the transplanted organ. There are obviously quite different risks for a female transplant recipient who is desperate to have a child, compared to a male with a kidney transplant. Decades later, many female patients have successfully given birth to healthy offspring with the help of careful management by their obstetric and the renal teams. This obviously brings immense joy to those who can have a family, as the desire to have children is a deep instinct. However, there are still many who are unfortunately unable to fulfil this dream. Some people of course have no wish to be parents but, for me, becoming a father has been one of the greatest joys on my kidney journey.

The months following Lucy's arrival brought unexpected changes in my feelings towards my dad. By now, the skeletons in our family cupboards were well known and I wanted my dad to meet his new grand-daughter. I had not seen my dad for 20 years. Our last encounter had been when he dropped by my school one lunchtime with Cornish pasties, and we had spent the break-time eating them on the sea front at Torquay. He had maintained contact with my brothers, who gave him updates on my life. After a few years, he had moved north to Ilkeston, Derbyshire, before returning to Newton Abbot in the late 1980s. After lengthy conversations, the need to contact him became more pressing, and I wrote a letter addressed to him at the Cider Bar, Newton Abbot, which was one of his favourite haunts. A couple of weeks later he replied, and we suggested he visit us by train one Saturday.

When the day arrived, I was nervous, having not seen him for so long. My mind was filled with questions as well as nagging doubts about whether I had done the right thing. However, there was no backing out, as the decision had been made. I arranged to pick him up that morning at Paddington Station while Ann stayed at home with Lucy, preparing lunch. I needed to be alone for our first meeting after all this time. I instantly recognised him as he walked towards to the platform barrier but managed to keep my emotions under control. After a slightly awkward handshake, there was a hug and relaxation from both of us, and the years of not seeing each other melted away. He had changed little during this time, still being a tall, rather well-built chap, with a very loud booming voice! Despite all the time that had passed, it was as if we had never been apart.

On the drive to our house, I kept the conversation on neutral topics. He was overjoyed to meet his new grand-daughter; and we spent a lovely after-noon on the patio, mostly talking about our current work and of course Lucy, who was the centre of attention. The afternoon quickly came to an end and it was time for me to drive him back to Paddington. On the way to the station the conversation revolved around how enjoyable the day had been and that we must repeat it sooner rather than later. When I returned home after safely putting him on the train, there was much to discuss. It was hard to explain to Ann how and why we hadn't seen or spoken to each other for all this time. He had bravely and without hesitation given me the gift of life in October 1970 and his own operation was not without significant risk. Without his kidney, I would probably have died many years earlier and there would have been no Lucy. From that day on, we maintained contact and a few months later we went to visit him in Newton Abbot. Our relationship was re-established, although there were always certain subjects that were never discussed, including my loss of his kidney and my current transplant. The past was kept safely in a box – while our current work and family life always gave us plenty to talk about.

With Lucy still only five months old, Ann and I decided to try to attend a scientific conference in Prague in September 1992. The country had only just overthrown the communist regime and was desperate to attract people and researchers from outside the former 'iron curtain'. We found accommodation in Prague for the conference and planned to have a week's holiday in southern Bohemia, driving there in our Ford Escort. On the morning of the conference, we duly turned up at the back of the auditorium with Lucy in a backpack, hoping she would sleep for a couple of hours while we listened to the talks, as we had occasionally seen other couples do. This was a big mistake, as she had other ideas. Despite all our attempts to keep her quiet, she noisily joined in with the proceedings! We had no choice but to abandon the meeting and show Lucy the delights of Prague instead.

At the end of the week, we drove to a delightful old farmhouse to spend the rest of our time in southern Bohemia. Here we met a retired Professor of Physics whose wife was literally painting the door of her newly opened estate agent's office. Before leaving London, I had seen reports of people buying property in Prague and elsewhere and wondered if we could do something similar. We floated the idea with the retired Professor and started planning to set up a property company with him as a sleeping partner. At the time there was no property market there, as it had been forbidden under the communist regime; consequently, houses and land had negligible value. When we got back home, we had to buy a fax machine to communicate with our friends in Bohemia, as email communication was still unavailable to the general public.

Sorting out the paperwork for the creation of the property company took many weeks. Meanwhile we were moving towards our first Christmas as a family with Lucy. Ann had secured a Diabetes Consultant's post at the Royal Free Hospital in Hampstead. We now had to decide whether to move to North London to avoid her spending hours commuting each day. In the end we never had to make this decision, as we received a telephone call from Professor Wilkin who had just taken up a position in the newly created Plymouth Postgraduate Medical School. He asked if we would like to consider moving to Plymouth and join him in setting up the new medical school and establishing diabetes research there.

Christmas and New Year came and went with many discussions. There was a great deal of upheaval and reorganisation going on in medical schools in London at that time, creating uncertainty among the academic community. A fact-finding trip to Plymouth was required so in January 1993 we set off early in the car, dropped Lucy at Derriford Hospital's Busy Bees nursery and made our way to the South-West to Plymouth University. Professor Wilkin had organised meetings with Karl Rosen, the first Dean of the Postgraduate School, as well as the Deputy Vice Chancellor of the University. There were lots of opportunities on offer, including newly refurbished laboratories, technical help and funding for PhD studentships. Once back in London, we consulted with our friends and colleagues and the overwhelming consensus was that we should move to Plymouth. We therefore started to plan for a new start and new challenges in the South-West, which also meant that we never completed the creation of the property company in southern Bohemia.

With our beautiful house in Forest Hill up for sale and our offer accepted on our future home in Cornwall, we left London on Friday 30th April 1993. For the first few weeks, we stayed in a holiday flat overlooking the sea in south-eastern Cornwall, returning to London each Friday for the weekend. It was idyllic, waking up to see the sea and having a walk on the beach with Lucy before work, though the accommodation was damp and felt rather like camping.

Finally, the news came through that we could move into our future house on Friday 28th May, and we returned to London a few days beforehand to start packing. The removal company took two days to help us pack all our belongings and left early on the Friday morning, agreeing to meet us the next day at our new home. It was a bizarre feeling, seeing a lorry drive away with all our worldly possessions. Would we ever see them again?

After waving them off, we put the last of our personal items, with overnight bags, food and essentials for Lucy and our adorable cat Calico, into the car. We said farewell to our neighbours and drove off to begin our new life, away from the hustle and bustle of London, amid the tranquil beauty of Devon and Cornwall. We have never doubted that we made the right decision, even if it felt strange to be returning to a part of the world I'd left behind so many years before. When I had caught that London train in September 1979, I never dreamed that I would one day return with a wife and young family, having attained an international reputation in kidney disease research.

Chapter 12: Plymouth and Another New Beginning

There was a lot to do when we arrived in Plymouth. There were laboratory facilities in a newly refurbished area, but most of the equipment had to be sourced and purchased. The university had been very generous with funding for equipment and technical support. However, while we received overwhelming support at senior management level, this did not necessarily feed down to the grassroots. We were housed in a space previously allocated to Biological Sciences and, not surprisingly, this led to some interdepartmental tensions. There was also a considerable amount of red tape to deal with. The university had no experience of clinical laboratory research, so I had to call upon my experience of setting up the laboratory at Guy's, and to a lesser extent KCMD, to deal with the tremendous amount of administration required for it to work efficiently. More importantly, I had to get licences from the government agencies that enforced health and safety legislation, such as 'Use and Disposal of Radioactive Substances'. These government bodies included the Environment Agency and the Genetic Manipulation and Advisory Group.

We were extremely busy, establishing this new research group; and our new house in Cornwall also needed some work. However, there was little time available for home improvements, with Lucy now just over a year old and our second child due very soon. On 25th July 1993, Ann gave birth to a healthy baby, Thomas Jack, born a week early in Freedom Fields Hospital, Plymouth, one of the last babies to be born there before all obstetric and paediatric care was transferred to Derriford Hospital. The delivery was complicated, with Ann losing a considerable amount of blood and requiring a lengthy recovery period. The addition of a new family member also brought added complexities, in terms of balancing home and work commitments. Later in August, just as we were getting into a routine with baby Thomas, I started to develop a fever. I had already been seen by Dr Richard McGonigle, Consultant Nephrologist at the Renal Unit, when I first arrived in Plymouth. At the beginning of the year, I had also contacted Dr Bisson at Exeter to determine whether they should take over my care, but he wisely suggested that I be looked after by the Plymouth unit at Derriford Hospital.

In August, I had experienced dry coughs for a couple of weeks, for which my GP had prescribed amoxycillin and ciprofloxacin for a presumed chest infection. However, at the beginning of the August Bank Holiday my condition deteriorated, with high fevers and then rigors. Around midday on Sunday 29th August, we called Derriford Hospital, and were told to go straight to Haytor Ward, where I arrived at 1.30pm to be met by Dr Clive McGavin, a Consultant Chest Physician. This was the first time I had needed a hospital admission for over ten years, since I had developed osteomyelitis with septicaemia at Guy's. This time, there was more to contend with. We had to organise childcare for Lucy and Tom. In addition, Ann was still on maternity leave and breast-feeding Tom, and she was still anaemic after the difficult delivery.

On admission, I was started on the antibiotic doxycycline, as it was assumed that this must be an atypical pneumonia, but for a week there was no improvement in my symptoms. The doctors persisted with their working diagnosis of an atypical pneumonia. Several clinical tests were performed, including blood cultures, a bronchoscopy searching for atypical organisms, and a bone marrow biopsy, to rule out a possible lymphoma, a known long-term complication of transplantation, which can present with a fever. All these investigations were inconclusive, but my condition continued to deteriorate, and tuberculosis was then added to the possible diagnoses. It was a worrying time for all.

On the Wednesday I was transferred to Hexworthy Ward, and by the afternoon of Thursday 2nd September my temperatures were swinging to over 40 degrees centigrade with rigors. It was the start of a full-blown fever! Paracetamol had little effect on reducing my temperature and blood cultures were taken once more. I can distinctly recall how violent the rigors were, as they were frightening, uncontrollable and made the bed rattle. They were rather reminiscent of the *grand mal* fits I had suffered when I was in kidney failure. Until this point, I had been a healthy and extremely fit, normal chap in his mid-thirties in my relationship with Ann. This was the first time she was seeing me severely ill. Despite being a doctor herself, it must have been hard seeing her husband like this, with our baby son Tom still needing so much care.

I wasn't in a fit state to think about all the possible scenarios, but this was not the case for my wife and family. The nurses were carrying out continuous tepid water sponging and there were fans on each side on my bed to cool me down. This continued throughout the night and the nursing notes remarked, 'Andrew is becoming peripherally shut down, with multi-organ failure becoming a real possibility'. Paracetamol reduced my temperature slightly for about two hours but then it would rise again sharply, by about 1 degree an hour. At this stage, the antibiotics were changed to intravenous gentamycin and flucloxacillin, as well as adding oral metronidazole and ciprofloxacin.

There was little change in my condition over the next two days and on Monday 6th September the renal consultant inserted a central line. He prescribed the anti-viral agent, ganciclovir 400mg twice-daily and he began to consider that cytomegalovirus (CMV) infection could be a possible cause of my symptoms. CMV was first described by Ribbert in 1881, after he saw large cells in histology sections of a kidney of a stillborn baby and glands of children. Jesionek and Kiolemenoglou also described similar cells as 'protozoan like' in the lungs, kidneys and liver of a near full-term baby. But it was not until 1956 that CMV was isolated from the salivary glands and kidneys of two dying infants. Two other laboratories isolated CMV at approximately the same time. It was initially called 'salivary gland virus' or 'salivary gland inclusion disease virus'.

But in 1960, Weller proposed the use of the term *cytomegalovirus*.

In 1965, Klemola and Kaarianien described CMV mononucleosis, the principal clinical presentation of previously healthy individuals, and in the same year it was first isolated in a renal transplant patient. Today it is recognised as a common infection in all solid organ transplant patients. It is a challenging condition, as many patients have asymptomatic CMV viremia. CMV infection is particularly important in the early days following kidney transplantation as it may enhance the immune response to allo-antigens, which itself may lead to increased risk of acute rejection and loss of the kidney.

Ganciclovir was the first antiviral agent approved for the treatment of CMV infection. It is now widely used for the treatment of CMV among patients with impaired cell-mediated immunity, particularly those with poorly controlled and advanced HIV/AIDS, as well as recipients of solid organ and bone marrow transplants who are at high risk of invasive CMV disease. Valganciclovir, an oral pro-drug that is rapidly converted to ganciclovir, is also used to treat and prevent CMV infections in immunocompromised hosts. When my CMV results came back from the laboratory, they showed a marked increase from a titre of 1/10 on admission to 1/160 the previous day, which indicated active CMV infection. Finally, the medical team had a definitive diagnosis and could treat me accordingly. This included giving me intravenous fluids to try to keep me hydrated, even though – as always – I was drinking large amounts.

There was no longer any need for the antibiotics, and these were discontinued on Tuesday 7th September, although my temperature was still stubbornly peaking at over 40 degrees centigrade with the fever rigors. However, things changed for the better by the following afternoon and for the first time in many days I had a normal temperature, with just a small peak later that evening. By Sunday 12th September, I was stable enough to be allowed home for the day. This was quite emotional, as it was the first time I had been home for two weeks. With Lucy nearly 18 months old and Tom having been born only eight weeks before, it had required considerable juggling with childcare arrangements for Ann to visit and stay for any length of time by my bedside. Having only recently moved to the area, we hadn't yet had time to build up the usual network of friends who might have helped. However, my mum and Ann's parents came down from Halifax and London, respectively, as soon as they could.

This was still a worrying time for Ann. She was now finding out first-hand what life would be like, being married to a person with a kidney transplant. Despite all her prior medical knowledge, nothing could really have prepared her for the reality of seeing her soulmate succumb to the ravages of kidney failure or its complications. Events such as infections often occur with no warning, with early symptoms often remaining hidden due to immunosuppressive drugs. Such challenges can ruin the best-laid plans, even the joy of having a new arrival in the family, and my wife's anxiety about my health was giving her sleepless nights.

Thankfully, the ganciclovir started to work its magic, and paracetamol was able to control the small temperature spikes so my symptoms and fever subsided over the next six days. The ganciclovir was stopped after 12 days so the central line could be removed, finally allowing me to be discharged on Saturday 18th September. I was delighted to be back home with my family and our new baby boy, whom I had hardly had an opportunity to get to know, and I was now recuperating from this nasty virus infection. It had been an exceedingly difficult time for all concerned. It seems to have been a primary CMV infection and had appeared out of the blue. One plausible explanation is that I might have picked it up while meeting the young children at Busy Bees, the hospital nursery Lucy attended. At the time, Lucy had a persistent cough! But it will always remain a mystery.

It wasn't possible to recuperate for too long as there was much to organise with the research in the laboratory, but it was time to alter our work-life balance, with two highly active toddlers in tow and Ann also working full time. Our delightful Georgian home needed much refurbishment. It had been built of stone in around 1850 and the central heating consisted of an old Parkray coal burner and three small radiators. It had many air leaks, so it was either unlit or raging hot, burning itself out within a few hours. We also had to deal with the intricacies of a coal-fired Aga cooker. Our first Christmas was spent in a cold house, relying on open fires while trying to cook a turkey in the Aga whose temperature refused to get above warm. We did not sit down for dinner till after 6pm. It was obvious that a coal-fired Aga needed considerable love and attention, together with the right type of coal. It was like having a third child!

Work progressed apace. Once again, various health and safety protocols needed to be established, including safe ways of disposing of genetically modified organisms. Professor Terry Wilkin was keen for us to be involved in a project he'd long wanted to carry out. This involved screening newborn babies for early immunological markers of type 1 (childhood) diabetes. It was an extremely ambitious project that needed a considerable amount of funding. We were all keen at the outset but realised after a while that there were considerable scientific flaws in the study's design and application. My focus therefore had to remain on ensuring that our own research projects were funded and carried out properly. Ultimately, this would cause an irretrievable breakdown in our collaboration.

Within a few years of our arrival, the founding Dean, Professor Carl Rosen, returned to his native Sweden, and the university sought a new leader to take the fledgling postgraduate medical school to a new level, with the possibility of becoming an undergraduate school. The Deputy Vice Chancellor Academic (DVCA) of the university sought my advice in identifying possible candidates and involved me in the interview process. I was responsible for contacting short-listed candidates and organising their visits to Plymouth to meet academics and clinicians, as well as entertainment and accommodation. Out in the wider world, Plymouth was becoming known as an excellent place to work and attracted several exceptional candidates. At the end of the process, the university appointed Professor Ken Rogers who had been a leading academic surgeon and Dean of Admissions at the University of Sheffield Medical School.

Before his arrival, Ann and I had also been head-hunted by various universities and pharmaceutical companies but nothing concrete had materialised. His arrival quelled questions about the future of the postgraduate medical school, including our own, which may have impinged on future employability. The Department of Biological Sciences were putting me under great pressure to take on a large teaching commitment, which would certainly have detracted from my ability to develop the research. Ann had also found out that her contract was not as secure as we had been led to believe by Professor Wilkin and we were both facing the possibility of finding ourselves unemployed, with a young family in tow. Fortunately, the arrival of Ken Rogers signalled a 'sea change' for the future direction and security of the school. It remained an exciting prospect. Ken Rogers would often drop by my office and chat over a coffee about numerous aspects of developing the school, as well as research and academia. These conversations were akin to the ones I'd had during my time at Guy's with Ken Welsh.

Ken Rogers now set about giving the postgraduate school a management and academic structure that had previously been absent. One of the first tasks I took on was the creation of the master's postgraduate teaching programme. I had no prior experience of this but – working with enthusiastic clinicians and scientists in the university and hospital – I soon developed the skills needed to write the programmes from scratch. Again, there was considerable documentation that would need to be validated and scrutinised by internal assessors as well as external academics. Course module leaders were identified and approached within the university and hospital. I really enjoyed the challenge of learning these new skills, which also brought me into contact with senior academics as well as regular contact with the DVCA. The programmes included MSc degrees in Cancer Studies, Remote Health Care, Biomedical Studies and Clinical Studies, some of which still exist in one form or another.

The research programme was expanding quickly, with new doctoral students joining the group. The laboratories were becoming crowded, and an opportunity arose to move from the main university campus in the city centre to the new Tamar Science Park, next to Derriford Hospital. The university had shown great foresight in developing this site in conjunction with other stakeholders in Plymouth City, but at this point, most of the units were still unoccupied. Having new laboratories that were a hive of activity would probably attract new tenants from the private sector, or at least that was the hope. The DVCA gave us a choice of empty units that could be used for laboratories and offices.

The challenge was to come up with a design and costings for the conversion as well as new equipment. Initially, this had to involve the University and Hospital Estates Departments who, as expected, gave a high estimate of well over half a million pounds. The DVCA's office informed me that this would be impossible, so I needed to think of another way. The DVCA gave me a few words of advice and suggested a ballpark figure that would be acceptable. Thinking laterally, as the space was 'off-campus', it was in fact possible to use private contractors to tender for the work, rather than the Estates Department. This was extremely exciting, and very quickly quotes came in at less than half what the University and Hospital Estates Departments would have charged. The project was signed off by the Vice Chancellor and work started on the new laboratories.

It was very satisfying to be able to design from drawings and create functional molecular medicine and biology laboratories from start to finish, including sorting out all the necessary health and safety licences. Everyone involved was extremely happy with the result and we were all on a bit of a high. Indeed, our efforts attracted the attention of academics and professionals from the hospital and university who were complimentary about what we had achieved with such a small budget and in such a short space of time. The standard of the floors and benches was identical to those found in NHS laboratories but had been delivered at less than half the price. The extra facilities were within walking distance of the hospital, and over the next few years this allowed for many collaborations between enthusiastic clinicians and joint research students. It also resulted in an enormous research student supervisory load, but this was thrilling. Indeed, I would say that one of the greatest contributions I was able to make over my research career was enabling many MD and PhD students to complete their higher degrees, PhD, MD, MS, totalling over 45, in addition to innumerable MSc dissertations. This number was considerably higher than most senior academics throughout the UK and certainly substantially greater than anyone within my own university.

We were already aware of national discussions about starting up new medical schools as Ken Welsh had tipped us off that Plymouth might be a possible site for one, and this had been one of the reasons behind our move. Towards the end of the millennium, the government officially announced plans to create a handful of new medical schools. The universities of Exeter and Plymouth put together a bid for a joint new school. This was originally led by our Dean, Ken Rogers, along with Professor John Tooke from Exeter. Unfortunately, while putting together the bid, Ken Rogers had to take early retirement due to ill-health, leaving a 'power vacuum' at Plymouth that was difficult to fill and ended up dictating Plymouth's future direction over the next few years. There followed a great deal of hard work, political jockeying and bargaining between the two universities, and in August 2000 it was announced that our bid had been successful. Two years later, the first cohort of 130 students arrived, with equal numbers on each university site. However, the loss of Ken Rogers had a profound effect on me personally as I had lost a friend, a mentor and a highly supportive line manager.

This all came at a time when I had been seeking promotion to become a Reader in Molecular Medicine, having more than satisfied the necessary university criteria. Unfortunately, the acting Dean, standing in for Ken Rogers, refused to support my application – for what later turned out to be political reasons. The DVCA had given his advice and supported my application and immediately saw the injustice of the acting Dean's lack of support. I was indebted to the DVCA for nurturing my career over the previous years and when appropriate I had used him as a referee. Following discussions at the highest level in the university, he was instrumental in side-stepping my new line manager to ensure that my application was not blocked.

My application then went to the Universities Professorial and Readership Committee where it was properly scrutinised and, following referees' reports and an interview, I was promoted to Reader in Molecular Medicine in September 2000, just as the new undergraduate school came into existence. The university then went through a period of turmoil, losing firstly the Vice Chancellor, who retired, and soon after that, my mentor the DVCA who, not having been appointed as VC at Plymouth, soon moved to a prestigious post elsewhere. This meant that the new Peninsula Medical and Dental School (PCMD) now had its centre of power shifted to the University of Exeter, with Professor John Tooke becoming its very worthy inaugural Dean.

Before the DVCA left Plymouth, he was able to advise me on my application for academic promotion to a Professorship. Ken Rogers, with whom I was still in contact, also gave me guidance. My application went to the University of Plymouth Professorial Committee, rather than using the new and probably convoluted route through the new medical school, which would have been dominated by academics from the University of Exeter. Once the application was submitted, it went out to international referees to assess. If the reports are satisfactory, there normally follows an extensive interview. I patiently waited to hear from the Professorial Committee but heard nothing.

Eventually, the Dean came to see me and told me that the new Vice Chancellor of the University of Plymouth, Professor Roland Levinsky, himself a clinical immunologist, had made an executive decision to promote me to Professor without any need for an interview panel. This was shortly after I had been promoted to Reader. He had commented that he had not seen anyone with as many successful higher degree completions as I had. Together with the number of research papers I'd published, he decided I was easily worthy of being a professor in any UK university.

I was thrilled. I had finally achieved one of my long-term ambitions. Never in a million years would I have thought it possible, when I looked back over my years of interrupted schooling and illness. But it was even more important to me that it had been achieved without any special allowance being made for my illness. Life is full of compromises and, although I had been Reader in Molecular Medicine, the University of Exeter faction of the PCMD objected to this title, despite having run an established Molecular Medicine Research

Group for many years. My new title was Professor of Cellular and Biomolecular Sciences, though most people still referred to me as Professor of Molecular Medicine. This was just one of the many examples of trivial red tape and politics that would dominate the next decade of our lives.

In late 1995, we had the exciting news that Ann was pregnant again, with a due date in July 1996. A normal healthy baby boy, Olly, was born on 19th July in the maternity unit, at Derriford Hospital. During the intervening period, family and home life had become extremely busy and rewarding. We had been doing a lot of home renovations and alterations, including extending the kitchen area, all of which took time and energy to organise. Just before we had moved to Plymouth in January 1993, we had our first family ski trip to Morzine, France. We made friends in our chalet there with a family from deepest West Cornwall. Our children were similar ages and we met regularly at weekends, enjoying the beaches and boating, as they lived on the Helford River.

This rekindled my interest in sailing, and in the spring of 1994 we bought our first sailing vessel, *Sylvia*, a traditional Cornish 19-foot open boat with square-shaped sails, rather than the modern triangular ones. We kept our boat on the quay in the village and spent many days and nights sailing on the river and out at Plymouth Sound and on the beach. It was idyllic. A highlight of that summer was joining in with the 50th D-Day Anniversary Parade in the Sound. Having enjoyed this experience a great deal, the following year we sold *Sylvia* and bought *Abigail*, a larger, 24-foot gaff-rigged Cornish crabber with four berths. Gaff-rig sails are also traditional square sails. We were now able to stay overnight on the boat in a little more comfort. The arrival of Olly in 1996 did make it rather squashed down below, but the children just thought of it as a big tent on the water. Having a larger boat meant that we were able to venture further away from our home port, with voyages to other local ports in Cornwall and Devon.

One of the great joys of sailing a traditional boat in the South-West was that we could participate in the West Country 'classic boat rallies', which often include singing sea shanties as well as sailing beautiful old and replica boats. We all threw ourselves into these rallies with other like-minded sailors. Our level of participation grew quickly, and I was soon asked to join the organising committee of the Plymouth Classic Boat Rally and then become Chairman. Indeed, the entire family got involved in stuffing envelopes, handing out breakfast bags to skippers and crews, and eventually, when they were a bit older, driving the ribs to help moor the old boats.

While Olly was still in nappies and sleeping on top of the Portaloo aboard *Abigail*, he would sneak into Ann's sleeping bag in the middle of the night. A few years later, when we were alongside the pontoon at Falmouth and about to leave, Olly watched me turn the seawater inlet valve on. We cast off our lines and a couple of minutes later smoke was pouring out of the engine. Fortunately, we had already hoisted the sails and were able to get back to the pontoon under sail. A quick inspection of the engine showed the seawater inlet valve was now off and the engine had overheated. Olly's little fingers had copied his dad's but in the opposite direction! This was just one of many interesting events that occurred while taking our young family out on the water.

During the summer of 1999, we realised we had outgrown *Abigail*, which had almost no headspace down below, and it was time to think about getting a larger vessel. We had fallen in love with the traditional gaff (square) rigged Martin Heard Falmouth working boats built in Mylor near Falmouth. We went to see Martin one wet morning and plumped for his newly designed 35-foot gaff-rigged cutter boat with a flush deck. The boat would be built from new with a waiting time of two years, making it a perfect 10th wedding anniversary present, ready for June 2001. We decided to call her *M'Yvonne* (Margaret Yvonne) after our two mothers, following the Cornish tradition of naming working boats after significant female family members. This was the start of a new chapter in our adventures, sailing off the Cornish coast and then to Brittany in a sound seagoing boat.

Over the next few years, we spent most weekends and (thanks to academic holidays) as much as a month during the summer on board *M'Yvonne*. As our confidence increased, we started taking her to some of the Breton sea shanty festivals in quaint ports such as Paimpol and Binic in the St Malo Bay. We sailed with our friends and their family from Hastings and elsewhere all around the Brittany coastline, including down into North Biscay. I felt completely at home on the water and *M'Yvonne* is such a forgiving boat that we knew she would keep us safe no matter what the elements threw at us. One of my greatest thrills was the overnight crossings to Brittany. It was only a distance of just over 100 nautical miles from Cornwall, but it would take us anything from 18 to 24 hours.

There is something mystical about being at the tiller of a boat, out on the open sea, often with no other vessels in sight and dark starting to fall, with phosphorescence sparkling in the water. There is no turning back, you cannot ring up for 'roadside assistance', you are on your own, and you have to rely on your own experience, seamanship, and your trusty boat to get you through the night. For many years, the family would bed down after Ann's delicious passage-supper and leave me on the tiller. It was bliss. Sleep would finally catch up with me in the early hours and Ann would have to be woken to come and take over for a short time. By then dawn would break and a new day began. Again, this was an experience to be cherished. Both boys effectively learnt to walk on the boat at the same time as they did on land. None of the boats had upright guard rails and it became instinctive to be aware of the sides. In the words of the old fishermen, keep 'one hand for yourself and one for the boat'. All the children turned out to be excellent sailors.

Another pastime I had longed to try was skiing. Ann and I had booked our first skiing holiday for a fortnight in Fieberbrunn, Austria, at the end of March 1989. Being a novice, I spent Sunday mornings in January 1989 on the dry ski-slope at Crystal Palace, trudging up and down artificial snow, learning how to snowplough and do stem christies. We had a fantastic holiday with superb snow, and I was hooked. From then on, a fortnight's skiing in the Alps became a regular event that always included the children. From about the age of three, they all went to Austrian ski school for the two weeks. We would drop them off at 10am at the ski-school office and pick them up again at 3pm. They all very quickly became very competent skiers, having no fear of falling at such a young age.

One of the most enjoyable aspects of these holidays when they were little were the Friday morning ski-school races and our home is full of the medals they won. In later years, when they were all teenagers, the fortnight would be spent skiing together as a family. From early 1997 and for many years following, we would book the fortnight over the February half term in the Hotel Staddtor, Schladming. This was a delightful family-run traditional Austrian hotel that had its own crèche for babies and toddlers when we first went there with a ski company. The hotel was so good that we returned under our own steam for the following ten years and the children spent many happy times attending the Planai 'Hopsi' Schischule and then later skiing as a family. We did break from the tradition of Austria for a couple of years, going to Killington, Vermont, New England, where we also had a fantastic time enjoying American East Coast hospitality.

Once Tom had reached the age of six in 1999, we decided to take him to the local rugby union club in Liskeard (Liskeard & Looe RFC). We all went along to the first session which happened to be a game of tag against Exeter Saracens in Exeter. The under-sevens team had no coach (under-sevens teams never have a coach at the start of any season!), so I was asked if I could help as I 'looked like someone who knew about rugby'. I had not played since breaking my leg.

We hadn't thought about Lucy playing until she asked whether girls could play too. They took one look at her long legs and immediately invited her to join. Of course, she said yes. Over the next few years, we all became active participants in the club. At the beginning I took the basic coaching course and eventually coached all the children through the early age groups. Later, I took on more responsibility, became Chairman of the Youth Club and developed my interest in coaching, taking higher-level courses.

Ann took on responsibility for Safeguarding at the club and then later with Cornwall Rugby Football Union. Lucy was unable to play rugby with the boys after the age of 12, so we decided to set up a girls' team in Cornwall. This took up a huge amount of time but was very rewarding, with many girls from all backgrounds joining the teams. Our winter weekends became very busy, with rugby training and matches, and Lucy, Tom and Olly often travelling to different venues across Devon and Cornwall.

The development of our girls' rugby team (nicknamed 'the Leopards'; the men were called 'the Lions') coincided with considerable development of the female game in England through the Rugby Football Union, supported by Sports England. This led to fantastic opportunities for regional coaches, with opportunities to attend training courses at national level. By the time Lucy was 14, it was apparent that she was an exceptionally talented player, following trials at Rugby School the original seat of rugby when Webb Ellis picked up the ball! She was selected for the England women's and girls' talent development group. This involved driving her to various venues around England for training sessions and later watching her play matches. As our own girls' rugby team developed, we decided to create a separate and unique type of rugby club to fill the need for local girls. It was mobile and could move to various schools and venues to engage girls in playing the sport throughout the county. This continued for several years, until the national Rugby Football Union drive led to most clubs establishing women's and girls' sections.

There have been many highlights during my own family's rugby career. One of the most enjoyable was to see Lucy play for the England Under-20s in the 2011 Nations Cup in Santa Barbara, California. This was at the end of Lucy's first year at medical school and we dropped her off at Heathrow Airport to join her team, while Ann, Tom, Olly and I booked into a hotel for our flight the next day. We had a fantastic holiday, watching Lucy play rugby at the University of California, Santa Barbara, visiting Universal Studios in Los Angeles with the boys, and having a picnic in the National Park at Lake Cachuma. Lucy was training and playing hard, as she always reminds us, but we were very proud to see her and her team win the U20s Nations Cup.

Some years later, we were also lucky enough to watch Lucy obtain a full England Rugby Union cap playing against Scotland. In her first game she came on as a substitute for the last ten minutes and scored the winning try. We also had great joy and pride watching Tom and Olly play in their own matches and competitions. For a while I even started to play rugby at Liskeard in the vets/ second team matches, taking up my old position of prop forward, and was quite pleased with my level of fitness compared to some of the players in the team. But then I have never been a smoker! I have often wondered why I have such a strong passion for rugby and wondered if it had anything to do with my kidney coming from Wales. Many people will think I am crazy to say this but there have been many stories of recipients' personalities changing after a transplant and taking on the characteristics of the donor. I will never know, as it is impossible to contact my donor family to find out if he was an avid rugby player or fan. In the 1970s contact between the recipient and donor family remained strictly confidential. Today, recipients are offered the opportunity to write a letter to the donor's family. For those who do write this is done through an intermediary and the donor's family have the choice whether to receive it.

The Peninsula Medical School students had formed a rugby club whose team participated in the National Medical Schools' competition (NAMS). They were looking for a coach and my offer to help was quickly accepted. Coaching the students was extremely rewarding as well as challenging, as several of them had previously played at regional and national level before starting their degree course. As Tom had now embarked on his Biomedical Sciences degree at Plymouth, he was also eligible to play for 'the Medics'. This was the first time since Tom had played mini rugby that I had an opportunity to coach him, and he was a very active member of the team. Like his dad, he was a prop!

In 2010, the Medics beat the Royal Marines 22–7 in the second annual 'Help for Heroes' charitable match at Plymouth Albion's ground at Brickfields in front of a capacity crowd – the only time (to date) that the Marines have been beaten in this match. Being very competitive and feeling aggrieved at their defeat, the following year the Royal Marines ensured that they fielded a strong team of players and duly triumphed, as they have ever since. I carried on coaching the Medics team for another two years, before having to stop due to knee and shoulder issues.

In the mid-1990s, research into a particular gene (aldose reductase) that might affect the susceptibility of people with diabetes to kidney disease became a focal topic at international level and dominated our own research. As a group, we wanted to try to discover a gene or genes that might put some people with diabetes at greater risk of developing diabetic renal disease. Several large pharmaceutical companies were also trying to develop new drugs to stop the action of aldose reductase and thereby prevent the devastating long-term complications of diabetes. Because of this, I developed a very fulfilling collaboration with Dr Peter Oates who, at the time, was a senior scientist working on aldose reductase at Pfizer Inc. Groton, USA. Over the next few years, we worked together to see if we could use molecular markers to identify those patients who might benefit from the drug. For me, this meant many trips to Groton, Connecticut, to discuss and present data.

Our collaboration was cemented while Peter was attending the European Diabetes meeting in Glasgow on 11th September 2001, a day never to be forgotten as it was when the Twin Towers in New York were destroyed by terrorists. As all transatlantic flights were suspended, there was no way for Peter to get home to his family. I had his mobile number and called him in Glasgow, inviting him to come and stay with us for as long as he liked. Hotels throughout the UK had quickly begun to fill up and flights across the world were cancelled for many days. He immediately agreed to stay, and we advised him to catch the train to Plymouth. It was a terrible time for many people, Peter included. His son had left one of the Twin Towers only ten minutes before one of the planes struck, but fortunately he was safe.

A high point of our collaboration was when I joined Peter as Session Chair/ Co-Organiser of the US-Japan Aldose reductase workshops in Kona (Big Island), Hawaii in January 2000, March 2004 and again in 2007. The 2007 workshop was the last of these successful scientific workshops which had started in the 1980s in Honolulu. Around 100 researchers from around the world would attend the workshop over a three- to four-day period. I am often wryly asked why Hawaii? When the workshop was first established, it mostly attracted researchers from the USA and Japan so Hawaii, being equidistant between the two, was an obvious choice as a venue. The months just after Christmas are also the low season, making accommodation relatively inexpensive.

Until 9/11, Hawaii had also been suffering a long recession, being out of favour with many tourists who were now travelling to more exotic places such as Vietnam and Thailand. Indeed, one of my main impressions from our first trip was how very run-down Kona-Kailua was. This was a town on the 'Big Island' of Hawaii, with houses that looked as if they had seen better days. We stayed in a modern 1960s hotel on the west coast, a 20-minute drive from the main town centre and we were nearly the last visitors, as it closed its doors not long afterwards. At the time, you could buy a two- or three-bedroomed house there for a similar price to one in Cornwall.

On returning to Kona in 2004, it had noticeably changed. It was now post 9/11 and the US tourists were flooding back to the island, thanks to terrorist threats abroad. New roads had replaced the old, dusty tracks and this was accompanied by housing and commercial developments. The price of houses had more than doubled since my previous trip. As organisers, we were fortunate to obtain sufficient sponsorship to subsidise the meeting in a hotel (as I recall, it was the Outrigger Keauhou), some five minutes closer to the town centre. It was an idyllic setting. The dining area had been built above rock pools where you could watch green-backed turtles swimming while eating your breakfast. At around 6.30pm, when the sun set, traditional Hawaiian singing and music entertained us. This ritual also attracted some 'sun worshippers' who would sit in a trance, watching the sun set.

The scientific recognition I received at these and other international workshops and meetings was, sadly, in stark contrast to the uphill battle I faced at my home institution. There is something special about being among like-minded researchers and scientists, sharing ideas in a workshop or forum, which is small enough for everyone to get to know everybody else. There is a real buzz and sense of euphoria when ideas are shared, with a collective desire to push forward the boundaries of knowledge. No doubt my feelings were no different from those experienced by countless other scientists throughout history. Gaining the respect of your international peers is humbling, and also gives you an adrenaline rush. Once the workshop or meeting is over, you just want to get back to the laboratory to start the next round of experiments and share the knowledge you've gained. This sense of excitement never goes away, no matter how many years you have been involved in research.

Flying directly back to the UK from Hawaii requires a two-night flight with an entire day spent waiting in a US West Coast airport such as Los Angeles. And by the time I got back to work to find all the usual petty problems and issues waiting, some of the euphoria usually dissipated! People tend to become preoccupied with their own research, and those involved in other spheres may not be interested in someone else's scientific standing in their field. The usual small-minded politics and competition between groups also kicks in. By the time I attended the last US-Japan workshop in 2007, I was beginning to develop the side effects of the statin treatment I had been prescribed for high cholesterol. At the time, I didn't realise that over the next few years I would be struggling with severe memory loss and impaired cognitive function. In addition, there were organisational changes afoot. In 2009, Sir John Tooke left Exeter to take up a new prestigious post in London. After Ken Rogers had retired, Sir John had led the original bid to form a joint medical and dental school and he was one of the last links to the old postgraduate schools. In any organisation, losing a chief executive can cause uncertainty and disquiet.

We also had to deal with the 'Research Assessment Exercise (RAE) or Framework (REF) every six years. This is a process whereby the government audits the effectiveness of university research. Universities ask their academic members of staff to submit evidence of their research output during the period since the previous assessment. Some universities have been criticised for trying to manipulate the audits by buying in entire research groups (and their academic outputs) just before the cut-off date for submission. Others are said to have hidden or even fired academics whom they consider have under-achieved during the audit period, even though this might have been for genuine reasons such as maternity leave, sickness, or excessive teaching or administrative loads. Each time the audit comes along, the government department responsible for administering it tries to refine the process to deal with these underhand tactics.

Plymouth and Exeter Universities agreed to submit the RAE jointly for the 2008 audit. At the end of the process, the results showed that my own research output, as well as others in our group, was highly rated and our medical school was placed in the top 50 percent of all UK medical schools. This was a great achievement for a new academic institution; and for the team it built on the high grade we had previously received in the RAE 2001 when we were simply the Postgraduate Medical School.

However, by the middle of the first decade of the new millennium, I had started to develop severe mental health issues, particularly amnesia and loss of cognitive function, even though I wasn't fully aware of it at that time. The cause of my mental incapacitation would remain elusive for several years. I had first become aware that I had a raised cholesterol level after giving several oral presentations at a British Society for Immunology meeting in South Kensington Town Hall in the mid-1980s. After I left the podium, a middle-aged Polish medical doctor came up and started telling me in Polish and broken English that I needed to check my cholesterol. She was pointing towards my eyes and the 'lipid arc' that was visible. I did not appreciate the significance of what she was saying on that occasion.

The first time any of my own doctors mentioned my high cholesterol level was on 14th December 1993, when Dr Richard McGonigle (my Renal Consultant) copied me into a clinic letter. He suggested I should start simvastatin or lovastatin (10mg daily). The lipid arc had been present since I was first ill, so I was indifferent to the risks of cholesterol and heart disease and have always been reluctant to start new medications. Over the next few years, however, I was repeatedly told by my renal clinic doctors that I needed to take a statin, as my cholesterol was often around 7.4mmol/l. By now, I had done my own research on the risks and benefits of taking statins to lower cholesterol and I believed the entire field had become controversial, with a confusing array of claims and counter-claims. Even the role of cholesterol, in causing coronary and other heart disease, was being questioned.

Nevertheless, I came under intense pressure from the clinic to start taking atorvastatin (Lipitor), 20mg daily, from around 1997. It reached the point where I dreaded going to the outpatient clinic because of the pressure I was under, despite my being a professional colleague. In May 2003, after five years, I was finally sufficiently browbeaten to agree to start taking the statin. After a few years of taking atorvastatin, it was suggested that I should switch to rosuvastatin, but I resisted. This latter drug was already known to have side effects, including some affecting the kidney.

There was also a discussion about switching my immunosuppressants to sirolimus, rather than azathioprine. I asked my nephrologists, all of whom are excellent, empathic doctors, if they could provide 30 years' kidney function and survival data with sirolimus, to compare with the azathioprine that I was taking. These records are clearly not available for any of the new drugs, so I rested my case. This is a question I often ask consultants from all specialities that I come across during such discussions. I have yet to meet one who would change their immunosuppressive regime if they were in the same position as me. 'If it ain't broke, don't fix it' is a very good motto!

Gradually, over the next few years, I started to develop new symptoms. They were mild at first, and I only became aware of them as they worsened. At this time, I was supervising a great many research students and there were some meetings in which I would withdraw almost entirely from the discussion. As the Director of Studies, I should have been leading these discussions, coming up with new ideas and challenging the students. But as time passed, it became increasingly difficult to hold the meetings at all. When I did, I found ways of prompting others to continue the conversations without having much idea myself of what was being said.

As well as being unable to hold meaningful academic debates with students and my colleagues, I started having difficulty in reading scientific papers. I seemed to have lost my ability to assimilate the content of a paper beyond the first few lines. I would pick up a hard copy, start to read it and perhaps take some notes, but by the end of the first paragraph I had to put it back on my desk. I had similar issues with writing research papers and grant applications. My previous 20 years of high output now seemed a distant memory. It was simply impossible to string my thoughts together. I might still have been able to come up with great ideas but getting them down on paper was out of the question.

Fortunately, I had my own office in the John Bull Building on the medical school Plymouth campus and was able to hide myself away there. My enthusiasm drained away, and I dreaded being in the building, let alone going into the laboratory. I now went to my office late, usually after everyone else had arrived, turned on my computer, looked through emails and opened post. Within a short time, my mind would become cloudy and I would lose my ability to concentrate and deal with anything. After I had settled into my office, my secretary, Julie, would bring me a cup of coffee and we would have a chat about day-to-day matters. Sometimes this was the only conversation I had – talking to my secretary became the highlight of my working day! I had always worked closely with my wife Ann, but she was having to deal with an increasing clinical load in the hospital as well as having to organise clinical trials. These activities all took place in separate buildings. The new medical school had physically and emotionally broken our professional relationship, and this came at a time when my mental illness was having its most profound effect on my ability to function.

As my condition worsened, it could only be described as living in a 'brain fog' and being unable to communicate to let anyone know that I was there. By now, I was also experiencing episodes of 'transient amnesia'. The most striking example of this was the difficulty I had in remembering people's names. This included my own research students working along the corridor, as well as close relatives outside my immediate family. The memory loss exacerbated my growing feeling of isolation. In professional and academic conversations, I found it incredibly difficult to concentrate on what was being said or to comprehend the context. It was easier to stay silent or limit my replies to vague phrases. A more tempting option was to cancel and reschedule the meeting, as my confidence in these settings was now non-existent.

By spring 2010, I had severe loss of memory and cognitive function, though I had not yet sought my GP's help as I was too embarrassed. I had been asked to chair some oral presentations at a meeting of the European Diabetes Nephropathy Study Group (EDNSG) in Poitiers, France. I had planned to fly from Exeter to Charles de Gaulle airport, Paris, on Thursday 20th May and then take the TGV train direct to Poitiers. Everything went according to plan, and I left the plane and made my way to the air-rail transport terminal. I followed the crowds and headed for the escalators down to the train platforms but there the 'brain fog' descended. I had no idea where I was, what I was doing on the platform or why I was there. I had little recollection of the plane journey and couldn't understand why I was surrounded by people speaking French, with French signs everywhere. I started to get into a massive panic, something that had never happened to me before, even during all my crises on dialysis. My eyes became teary and wet, and I went and sat down on a bench. Why was I here? It was as if I had just been beamed down from another planet.

I eventually calmed down, went through the documents in my bag and found the letter of invitation and details of the EDNSG meeting. At the same time, I found the TGV tickets for Poitiers. The 'brain fog' cleared slightly and I realised I needed to catch my train. Fortunately, the train hadn't yet arrived, and my tickets included seat reservations. However, I realised then that my life was a mess and that I was no longer in control of my memory and senses. It was a really depressing feeling.

I somehow got through the meeting and returned home without any more problems. I explained to Ann what had happened, having already phoned her numerous times while I was away, and we both started to worry about my mental health. I had been doing some laboratory research on statins in kidney disease and had become acutely aware of the mounting number of papers reporting side effects. The use of statins in healthy individuals, as well as those with cardiovascular risk factors, had become a controversial subject, with claims that some pharmaceutical companies had 'hidden' the data on side effects. Around the same time, Ann had been asked to debate the benefits of statins with Dr Malcolm Kendrick who was leading the campaign highlighting the dangers of statins at a local GPs' educational meeting. The jigsaw pieces were starting to fit together.

Around three weeks after the episode in Paris, I suffered another severe 'memory loss' event but this time in my own workplace. Halfway through the morning I left my office and went upstairs. I then opened a door and walked in, to find a senior member of the school sitting in what was clearly his own office. He looked up, rather astonished, recognising me from a few years earlier when we had both been situated on the main campus. As soon as I saw him, I realised I had made a mistake. Fortunately, after a quick apology I was able to retrieve the situation by making light conversation about his current work. However, when I went back down to my own office, I was distraught and unable to comprehend how I had just walked into a senior person's office without any invitation or explanation for my presence.

My lapses of memory and cognitive function were now affecting many aspects of my life and I felt I was on the verge of some sort of breakdown. It was time to talk to my GP who was incredibly supportive and understood the issues I was experiencing. He advised me to stop taking the statins immediately. He wanted to rule out the possibility of a brain tumour so he referred me for an MRI scan at Derriford Hospital. He also thought I might be depressed. An appointment was made for me to see a Consultant Psychiatrist to investigate this further, and my GP arranged some counselling while also starting me on anti-depressants.

Thankfully, the MRI scan showed no evidence of a tumour, nor of dementia; and over the next few months my condition started to improve. Ann came to all my consultations with the Psychiatrist to provide support and help explain my condition. He confirmed the diagnosis of severe depression, although my short-term memory did not appear to be affected. I had by now started my counselling sessions and these continued into a second set. This was the first time during my entire illness that I had ever had any counselling. I was finally able to open up and discuss the contents of many 'black boxes' that had remained securely closed from as long ago as my childhood years of illness. These counselling sessions were extremely valuable, although sometimes also very emotional with a few tears being shed. Previously, I had always been sceptical about counselling, and suspicious of the idea of 'opening up' about one's feelings to a stranger. However, I obviously became a convert after taking part in these sessions. I would strongly advise anyone for whom counselling has been prescribed to take up the offer. There is controversy about the use of anti-depressants alone in the treatment of depression – and the most effective treatment comes from combining medication with talking therapy.

Eventually after several months my memory started to return, together with my cognitive function. It was as if the 'brain fog' had lifted, and I was back in the sunlight. I continued to see the Psychiatrist and take anti-depressants for around three years, by which time my recovery was almost complete. There is no doubt that statins caused my symptoms and fortunately the side effects were reversible, although I lost several years of my life and work. The side effects had a severe impact on my professional life as well as my recreational and family life. I will always be grateful to my GP, and to Ann and my family who were extremely supportive through a very difficult part of my kidney journey.

My field of scientific research, as others, is extremely dependent on one's ability to remember, conceptualise, review, and assimilate information. Research ideas are generated from one's prior knowledge and knowledge of the scientific literature, presenting, and discussing results in various scientific and academic fora. The catastrophic effect of the statins to close off my memory and cognitive function made it impossible to be effective in my professional life. I find it surprising now to think that my condition was never noticed in the workplace and there was no intervention. One of my direct line managers occupied the office next door and I met other senior line managers from time to time. The deterioration of my mental health occurred over several months, if not years. However, memory loss and cognitive dysfunction aren't easily recognised, in contrast to a broken leg! Before my problems with statins, I had been extremely productive, at the forefront of my field and held in high esteem by researchers all over the world. I also had an excellent track record of successful grant applications and a remarkable number of higher research degree completions. These areas of activity all ground to a halt during the days of 'brain fog' when it was impossible to achieve anything. I myself failed to recognise the problem until it reached crisis point. On reflection, my wife now recalls numerous pointers (such as mood swings and memory failures) indicating that I was having mental health issues; and in many ways, she tended to compensate for them when we were together.

There is often fierce rivalry between research groups within university departments (for example, competing for access to laboratory bench space) and the Peninsula was no exception to this rule. Cohesion and teamwork could be in short supply, and professional rivalry was to be expected. Consequently, it is hard to admit to having any problems. I went for months without hearing from the senior line manager who was responsible for my appraisal or, indeed, any other senior member of the school. Mental health issues in the workplace are often overlooked, as they are in the community. The 'grin and bear it' and 'pull your socks up' attitude still prevails. But I worked in a medical school where understanding mental health formed a major part of the curriculum! Thankfully, our attitude to identifying, treating and supporting mental health in the workplace has changed dramatically over the past few years.

By 2013, my memory and cognitive function had returned to near normal. There were attempts in renal outpatients to try and persuade me to change to another type of statin, but I refused – pointing to the accumulating evidence of their side effects and challenging the whole premise that cholesterol played a pathological role in heart disease. I was also able to add statins to the list of drugs (along with 'Fortral') that I was 'allergic' to in my hospital notes. Unfortunately, by the time I had recovered from the statin side effects, I was facing several problems arising from the long-term complications of transplantation and immunosuppression.

The latter period of my mental health issues also coincided with the break-up of the Peninsula Medical School by the two universities. The reorganisation of the structure on the Plymouth site left us completely exposed, with no support – not even our secretary. Everyone was now talking about the next research audit, which would be REF 2014. This would cover the period when the dramatic side effects of statins had really taken their toll on my mental capacity and professional performance. The Equality Act 2010 states that protection should be given to people with certain characteristics such as disability, chronic health conditions, sexuality and religion. The REF 2014 had a large section devoted to ensuring that researchers with 'protected characteristics' would not be discriminated against in the forthcoming audit. Yet my line manager offered no support regarding my ongoing health issues, and it became clear that I and my entire research group were facing a bleak future, despite my mental incapacitation and extensive medical history having been reported to the University Occupational Health Department. While I was on sick leave following my right knee replacement in spring 2013, a newly appointed senior academic in the school began holding talks with individuals working on diabetic kidney disease about possible voluntary redundancy.

Ann was also facing the prospect of being made voluntarily redundant, despite holding a clinical contract with a heavy NHS commitment and with no discussion taking place between the medical school and the hospital. We discussed our options: either taking a generous enhanced early retirement package; or fighting what we saw as an injustice that breached NHS Consultant Clinical Academic Guidelines and the Equality Act. We had never lost a battle like this before, but, in the end, neither of us had the energy to take it on.

In June 2013, I suffered a pulmonary embolism, requiring more sick leave. I never returned to my office. Ann and members of the research group cleared my desk and office Thankfully, my laboratory books going as far back as Guy's were recovered. The laboratory had numerous freezers holding literally thousands of DNA and other samples collected since I had been at Guy's in the 1980s. Some of them were incredibly precious and included samples from non-renal diseases, such as myasthenia gravis, from collaborations with Professors John Newson-Davis and Nick Willcox. Many other samples were part of a UK DNA repository of families of people with diabetic kidney disease. We also had an extremely valuable collection of Cornish Celtic DNA samples that had already led to prestigious publications examining European population migration patterns over the past 40,000 years. These were irreplaceable.

In 2006 the Human Tissue Act 2004 came into force, which regulated the removal, storage, use and disposal of 'Relevant Material'. There are many different types of human tissues and cells, including skin, body parts, blood and bone. The Act was passed partly because of incidents in which children's organs had been retained by the Alder Hey Children's Hospital without consent. The Kennedy inquiry into heart surgery on children at the Bristol Royal Infirmary also led to great concern about these issues. Any sample derived from a human body that contains even a single cell is deemed to be 'Relevant Material'. I was the 'Designated Individual' for the medical school, and this meant that I was responsible for ensuring that samples were stored and archived properly.

Before our departure, there were fraught discussions about the future of such samples which had been collected over many years. There were important ethical issues at stake, as patients had consented to donating their blood because they expected it to be kept and used for the research they had signed up to. The medical school staff were keen to clear out and throw away the samples – until we pointed out that this would be a criminal offence, as it would be a clear breach of the Human Tissue Act. Senior members of the medical school had not appreciated the ethical issues or the enormous cost of dealing with the samples and were at a loss as to what to do next.

Ann had a meeting with some of the patients in her diabetes patient participation group, many of whom had also donated samples. We then managed to arrange for many of the diabetic kidney disease samples to be sent to a colleague and collaborator in another laboratory where they could be used. However, until the charities (which had spent millions of pounds for the studies to take place) became involved, the medical school refused to pay the relatively minor cost of transporting the samples to the other laboratory. The final whereabouts of these thousands of samples were not communicated to us.

This unhappy episode raises some major ethical questions about the rights of the donor (the person donating the biological sample), the recipient who is likely to be the researcher, the institute holding the samples and personal data, and the funding bodies paying for the work. In the 1980s, when I first got involved in research, it was very straightforward. You would simply ask a patient whether they minded if an extra tube of blood was taken for research, to which the patient (trusting their doctor or researcher) would just give verbal consent. Later, as projects became better defined and involved the storage of DNA extracted from the blood, a patient information sheet explaining the study would be given to the patient, who would give written, informed consent after a suitable time for reflection. This was at a time when as much as 30–40ml blood was needed to be able to extract sufficient DNA and the entire process could take up to a week to complete! Arrangements for obtaining informed consent for research, scrutinised by research ethics committees, have advanced out of all recognition since those early days, and understandably so.

The phenomenal advances in molecular genetics in the 1990s, together with such ambitious projects as sequencing the entire human genome by the early part of the 21st century, and the above-mentioned scandals, stimulated discussions among interested parties and the public on how this area of research should be regulated. This has become even more important, with collections of samples that are now being proposed or are already taking place. There is also the critical matter of ownership of clinical data, which has become a very controversial topic in the post-pandemic era. Some of these collections involve whole DNA sequencing of hundreds of thousands of samples from individuals. The ethical issues around these collections are enormous and will no doubt be debated for many years to come.

Ann leaving her post gave rise to severe problems in the clinical arena and Derriford Hospital had not been party to any of the discussions. However, the hospital quickly sorted out the issue by giving her a clinical contract. The other members of the research group all left laboratory research but fortunately found good positions elsewhere in the NHS. On reflection, perhaps my problems in the workplace were no different from those encountered by numerous patients with kidney failure. Mine just happened to be particularly complicated and involved other people. These issues have become very pertinent during the Covid pandemic when transplant recipients have sometimes been asked to work in high-risk areas when they are supposed to be shielding. If they do not turn up for work, they face the sack; but going to work may put them at severe risk. This is the kind of injustice that patients with kidney failure regularly face.

Chapter 13: Long-Term Complications of Kidney Transplantation

Renal transplantation has been a life-saving treatment for tens of thousands of people with kidney failure, giving them back a good quality of life. For me, this included returning to full-time education, finding work that I enjoyed and having a family. In the pioneering days of transplantation, doctors were mainly concerned with the treatment of hyper-acute and acute rejection of the newly transplanted kidney. For many years, scientific research was rightly focused on, firstly, developing the best protocols to ensure that the kidney wasn't rejected in the short term; and secondly, on optimising maintenance of kidney function over the first decade after transplantation.

Over time, transplantation results improved, as surgeons and doctors gained experience in the procedures, and new immunosuppressants and other drugs (particularly anti-hypertensive agents to control damaging high blood pressure) were developed. Consequently, over the past 50 years and particularly in the last two decades, there has been a great deal of success in preventing and treating rejection of the kidney, and overall patient morbidity and mortality have substantially decreased.

This massive improvement in post-transplant success has been accompanied by a growing understanding that there are also long-term complications associated with transplantation. In recent years, it has become clear that long-term dialysis and immunosuppression in patients with kidney failure leads to an increased risk of cancer, post-transplant malignancy (PTM), and accelerated cardiovascular disease, as well as other conditions that can reduce the life of a transplant recipient.

Immunosuppressive agents are extremely powerful drugs that usually work by preventing the proliferation of T-cells and other cells in the immune system. This has the effect of dampening down the immune system, to ensure that the transplanted kidney is not rejected. Unfortunately, this also means that the immune response needed to identify and destroy rogue tumour cells is reduced. The immune system normally undertakes constant 'tumour surveillance', destroying many thousands of potentially dysfunctional cells every day. It is now thought that long-term continuous exposure to immunosuppressive agents in transplant patients results in an increased risk of clinical cancer because of the decreased tumour surveillance and the accumulation of mutations in the DNA. By impairing T-cell function, immunosuppressant drugs also reduce the destruction of oncogenic (tumour-producing) viral infections.

Cancer-related mortality rates are particularly high in solid organ transplant (SOT) recipients. Recent studies from the UK, Europe, US, South Korea, Australia and New Zealand (ANZDATA) all confirm that kidney transplant recipients, as well as other SOT recipients, have nearly three times the risk of developing a life-threatening tumour, compared with ordinary members of the general population of similar age and gender. Indeed, it is predicted that death from cancer will soon be the leading cause of death in people with a kidney transplant. While early diagnosis may improve outcomes, the best methods of screening for cancer are still being debated, and identifying effective treatments can be challenging, mainly because of the difficulty in performing randomised controlled trials in these SOT groups.

Personally, I have suffered from skin blemishes (such as common warts) since my first transplant in the 1970s. Warts were so common then, especially in children, that I never bothered seeking any professional help. When I was at grammar school, I had many warts on both hands so I bought a tube of 'wart remover' from Boots chemist. This consisted of silver nitrate, which I diligently applied to all the warts on the top of my hands, not realising the consequences of the reaction of the silver nitrate with skin. Within minutes, my skin turned white (where I had applied it) and my entire hands were gleaming!

It was so noticeable that I decided to wrap my hands in bandages. This became another reason for bullying and name-calling at school, which I tried to deflect by saying I had cut my hands. But people had previously noticed the warts and realised that I had been trying to get rid of them. The bullies referred to me as the 'scabies boy' or 'leprosy boy' or worse. I was so distressed by it all that I didn't go into school for the next couple of days and used the time to try and remove the silver nitrate and the scabs. This of course just made my hands look even more unsightly. The warts and skin blemishes have never gone away.

Funnily enough, in these early years at school I never had the same self-consciousness about my many operation scars, including the three exceptionally large ones that dominate my abdomen and numerous areas of my arms. They were just war wounds and part of my kidney journey. They were also hidden underneath my school uniform and weren't seen, as I never changed with the other boys. When my native kidneys were removed by Mr Shaldon in 1969, he used a rather unconventional method, making a vertical incision of around 16 inches (I was only 5 foot 2 inches tall at the time), from the base of my ribs to the suprapubic area. He then used staples to hold the massive operation site in position and this produced a raised scar that in places was nearly half an inch wide. The two operation sites for the transplants involved conventional incisions which were commonly used in those days, before the advent of keyhole surgery.

While under the care of Guy's Hospital, I was referred to the Dermatology Department to check out my warts. This was in the early 1980s, when long-term complications due to immunosuppressants received little attention. My first consultation was with a Professor of Dermatology who quickly confirmed that they were common warts, although they were of differing types. I was passed on to a medical student who used an orange stick with cotton wool on the tip that had been immersed in liquid nitrogen to 'burn off' the warts. This was quite a simple technique that simply required the nitrogen-soaked cotton bud to be held against the wart for as long as you could bear the pain, often for up to two minutes with pressure. The method worked reasonably well, and within a few days the wart dropped off and was replaced by new skin.

While watching the medical student performing the technique, I realised that this was something I could do myself, as my laboratory also had a plentiful supply of liquid nitrogen, cotton wool and wooden sticks. Indeed, I found using plastic petri-dish spreaders particularly effective! I decided not to waste any more NHS resources going to follow-up appointments in the Dermatology Clinic and, over the next decade or so, I burned off my own common warts to great effect. I even managed to acquire a small Dewar flask to store the liquid nitrogen. These flasks have a metal casing. Inside, they look like a conventional Thermos flask but they can withstand the extremely low temperature (-196 degrees centigrade) at which nitrogen is stored as a liquid. Often, I would attend to the warts in my office or bring the flask home and do it there. I managed to keep control of them for many years, although I suspect this is not a method to be recommended for patients in general!

In June 2004, now at Plymouth, I had my first outpatient appointment with a Consultant Dermatologist for around 15 years. Over the previous few years, numerous skin cancers had developed, particularly on my shoulders and back. Some had become quite large and ulcerated. Dr Peter Kersey kindly saw me, and his clinic letter mentioned my extensive collection of skin cancers and other abnormalities, which included squamous and basal cell carcinomas, Bowen's disease and actinic keratoses. It reads like a fact sheet listing commonly found skin lesions in a long-term immunosuppressed patient!

Over the next year, he removed many of my skin cancers under local anaesthetic. The limiting factor during these procedures was the total amount of the local anaesthetic (lignocaine and adrenaline) which could be injected in one go; so I would generally have six excised at a time, some of them requiring substantial stitching. The procedures were carried out in a clinical room in the Dermatology Department. Sadly, I would often have complications following the operations. The dermatologists liked to use 'dissolvable' stitches that were aesthetically pleasing and didn't need to be removed. However, I had thin skin, due to long-term steroid use, which meant that within the first week of the operation the dissolvable stitches just pulled away from my skin and the wound. Invariably, the site would then become infected, thus requiring antibiotics for up to two weeks and resulting in even more scarring.

As well as the skin lesions, I also had an exceptionally large and nasty hypertrophic, highly keratinised viral wart deep within my right heel, which I had lived with for a few years. It had gradually got bigger; the heel was deeply split, with a gap of a couple of centimetres which had become difficult to walk on, and it was continually bleeding. More importantly, it interfered with sailing, as I usually went barefoot on the deck! It became clear that some treatment was needed, and I received intralesional Bleomycin.

Bleomycin is normally used to treat cancer, including Hodgkin's and non-Hodgkin's lymphomas, testicular, ovarian and cervical cancers. It is typically used with other cancer medications, and can be given intravenously, intramuscularly or under the skin. Due to the cytotoxic nature of the drug, it had to be specially purchased for me as an individual patient, which involved a lot of red tape. I ended up having to have two injections of around 10ml Bleomycin solution directly into the open lesion on my heel. It was an incredibly painful procedure, done without any prior local anaesthetic. Thankfully, after the first injection, the lesion started to heal; and after the second injection it never reappeared.

The Dermatology Department continued to treat the skin cancers in this way until the end of 2006 when Dr Kersey retired, and unfortunately, there was a long gap before his replacement was appointed. On reflection, it seems rather remiss that the care for my skin cancers was abruptly stopped, given that I was a high-risk patient. This was a case of poor communication, with my clinical care not being transferred to another department, leaving me in limbo. However, in September 2009, my GP referred me back to the Plastic Surgery Department for continued treatment.

Over the next ten years, I attended the equivalent of six-monthly outpatient appointments with my surgeon, which usually resulted in surgical excision of the lesions in the day-case Freedom Unit, Plymouth. This system worked extremely well. Occasionally, a basal cell or Bowen's carcinoma, which had been earmarked for removal at my outpatient clinic appointment, had disappeared by the time of surgery, while new ones had erupted. While I was being operated on, we would often discuss the intricacy of the immune system, which could destroy certain malignant cells without any intervention, while others would flourish and become a major problem. One explanation may be that the cells destroyed by the immune system displayed certain 'foreign antigens' on their surfaces, while others did not. If we could identify which antigens were recognised by the immune system, this might lead to an effective treatment for cancer. Indeed, some cancers are now treated using this type of immunotherapy.

Looking back at my hospital notes, I was amazed to find that I had at least 160 lesions removed between 2004 and 2020. At the beginning of this period, most of these lesions were basal cell carcinomas and Bowen's patches (disease), which were less aggressively malignant. Over time, the number and presentation of the lesions has changed and now there are more squamous cell carcinomas (SSCs), which are far more dangerous. Over the past five years, I have had several SSCs which have grown exceptionally quickly over a couple of months and have been intensely painful and sensitive to the touch. Another difference is that the lesions were initially found on my shoulders and upper torso, but in the last few years they have increasingly appeared in non-sun-exposed areas, which were previously unaffected.

My surgeon briefly left Derriford Hospital in 2018 and arranged for my care to be transferred to a colleague in the Plastic Surgery Department. To begin with, this system worked well, and I had a few more lesions removed, some of which were urgent and required skin grafting. Indeed, two of these procedures were performed while I was an inpatient with sepsis. There was then a period of a few months when I seemed to get lost again in the 'black hole' of hospital administration, resulting in my care suddenly being moved to another department. After some to-ing and fro-ing, I managed to re-establish my care with the Plastic Surgery Department. In this case, as so often with patients who have long-term complications, getting appropriate care largely depends upon establishing a relationship of trust between the patient and their healthcare team.

In the interests of balance, I should say that, in over half a century of being an NHS patient, I have only had cause to be concerned about my care on a handful of occasions. This time, my major concern was that at no point had anyone sought my opinion (as the patient or service user) about what I thought might be the best option for my long-term care. The old-fashioned, paternalistic approach was reminiscent of Professor De Wardener trying to take over my renal care while I was lying in a hospital bed at Charing Cross Hospital with fractured lower limbs. I had been confident enough then to challenge and overturn his decision; and this time I again took the initiative. In contrast, when I had given in to pressure to take statins and accepted what I believed to be incorrect treatment (against my better judgement), the consequences had been devastating.

All healthcare workers and patients, as well as their carers, should bear in mind that patients need to learn skills that empower them to challenge treatment and care plans they feel uncomfortable with. Most long-term patients are experts on their own diseases, be they renal or other long-term conditions, and their voices need to be heard. This problem of lack of patient empowerment, and how to change it, has been the focus of several studies in recent years by NHS England, among other organisations. With additional support and coaching from healthcare workers and peers, patients with chronic diseases (such as kidney failure) can become more confident, 'activated' and empowered. Such empowerment has been shown to reduce hospital admissions as well as helping the individual to deal with their condition in a positive manner – a win–win situation for everyone.

Back in Plymouth, a very efficient system is now in place for me with the Plastic Surgery Department, allowing me to phone up a cancer specialist nurse and discuss any new lesions that may be worrying me. This includes sending a photograph of the new lesion to a skin cancer nurse, rather than having to attend an outpatient clinic. The details are passed on to the surgeon and a decision made to see me face-to-face, before booking a date for the lesions to be removed. This all takes place within a few weeks and is immensely reassuring, giving me confidence that any cancerous lesions will be dealt with quickly and effectively. With lockdown and shielding during the Covid-19 pandemic, this system became invaluable. Over the past few years, the once relatively simple procedures needed to excise small, slow-growing lesions have become more complex, due to the additional complications of taking immunosuppressants for over half a century.

Another area of concern for kidney and SOT recipients on long-term immunosuppressants is the development of possible cancerous lesions or polyps in the large intestine. For this reason, in recent years I have also required referrals to a colon surgeon to deal with polyps that have popped up in various parts of my mid and lower gastrointestinal system. To screen the large bowel, a dreaded colonoscopy is needed! Drinking the solution required to clear the bowel is not pleasant, but it is much better than the alternative – the risk of missing an early bowel cancer and failing to treat it.

Given the high prevalence of skin cancer in organ transplant patients, national guidelines for skin cancer screening of kidney transplant patients have now been established. No matter what type of immunosuppressant drug is taken, kidney transplant patients are at least 40 times more likely to develop non-melanoma skin cancers (NMSCs). NMSCs are the most common malignancy in patients with a kidney transplant, with squamous and basal cell carcinomas accounting for over 90 percent of all skin cancers. Professional bodies, such as the Renal Association, recommend that patients be informed about the adverse effects of exposure to the sun and have an individualised assessment based on their unique risk factors. Sensible preventative measures should be taken, such as the use of sunscreen, hats, and avoiding exposure to ultraviolet radiation during peak sun hours. Patients are advised to examine their skin themselves and with the help of a partner. In addition, there should be reviews by a trained healthcare professional at least once a year, particularly when NMSCs have already been found.

In contrast, there is still no consensus in the UK on how best to screen for colorectal tumours, even though there is a two- to three-fold increased risk of colorectal cancer (CRC) among kidney transplant recipients. The Renal Association recommends a screening programme like that in the general population, checking for blood in the stools every two years using the faecal occult blood test (FOBT) for men and women aged 60 to 74. In addition, over-55s may be invited for a one-off screening colonoscopy if it is available locally. In the USA, it has been recommended that patients with an average risk of colon cancer should be part of a screening programme from the age of 50 onwards, with a colonoscopy or sigmoidoscopy every five to ten years. The frequency of this is increased where polyps have already been found, or if there are other individual factors suggesting an increased risk of colon cancer.

Over recent years, I have developed a relationship with an excellent colorectal surgeon, who has ensured that colonoscopies and sigmoidoscopies have been performed and polyps removed from my lower gastrointestinal tract in a timely manner. This has again given me confidence that any potential cancerous lesions will be dealt with quickly and efficiently. However, the lack of any clinical practice guidelines in the UK for colorectal cancer screening meant that we had to have an informed discussion to determine an individual plan of action tailored to my specific situation.

Recent studies have shown that paediatric kidney recipients also have a substantially higher risk of developing cancer. Living longer with a successful transplant means that the risks become near exponential. There are also increased risks of tumour formation after having received a kidney transplant. In the first few years, these tend to include non-Hodgkin's lymphoma, Kaposi's sarcoma, and lymphoproliferative disorders. In later years, the most common cancers are those found in adults, such as skin, lung, colon, cervical and anal tumours. People who received their kidney during childhood (before the age of 18), as I did, have a risk of developing cancer at least eight times greater than the general population, regardless of whether or not the transplant has remained functioning. This number is considerably higher than the risk for other transplant patients who receive their kidneys in adulthood. It has been calculated that paediatric recipients, such as me, take on a risk and mortality rate of cancer that is akin to someone at least 20 years older. Based on this new research, my risk of cancer is off the chart!

However, skin and colorectal cancers have not been my only problem. In 2012, when I was 55, I started to develop severe pain in my right knee, associated with limited mobility. The problem became particularly bad while I was coaching rugby during cold evenings and weekends. I was finding it increasingly difficult to walk, let alone jog or run, on the lumpy grass rugby pitch. Eventually, when the pain became unbearable, I saw my GP, who referred me to Mr Patrick Loxdale, a Consultant Orthopaedic Surgeon working at the Nuffield Hospital, Plymouth.

My consultation and procedures were paid for by the local NHS commissioning group, even though they took place in a private hospital. On 27th February 2013, I attended my consultation with all the necessary X-rays and an MRI of my right knee. The imaging showed moderate osteoarthritis in the joint, together with tears and a cyst. My surgeon had assumed that the problem with my knee was due to long-term use of steroids. However, the images showed no evidence of steroid-induced osteonecrosis. In fact, the wear and tear within the joint was probably due to the slight misalignment of my right femur following the car accident in December 1971.

An operation was needed, and there were some concerns about infection developing within a replacement joint as a complication of the operation and immunosuppression, as well as the anti-coagulants I would need to take after surgery to prevent clots forming in my veins. My surgeon took advice from my renal doctors as well as an orthopaedic surgeon colleague in Oxford who was used to operating on transplant patients. To get me back on my feet and coaching rugby again, it was decided that a total knee replacement would the best way forward. This would require standard gentamycin antibiotic cover, followed by clexane (to prevent clots occurring in the veins) for 14 days post-operatively, as well as using anti-thrombosis leg stockings for six weeks. The clexane and leg stockings were preventative measures to guard against deep vein thrombosis and pulmonary embolism (PE). There are some moderate risks associated with knee replacements for all patients. Another precaution was catheterisation for two days to ensure that I had good urinary output post-operatively.

About a week before my operation, I was contacted by one of my university senior line managers, who told me they were going to be the anaesthetist for my operation. They wanted to know if I would be happy to come up to their office in the medical school to review my medical conditions. We seldom saw each other in the workplace and our relationship was not always straightforward. This proposition made me uncomfortable, but I also felt very vulnerable and unable to voice my concerns. It was explained to me that conventional general anaesthesia (GA) would be used, due to being unable to carry out spinal or other nerve blocks. (I didn't know then but I later found out that spinal or neural anaesthesia was in fact the gold standard anaesthesia for knee replacement surgery.)

On the morning of Tuesday 30th April 2013, I was admitted to the Nuffield Hospital where I was to be first on the morning's operating list. The morning did not start well, with the anaesthetist being unable to insert an intravenous catheter (Venflon). Four unsuccessful attempts were made to insert the Venflon into one of the veins in my hands, all the time the anaesthetist complaining that I had 'fat hands'. In a flurry of anxiety it was decided that I should be 'gassed' and deal with the problem once I was anaesthetised. Not very reassuring!

By the early afternoon I had returned to my room and was fully awake after the operation. I had been prescribed fentanyl for pain management which was dispensed using a 'patient-controlled appliance (PCA)' where the patient can control the amount of painkiller given by pressing a button to receive a dose of the drug over a set period. However, I was suffering from dreadful pain in my right leg, with a pain score near the maximum of 10. I'm not sure the severity of the pain had been relayed to the anaesthetist, who had written in my notes at 6.20pm: 'all is well, still a little sore'. Less than two hours later, the 'on-call' anaesthetist, effectively the senior house officer, had to be called by the nurses and it was decided that I could use my own pain relief tablets. The extreme pain continued during the night, as reported by the nurse at midnight.

The next morning, I was seen by the surgeon, who wrote, 'pain is a big issue' and stopped the fentanyl PCA system. Following a conversation with the hospital pharmacist, he suggested that I simply revert to using my usual prescribed painkillers. It emerged that the reason I was in such pain was probably because the fentanyl was having no effect. This was because fentanyl works through the same receptor as Buprenorphine. Transplant patients are unable to take non-steroidal anti-inflammatory drugs, like Brufen, as they are toxic to the kidney. For that reason, the GP had prescribed a buprenorphine skin patch, which is unfortunately an antagonist of the fentanyl receptor, blocking it for up to a week. No-one had stopped the patch or asked me to do so. This meant that the fentanyl's action had been blocked and it was as if I'd had no pain relief at all!

Having gone 48 hours with no pain control meant that it took me a lot longer to get out of bed and start mobilising, using my new knee. One of the older physiotherapists seemed to think I was being rather slow, which was true in the first two days. This was particularly noticeable when they attempted to assist me into the shower. I certainly felt pathetic, dealing with the acute pain from my knee, unable to make the joint move, and needing the physiotherapist and nurse to help me 'stand' in the shower. However, there seemed to be a lack of understanding of *why* I was in such pain. By this time, many patients operated on at the same time as me, some of whom were much older, were fully mobilised and zipping along the corridors on their Zimmer frames! Physiotherapists generally like to get patients mobilised in the first few days, setting targets and goals along the way. For instance, patients who arrive on a Tuesday would normally expect to be discharged by Friday evening or Saturday morning. In my case, progress was much slower.

The physios used ice packs and pumps to try to reduce the swelling around my knee. They also had a machine that held my leg in a frame, and it would passively bend or flex the knee. I knew how critical it was to get myself moving quickly in this first week, to ensure the best long-term outcome. It's important to flex the joint to prevent scar tissue building up, as this can permanently prevent good movement.

By Saturday 4th May, there were very few patients left on the ward and I was determined to break through the pain barrier to get my knee mobilised. With the help of the physio, who was on duty all weekend, we used the flexing machine to get the knee to bend to at least 90 degrees, the aim being to achieve 115 degrees of flexion. Around an hour after taking oxynorm, tramadol and codeine pain relief, I would strap my leg into the machine and spend the next hour or so getting the knee to flex. As there were few people on the ward, the physio was able to leave the machine in my room and I set targets to use it throughout the day and evening.

When she came to see me on Sunday 5th May, the physio was really impressed by the massive improvement in the angle of flexing of my knee – and I was grateful for her sympathy and support over this difficult period. I had spent hours the previous day working to get it to bend. I did the same on Sunday, and by the end of the day I was able to bend it beyond 100 degrees in a sitting position. The physio's notes over the previous days continually referred to the immense pain I seemed to be dealing with, as well as the swelling of the knee. As I was also now using crutches and had effectively achieved my goal with flexing the knee, it was possible for me to be discharged home the next day, Monday 6th May.

The management of my pre-anaesthetic appointment and subsequent pain relief raise many governance issues, both ethical and clinical. Even though I am an assertive person and an 'empowered patient', I found myself in a very difficult position. It was wrong of my senior manager to act as my anaesthetist, as it was impossible for me to refuse to have this person perform the anaesthetic. It also meant that they had access to my confidential medical records. As a high risk patient I should have been offered the gold standard form of anaesthetic. This was a situation that I should never have been put in, but I was. The thoughts that went through my mind at the time ranged from 'if I refuse, will it adversely affect my professional relationships and work progression?' to 'I can't believe this is happening to me'.

Some years later, I have reflected on all this and a number of issues occur to me. Firstly, the total knee replacement took place when I was still recovering from the devastating side effects of statins, and I was taking anti-depressants under the care of my Consultant Psychiatrist. This left me feeling vulnerable and unable to assert myself as I should have when my senior line manager first informed me of the plan to be my anaesthetist. Numerous papers have been published on the subject of treating employees and family members, under the auspices of institutions and professional bodies such as the American Medical Association, General Medical Council and the Medical Council of New Zealand, and the overwhelming consensus is that a doctor should *not* treat family members or employees. The onus was not on me, the patient, to make this decision, as the phone call should never have been made in the first place.

Treating an employee can strain the relationship with a senior manager and blur professional boundaries that should always be clear. My pre-anaesthetic consultation took place in an academic office environment, rather than a clinical environment. My Nuffield Hospital medical notes have no record of this, or any such consultation, ever taking place. This raises another important issue – the 'hasty hallway consultation' between the doctor and employee that creates a clinical relationship where none existed before. Such discussions are likely to fall short of the acceptable standard of care for a consultation, where there should be a professional and structured examination of the patient.

Institutions such as medical schools, which are part of universities, have occupational health departments to manage confidential medical and personal matters for employees. Having to reveal to my senior manager that I was being treated for depression, in addition to my detailed medical history, was incredibly embarrassing and humiliating. Once again, professional bodies highlight such situations (where employees must reveal sensitive information) as a specific area of concern. This type of information can jeopardise a professional relationship and even damage the employee's chances of continued employment. The informed consent requirement was certainly compromised in my case. When the doctor and line manager is in a position of authority and control over the employee, it becomes exceedingly difficult, if not impossible, to question the treatment being offered and to say 'no'. Hindsight is of course a great thing and, while I should never have received that phone call from my senior line manager, I could have refused to agree, as Ann told me when I rang her after that fateful meeting! It's true that if I hadn't been feeling so vulnerable at the time, I might well have asserted myself more, as I had done on previous occasions.

The question of treating employees often comes up in GP practices where an individual may have been a patient there for many years before obtaining employment at the same practice. The professional bodies and various ethical and medico-legal institutions are clear that this is frowned upon, except in the case of GP practices in rural areas where it would be impossible for the employee to register elsewhere. Many institutions have employment contracts which make it clear that employees at a practice should not be treated by the practice GP, with obvious exceptions in the case of emergency treatment or there being no practical alternative. Medical schools in North America (such as the one in Saskatchewan) explicitly state in their ethical guidelines that doctors should not provide medical treatment to employees except in an emergency or for minor ailments where no other doctor is available. As far as I am aware, the Plymouth University Medical School had no such policy in place, which flies in the face of its own teaching of students in matters of professional conduct.

These are important matters, as patients with kidney failure (as well as those with other chronic conditions) often wish to 'give something back' by working in their local hospital or clinic. These doctor/employee difficulties have been further highlighted during the Covid pandemic, especially in its early phase, when many older healthcare workers volunteered to come in to help, and then became infected. In Italy, their health service was under such pressure that choices sometimes had to be made between treating a work colleague/employee or a member of the public.

An anaesthetist who was unable to do spinal or regional nerve blocks for this type of operation should also never have been appointed for this ortho-paedic list. Although I was not aware of this before the operation, I later read numerous published studies which clearly stated that there was an increased risk of pulmonary embolism (PE) associated with GA, compared to procedures carried out with nerve or spinal blocks. Indeed, the International Consensus on Anaesthesia-Related Outcomes after Surgery Group (ICAROS) recently reviewed many research studies going right back to 1946. This comprehensive review showed that total knee replacement using neural anaesthesia (NA) gave rise to significantly fewer complications, such as deep vein thrombosis and PE, pneumonia, acute kidney injury and infections including UTIs. These highly significant differences in risk had not been explained to me beforehand.

The difficulty I had in getting moving following the operation was solely due to the severe pain, which was in turn due to the lack of adequate pain control. It appears to be common knowledge among professionals dealing with pain management that fentanyl cannot be used along with buprenorphine patches for the reasons mentioned earlier. My Nuffield Hospital notes continually raised the issue of inadequate pain control, but there was no intervention other than using my own prescription drugs. It might have been too late and certainly by day four I was starting to mobilise better, but I was probably still one or two days behind those who had undergone the operation at the same time.

Once back at home, I spent the next few weeks continually improving the movement in my new knee, using flexing exercises and weights to strengthen the muscles. To prevent blood clots, I was still taking the prescribed clexane injections twice a day for the first two weeks and I administered these myself. The compression stockings had to stay on for at least six weeks post-operatively. Nevertheless, in the early hours of Friday 14th June, I woke up with an extremely sharp stabbing pain in my chest. Our immediate thought was that I might have had a pulmonary embolism (PE), which I knew was a moderate risk following knee replacement.

A trip to the Emergency Department at Derriford Hospital became essential. A Ventilation-Perfusion lung scan (VQ scan) was performed, along with a chest X-ray and blood tests. A VQ lung scan is particularly useful to determine whether a person has experienced a PE. It measures both air flow (V = ventilation) and blood flow (Q = perfusion) in the lungs. The test is performed by injecting a radioactive version of the element technetium, mixed with liquid protein, through a vein to identify areas of the lung that may have reduced blood flow. Multiple images are taken from different angles, using a special camera that detects radioactivity. For half the images, the patient must breathe from a tube containing a mixture of air, oxygen, and a slightly radioactive version of the gas xenon, which reveals air flow in parts of the lung. For the other half of the images, the camera tracks the technetium, which reveals blood flow in parts of the lung. PE is suspected in areas of the lung that have significant 'mismatches' – that is, good air flow but poor blood flow. My scan results confirmed that I had three areas of poor blood flow in my right lung consistent with a PE, and this was confirmed by the chest X-ray.

I was bitterly disappointed, having taken all the right precautions and dutifully performed the various exercises to prevent a PE. I now had to start the treatment regime for PE, which included two weeks of clexane injections, followed by nearly six months of taking the anti-coagulant warfarin. Interestingly, my Nuffield Hospital notes mention in a letter to my GP (which I never received) that they needed to be informed if a DVT or PE occurred in the first three months following a joint replacement so they could review their procedures. As I was treated directly at Derriford Hospital, this important audit feedback and information was never provided by one hospital for the other.

This was an important feedback process in theory, but – like so many in our healthcare system – it often breaks down in practice.

Having the PE also delayed the date for my new total right shoulder replacement, which was scheduled with Mr Andy Murphy at Derriford Hospital. Before I had my right knee replacement, I was already having major problems with pain and lack of movement in my right shoulder. Again, the scale of the problem became clear on the rugby pitch, when I realised that I was unable to carry bags of rugby balls over my right shoulder or lift them over the joint. Finally, I lost all ability to move my right arm above the horizontal position – and reaching over my shoulder with my right hand was completely out of the question.

While waiting for my right knee replacement operation, I was therefore also referred to Mr Andy Murphy, Consultant Orthopaedic Surgeon at Derriford Hospital and a leading specialist in shoulder injuries and joint replacements. In early April, he examined my shoulder, ordered X-rays and concluded that it needed to be replaced. I was about to find out just how complicated a shoulder joint is, and mine had abnormal pathology of the gleno-humeral joint, as well as the main ball and socket. The joint was described as 'disorganised', with numerous enormous loose bodies of calcified material in the joint space, the size of large marbles. A total shoulder replacement was the only option if I wanted a joint with normal function and little pain.

In view of my upcoming knee operation, we discussed which joint should be replaced first. Although I had some concerns about using crutches while the shoulder was still painful, I decided the knee should be done first and the shoulder procedure could then be carried out in the autumn. Unfortunately, the PE meant the shoulder replacement had to be delayed until January 2014. Due to the complexity of the shoulder surgery, additional imaging was required, including an MRI to try and get a three-dimensional image of the joint. Due to the recent PE, it was decided that I should take clexane prophylactically, 40mg injections twice-daily for the first month after the operation.

I arrived early in the morning at the pre-operation Fal Ward on Thursday 9th January, and after the usual formalities I went down to the specialist Operating Theatre Twelve, which has 'negative laminar air flow' for joint replacement operations. The procedure took over six hours and I didn't return to Stannon Ward till mid-afternoon. Dr Ian Christie was the anaesthetist and he had inserted a small plastic tube into the shoulder joint where local anaesthetic was injected through a pump, all of which had been fully explained to me at a comprehensive pre-anaesthetic consultation (unlike the one I had for the knee replacement at the Nuffield Hospital). I had also been prescribed oral Oramorph (morphine sulphate) for general pain.

In contrast to my previous experience only nine months earlier, there was little discomfort and pain after the operation. Furthermore, while I was an inpatient, there were daily visits from the hospital Acute Pain Control team who reviewed my pain control and checked that the small cannula was still injecting the local anaesthesia correctly. The Orthopaedic Surgeon Mr Murphy commented on how awful my joint had looked and, despite the detailed imaging produced before the operation, it was worse than expected when he finally got inside, with even more large marble-size calcified loose bodies. This was probably largely due to the fact that I had taken prednisolone, often at exceedingly high doses, over several decades. The numerous arterio-venous dialysis access (shunt) operations may also have significantly modified the vasculature in my arm, perhaps reducing blood supply within the joint. Of course, it was critical for me to have those operations over 40 years before; they saved my life. No one could have predicted that they might lead to me needing a reverse total shoulder replacement half a century later, especially as the prostheses for reverse total shoulder replacement operations weren't even invented until the early 1970s.

My recovery went well, with no complications other than needing a urinary catheter on the second day. Orthopaedic surgeons are generally very reluctant to catheterise patients immediately, as it can increase the risk of infection. I now realised I had made a very poor choice when I had opted to have my right knee replacement performed outside the main hospital site. A private cubicle cannot outweigh the importance of the high-quality, multi-disciplinary clinical expertise that can be found in a large teaching institution such as Derriford Hospital.

By the end of 2017, I started to have similar pain and mobility issues in my left knee, and it was time to visit my Orthopaedic Surgeon Mr Murphy again. He had now taken over the follow-up care for my right knee as well as my shoulder, as my previous specialist had retired. Unfortunately, because that operation had taken place outside the Derriford Hospital system, no provision had been made for follow-up or review of the knee replacement. This important point was never mentioned when I had the operation. I had assumed a process would be in place with whoever provided the care to ensure that I was followed up, according to national protocols. Indeed, the NICE guidelines of 2013 specifically state that regular reviews should be offered to any individual with symptomatic osteoarthritis, and particularly those with comorbidities or taking regular medication for their osteoarthritis. Clearly, the system had failed in my case. While the private sector happily took the money from the NHS for the operation and the first annual follow-up consultation, there was no arrangement to transfer follow-up back to the NHS after this period or if the consultant left. Mr Murphy kindly took over the care of my right knee, along with that of my right shoulder.

The X-rays of my left knee showed osteoarthritis, probably exacerbated by the insertion of the K-nail in the tibia following my motorcycle accident in 1980. There was a slight misalignment of my lower limb, and this had caused abnormal wear and tear on the joint. The pre-operation anaesthetic appointment with the consultant Dr Cleland was extremely thorough. After years of experience, I know within minutes in any new consultation whether the healthcare professional has empathy and is 'switched on' to my needs. It starts with how they address me, and quickly progresses to whether they have read and understood my medical notes and are aware of my many comorbidities. It is surprising how many fall at the first or second hurdle. Dr Cleland immediately put me at ease and was able to recite back to me my extensive medical history. We also went through the risks and benefits of spinal epidural anaesthesia over a general anaesthetic. I had already had this discussion with Mr Murphy and had read the recommendations in the literature.

The date for my total left knee replacement was set for Thursday 31st May 2018. I opted for the spinal epidural (neural anaesthetic) using propofol (the agent thought to be implicated in the death of the singer Michael Jackson). In the anaesthetic room, once attached to the monitoring equipment and once the Venflon had been inserted, I was asked to sit up while the spinal epidural was injected. My surgeon had joked that I could watch the operation if I wanted by having only a small amount of propofol, but I quickly lost consciousness and was gently lowered on to the bed. The anaesthetist also inserted a cannula into my thigh, which blocked the major nerves of the leg.

During the preparation of my bones to accept the new prosthesis, the surgeon apparently had to keep replacing the saw blades, due to the hardness of my bone. Clearly, despite decades of taking steroids and endless research papers stating that osteoporosis was a major side effect, this had not happened in my case. My surgeon was unable to use the 'jig' to align my leg and instead had to rely on 'eyeballing' and experience to ensure that it was straight. I woke up in theatre recovery around 6.30pm and was relieved to feel only some discomfort, but no pain. It wasn't long before the theatre nurse asked if I wanted a drink and a sandwich. I was ravenous and aware that I needed to take in fluid.

The ward had contacted the recovery room to find out when I would be returning. Unfortunately, I wasn't allowed to leave recovery as my respiration rate was too low, being only around eight breaths per minute, despite being able to eat and hold a conversation! The on-call anaesthetist came to see me and agreed that I looked reasonably well but couldn't understand why I had such a low respiratory rate. Hospital protocols prevented me from leaving recovery until it was above 14 breaths per minute or so. My wife had been patiently waiting on the ward but had come down to the theatre recovery area where a kind nurse had 'bent the rules' and allowed her in to see me. It was all rather bizarre – eating and drinking and talking away but unable to leave. Finally, at 9pm the ward decided that I was probably well enough to return, but it was now late in the evening.

My recovery and rehabilitation were uneventful, with very little pain, thanks to the various nerve blocks and excellent care from the Pain Management Team who paid daily visits to ensure that I was comfortable, while the renal doctors came to visit to oversee my kidney function. The day after the operation, I was already out of bed and sitting up, ready to use crutches. Over the weekend, I continued to make great progress and went home on Tuesday 5th June with another new joint to add to my collection.

In recent years, there have been several studies on the outcome of total knee and other joint replacements in patients with kidney and other solid organ transplants (SOT). These sorts of operations and their follow-ups are now necessary because patients with kidney transplants are living longer and taking steroids for longer periods of time, and some now receive transplants at older ages. The existing studies show that around 40 percent of transplant recipients have had complications and those with kidney transplants are more likely to succumb to infection. Overall, those with a kidney transplant tend to do far worse than those with other SOTs, although, surprisingly, they have fewer DVTs or PEs. It is a great relief, and a credit to the healthcare professionals involved, that I have had exceptionally good outcomes overall, with only one PE after my first knee replacement. However, now that these studies are available, it is important that they do not deter orthopaedic surgeons from offering joint replacement as a treatment for those kidney transplant patients who endure severe osteoarthritis and necrosis.

I find it fascinating that, despite having elevated blood cholesterol levels as well as a 'lipid arc' around my irises, my heart, great arteries and veins were all found to be normal. This supports the decision I made not to take statins as, for me, there is no correlation between my high cholesterol level and actual pathological changes to my blood vessels. The medical literature has no reports comparing cholesterol values (hyper-cholesterolaemia) and real-time functional changes in cardiac tests. Likewise, after taking steroids for over half a century, the medical literature suggests that my bones should be in poor condition, but the two orthopaedic surgeons who have physically handled my bone both independently stated it was the hardest they had even seen or worked with!

A large-scale systematic review of the medical literature has shown that kidney transplant patients have over twice the risk of dying following elective routine surgery, compared to individuals without a transplanted kidney. The most common complication is acute kidney injury (AKI) in kidney transplant recipients. Interestingly, there is no difference in post-operative cardiovascular complications or rates of infection. Thankfully, my kidney function has remained good throughout all my elective procedures.

Chapter 14: A Terrible Loss and Further Health Challenges

The period since the end of 2012 and the publication of this book has been torrid; years of taking immunosuppressive drugs and countless interventions as a child and teenager seem to have finally caught up with me. Having spent the first 46 years since my current transplant with very few complications, other than some episodes of sepsis and in later years skin cancers, I have been plagued with various medical and surgical interventions. Since 2012, I have also been diagnosed with polymyalgia rheumatica following a random episode of an extremely painful left shoulder.

All through my half-century of living with kidney failure and taking immuno-suppressants, infections have reared their ugly heads from time to time. I had remained relatively free of these spontaneous infections since September 1993, when I developed cytomegalovirus (CMV) infection. However, this changed in March 2012 when Ann and I attended the Diabetes UK annual meeting in Glasgow. I had noticed a large firm lump at the base of my spine and had started to feel unwell with a slight temperature on the last day of the meeting. We travelled home on Saturday 10th March and by the next day (Sunday 11th March, which was of course my birthday!), we had to phone the renal team at Derriford, who saw me immediately. The medical and surgical registrars diagnosed a large pilonidal abscess that needed immediate surgical attention. The following morning, the surgeons incised and drained the abscess, irrigated the cavity with hydrogen peroxide, and started me on intra-venous flucloxacillin for 24 hours. I made a speedy recovery and was able to go home on Wednesday 14th March.

However, in the pre-operative assessment on the ward I vividly recall a conversation with the renal consultant. Previously, when having a general anaesthetic, I had always received 100mg of hydrocortisone, given intrave-nously by the anaesthetist just before surgery. I was therefore rather taken aback when he suggested that I would not need hydrocortisone and all I needed to do was double my steroids for a couple of days. Based on the theatre operation notes, I had a normal blood pressure during the 45-minute operation but, once I was in the recovery room, my systolic blood pressure remained below 80mm/Hg for the first 45 minutes and then became a concern, leading the nurse to call the anaesthetist back to check me over. The drop in systolic pressure was probably due to the lack of hydrocortisone cover. This was another occasion when, although I knew what needed to be done after years of taking steroids, I failed to be sufficiently assertive to ensure that I received appropriate care.

Decades of taking prednisolone have of course taken their toll on my adrenal glands. This was first observed in July 1974 after my dad's donated kidney was removed and I had numerous side effects from steroid withdrawal and was never able to come off them. The need for steroid replacement became noticeable with this episode of infection requiring surgery and continued following the joint replacements, with increasing clinical signs that I was deficient in cortisol. Cortisol is needed for the fight-or-flight response, which is a healthy, natural response to threats, real and perceived. I would become extremely tired in the afternoon, often falling asleep upright in a chair. It was like a switch being turned off, with an overwhelming desire to just lie down. My family would poke fun at me for falling asleep like this, but the tiredness made it impossible to do anything else.

I have always had excellent blood pressure, but now I noticed that I had occasional postural hypotension, feeling faint when I stood up, with a correspondingly large drop in my systolic blood pressure reading. Eventually, after discussing it with Ann, I had a consultation with my GP where it was decided that I should take some hydrocortisone replacement during the afternoon, which later increased to three times a day. My symptoms improved tremendously once I had reached the full replacement dose of hydrocortisone that someone with primary Addison's disease or pituitary failure might need. Addison's disease is a condition in which the adrenal glands are damaged and cannot make sufficient adrenal hormones, mainly steroids. The condition is named after a Dr Thomas Addison who first described it in 1855. Addison's disease is rare – just over 8,000 people in the UK have it at any one time.

Prednisolone is like cortisol, and it has been well documented that, if taken for several weeks or more, the pituitary hormone ACTH is switched off and no adrenal cortisol can be made. If steroids are suddenly stopped, it can take quite some time for the pituitary to be switched back on again, to make ACTH, which then stimulates the adrenal glands to make cortisol again. Therefore, people receiving steroids for any reason should wear a medical alert band so that healthcare professionals know they may need to give steroids urgently in an emergency.

Looking back, when my first transplant kidney was removed in July 1974, I was never in fact able to stop taking prednisolone, even though I no longer needed it for immunosuppression. My adrenals must have already been dormant. In addition, for decades I have had a salt craving and the family are always horrified by the amount of salt I put on food. I have always used a salt grinder and I tend to pile on the salt crystals. Salt craving is another classic sign of low cortisol, whose absence makes the body lose salt in the urine. While I was adjusting my hydrocortisone dose to try to get the right balance, if I had a mild form of what can be described as an 'Addisonian crisis' I would take 10mg hydrocortisone before I got to the stage where I needed to go to sleep. It seemed to do the trick and I would wake up after a couple of hours bright and fresh and ready to take on the world!

I have now realised that, while my small dose of 5mg prednisolone has been doing its job preventing rejection, it is presumably no longer sufficient to maintain normal cortisol homeostasis. The additional hydrocortisone I take has restored this balance. I have also ensured that my medical notes make it clear that I have secondary Addison's disease and hydrocortisone support is required. This episode shows the difficulties that both patients and healthcare professionals can have in dealing with the effects of long-term immunosuppression. There are no clinical trials or NICE guidelines covering these situations, and decisions must be made based on common sense, good practice and 'gut feeling'. The latter is critical for the patient who usually understands their own body better than anyone else. Feeling 'off-colour' or 'grotty' may indicate hidden health problems which are masked by immunosuppressive drugs.

The endless hospitalisations which characterised this part of my life continued when, on Monday 12th May 2014, I started to develop extreme pain on the right side of my abdomen just as Ann and I were going to bed. I had been well all day but suddenly this colicky pain developed that was resistant even to tramadol and oxycodone. With the pain increasing by the minute, Ann called Mayflower Ward who, once again, told me to come in immediately. Sitting in the passenger seat while Ann was driving was excruciating. When we arrived at the hospital at around 10pm, Ann quickly sought a wheelchair as it was becoming impossible for me to walk. On the way to the lifts, I recall vomiting all over the concourse and apologising to a nearby porter.

Mayflower had no beds, so I was shepherded into a clinical room with an examination couch. The pain and examination, taken together, made the renal consultant think my condition was likely to be due to gallstones. Intravenous morphine finally helped with the pain and the Renal Team sought out the surgeons who confirmed the suspected gall bladder problem and transferred me to their surgical ward. The next day this was confirmed on closer examination and imaging, and I was transferred to the care of Mr Bowles, a hepatobiliary surgeon who had previous experience of managing patients with kidney transplants. I was sent home and saw him in outpatients on 23rd May, when he informed me that my gall bladder needed to be removed due to some large stones. Mr Bowles was at first keen to do this using a laparoscopic (keyhole) technique, but I was not convinced this would be possible, given the extensive abdominal surgery I had undergone in the past. Together we decided that he would start trying to remove the stone using the laparoscope but if he encountered any issues he would revert to a conventional excision and removal of the gall bladder. The operation was set to be carried out on Wednesday 11th June.

This time there was no need to remind anyone about hydrocortisone cover, but interestingly, even with 100mg hydrocortisone, my systolic blood pressure dropped 90mm/Hg within 30 minutes of being anaesthetised and stayed there for another 30 minutes before jumping up to 140mm/Hg, presumably once the hydrocortisone had taken effect. As expected, although Mr Bowles started the operation using the laparoscopic technique, he soon reverted to making a full excision, due to the extensive scar tissue inside my abdomen.

My recovery over the next few days went well, although pain control was a concern, and I was again monitored by the excellent hospital Acute Pain Control Team. I had been prescribed fentanyl using a PCA system, but I continually had breakthrough pain and it was suggested that I should add oral tramadol and oxycodone. I was able to go home on Sunday 15th June.

As a member of the Patient Participation Committee for the NHS England 'Think Kidneys' project, I attended a meeting on Tuesday 15th September 2015, in Birmingham. I had travelled by train and was staying overnight at the city centre Travel Lodge as I was attending a Kidney Care (formerly British Kidney Patients Association or BKPA) meeting the next day, also in Birmingham. These were two of the new 'expert patient' organisations I had been volunteering with since I had left the medical school.

In the early hours of the morning, I was woken by my mobile ringing. It was Ann and her first words were 'Tom is dead'. He had been killed in a car accident just after midnight. Aged only 22, he had been driving home from Bristol to pack his belongings, ready to move into a flat in Bristol, where he had just been promoted to a new job. He was also preparing to take his examination for the Admiralty Officer Board, as he hoped to join the Royal Navy as an officer. His car had come off the road at Haldon Hill, near Chudleigh, on the A38 trunk road just west of Exeter and he had probably died instantly, possibly just before the actual crash. This was every parent's worst nightmare and for some minutes after that indescribable telephone call with my wife, I simply sat on the bed in disbelief. The shock then kicked in and with it some tears, together with a host of questions, thoughts and memories.

I then moved into practical mode, looked up the next train back home and found it would not be until nearly 7am. It was a long wait for the train, followed by a journey of nearly four hours. The train was crowded with commuters until it got past Bristol and I had to stand for the first part of the journey near the luggage racks. Tom's sudden death was devastating for the entire family. He had been flying high in his job and was so happy to be settling down in Bristol. His death was such a shock, I felt I'd gone completely numb, and for long periods of time over the subsequent days and weeks I was just working on autopilot. The funeral took place in our local church, the old Cornish Cathedral, and it was full to overflowing. His entire rugby team from the medical school had turned up, along with his friends from school, university and work.

The grieving process is unique to each one of us. In my case, there was the added awareness that I was only alive, with a functioning kidney transplant, because of the generosity of a family in November 1974. I knew they must have gone through similar experiences to those we were now having. There was also the obvious anger at the loss of my child. It seemed so cruel that, having gone through decades of near-death experiences and somehow managing to carve out a normal life, our family should be ripped apart by his unexpected death. It was also a perverse twist of fate that, because of the circumstances of his accident, none of his organs could be used, even though all our children were registered organ donors.

Tom had lived at home during his final year at university, when I was rehabilitating from my various operations. This turned out to be a very precious opportunity for us to spend time together, talking about science, research and current affairs. Consequently, we became extremely close. Perhaps, in hindsight, this period made up for my compromised bonding with Tom in his early months of life when I was hospitalised with CMV infection. Despite my grief that our family was experiencing this tragedy, at least I could reflect on those precious days when we had been able to enjoy each other's company. It was unimaginable that he had been ripped away from us so dramatically – but we simply cannot predict what joy or misery the next day or hour of our lives will bring.

Over the following weeks, as the results of the crash investigation became known, several questions were raised. Tom had had no alcohol or drugs in his blood (as we had fully expected), had not used his mobile phone since leaving Bristol and the speed cameras showed that he had not been speeding (with an average speed of 74 miles per hour). The car had been serviced very recently and new tyres had been fitted. However, there was no evidence that Tom had applied the brakes – his car seemed to have simply swerved from side to side before coming off the road and hitting several trees. The pathology results showed that he had a significantly enlarged heart with left ventricular hypertrophy, which was an unexpected finding and clearly pathological.

We wondered if he had suffered a dysrhythmia or a cardiac event which had led to the accident. Ann contacted Professor Sanjay Sharma at St George's Hospital, London, an expert on 'young sudden cardiac death syndrome'. He suggested we all come up to London to be tested for common congenital abnormalities of the heart. In Spring 2016 we all underwent various functional cardiac tests, including a cardiac echo, ECG, an exercise ECG and more. We were relieved to find out that we had values within the normal range although they suspected some ischaemic changes on my exercise ECG and suggested that this should be followed up. I had these tests done at Derriford Hospital and the results finally showed that there was no suggestion of ischaemia or infarction, and I had a completely healthy heart and major vessels. I underwent further extensive real-time functional tests in early 2018 which confirmed these results.

Cancer and – to a lesser extent – cardiovascular events are the major contributors to mortality in patients who have had successful kidney transplants. Infection is the third important cause of death in this patient group, although this has been markedly reducing in recent years. No doubt this may change again when there is more data available for Covid-19 and transplant recipients. I had been fortunate to have spent decades since 1974 with few infections – the only serious one being the CMV episode in September 1993.

This all changed in December 2018. I had developed a dry cough with occasional production of green sputum at the end of November and into December 2018 and had been prescribed clarithromycin and co-amoxiclav antibiotics by my GP for a chest infection. I normally have a low temperature of around 35 to 36 degrees centigrade. However, as the week beginning 11th December progressed, I started to develop high temperatures and needed to take more and more paracetamol. My condition deteriorated further during Saturday 15th December and into the Sunday. On Sunday morning I had been feeling feverish, but this was managed with paracetamol. Ann was due to take part in our local choir's carol service later in the afternoon. I really didn't feel like leaving the house but, as I had missed all her other Christmas concerts, I went along to support her.

The carol service was held in the Methodist Chapel at Downderry and the service was conducted by an old work colleague of ours who is a Methodist lay preacher. During the service I began to feel even worse – freezing cold and drowsy. One of Ann's fellow singers later commented that I looked like 'death warmed up' and I kept dozing off during the performance. It certainly wasn't due to the quality of the singing! When the service had finished, our old colleague came to say hello but it was impossible to engage in conversation, as I was desperate to get home and curl up in front of the fire. Once we were home and, after taking more paracetamol and hydrocortisone, I felt a little better. Later that evening, I was lying in front of the log fire covered in blankets, having occasional shivering attacks while watching the final of The Apprentice on TV. Before we went to bed, we discussed contacting Mayflower Ward (renal), Derriford Hospital, but as I had an outpatient appointment the next morning, I decided to wait until then. As it turned out, this was not a good decision! I was feeling feverish, and my temperature spiked to 38 degrees centigrade, which was extremely high for me. The next morning, Monday 17th December, Ann drove me to outpatients, where I was very quickly seen by one of the doctors and immediately sent to the ward.

At 1.25pm I was examined by one of the renal consultants and admitted, although I had to wait to be seen in the clinic room. Bloods were sent off for the usual measurements as well as blood cultures. By now I was dehydrated, and a Venflon was inserted for saline as well as starting me on the antibiotic Tazocin. My temperature had climbed to over 39 degrees centigrade despite the paracetamol, my heart rate was 119 beats per minute, and I was having rigors but did not show any obvious clinical features that might suggest an abscess. Thankfully, rejection of my kidney was quickly ruled out, although my renal function results later showed that my kidney had taken a hit and was not happy. By 6pm my condition had worsened, and I was prescribed paracetamol intravenously to control the fever. Ann stayed with me until almost midnight.

The night was extremely uncomfortable, I was hot and sweating and unable to settle. Just after 4am I took a turn for the worse, with more severe rigors. On reviewing my notes, my oxygen saturation had dropped to 67 percent, I had a racing pulse and my blood pressure had dropped to around 60mm/Hg systolic with an unreadable diastolic. The night nurse had already called the on-call doctor, as my cannula had blocked and the 'Doctor's Assistant' had already been, and failed, to insert a new one. This meant I was no longer getting any intravenous fluids.

After quickly assessing my clinical condition, the doctor managed to get a cannula into my left arm at the first attempt and the nurse presented him with the saline drip which was still attached to the infusion pump. I can still vividly recall him saying to the nurse 'we must get fluids into him quickly and do it by hand' – the pump was not fast enough. He attached a 500ml bag of saline to the cannula and squeezed in the saline by hand with some force. This continued until he saw my blood pressure starting to rise. He was also able to give me more paracetamol intravenously as my temperature had spiked again at over 39 degrees centigrade. The nurses managed to get another litre of saline into me over the next hour and by the morning my condition had stabilised, although I now had severe, watery diarrhoea, which as probably a side effect of the antibiotics.

My medical team had a working diagnosis of bacterial pneumonia, as there was no clear source of infection other than the minor cough. Later that day, on Tuesday 18th December, the antibiotic was switched again to Linezolid. My condition began to stabilise a little, with temperature spikes when the effect of the paracetamol had worn off. When I had the temperature spikes, I could predict when the rigors would start. They came just before the temperature spike on most occasions and this didn't seem to be a coincidence. I am sure this phenomenon has been previously described somewhere in the world's scientific and medical literature. It brought back memories from decades before, when I had rigors due to my kidney failure, sepsis and CMV infection. They felt remarkably similar.

By now my kidney function had deteriorated and I had developed an acute kidney injury (AKI) stage 2 with a creatinine that had more than doubled (to over 170μmol/l) with an eGFR below 40 from my baseline. This was my worst recorded renal function since the days following my transplant in 1974 and sepsis in 1982 following removal of the K-nail. My C-reactive protein (CRP), a marker of acute infection, was over 350 (when it should be 0–5mg/l). I was shocked to hear these results when my doctors gave me the news later in the day. There were concerns about my poor vascular access and plans were made for a central 'PICC' line (peripherally inserted central catheter) to be inserted. Venflon cannulas were meant to be changed every few days to avoid the risk of infection. Tuesday evening and night saw the temperature spikes recur, but these were now controlled with paracetamol and intravenous fluids.

Wednesday 19th December saw a change in direction in my treatment. In the morning, the results of the first two blood cultures came back and the laboratory had successfully grown Enterococcus faecalis (E.Faecalis) bacteria.

Enterococci are bacteria that are part of the normal intestinal flora of humans and animals. However, they have also long been recognised as important human pathogens. The genus Enterococcus includes more than 17 species, although just a few are responsible for clinical infections in humans. Since the beginning of the antibiotic era, these organisms have posed major therapeutic challenges, including the need for synergistic combinations of antibiotics to treat enterococcal infective endocarditis (IE) successfully. There are two types of enterococci associated with normal healthy people which can also occasionally cause human disease. They are called *Enterococcus Faecalis*, the one I had, and *Enterococcus Faecium*.

The most common infections caused by enterococci are those of the urinary tract and wounds. These, and a variety of other infections, including infection in the blood stream (bacteraemia), heart valves (endocarditis) and the brain (meningitis), can occur in severely ill patients in hospital. The bacteria also frequently colonise open wounds and skin ulcers. In these circumstances, the bacteria can be grown from a lesion, but they do not cause the patient any illness. Enterococci are among the most antibiotic-resistant bacteria isolated from humans. Minor infections can usually be treated by antibiotics such as penicillins, macrolides or tetracyclines, taken by mouth. However, only penicillins, or teicoplanin and vancomycin (two expensive and potentially toxic antibiotics which can only be given by injection) are reliably effective against serious enterococcal infections such as endocarditis or meningitis. Serious infections often need prolonged treatment, usually with several antibiotics being given together by injection.

The identification of the *E. Faecalis* was extremely helpful, as none of the other screens for viruses had shown anything. I was also lucky in that it quickly turned out that my strain was sensitive to the antibiotic amoxycillin, which is cheap and easily available. Many of the *E. Faecalis* strains detected in patients in hospital settings are vancomycin-resistant enterococci (VRE), which makes them extremely serious, with a high mortality rate, especially in patients with a kidney transplant.

With the sensitivity of the bacteria known, my antibiotics were quickly changed to amoxycillin (1g given intravenously every eight hours). However, the medical team still had concerns about the source of the infection within my body. The idea of its being a respiratory infection of some kind had been dismissed, as the chest X-rays were normal, so an abdominal CT scan was booked to look for any abscesses. A second concern was the strong link between E. *Faecalis* infection and the development of infective endocarditis (IE).

Endocarditis is characterised by lesions, quaintly known as vegetations, which contain bacteria that stick to the valves in the heart. Once the vegetations have stuck to the valves, the bacteria may spread to other organs (pumped by the heart itself) and cause infection in those organs as well. They also damage the valves so the heart cannot pump properly. The diagnosis of endocarditis is based on clinical features, imaging of the heart with an ultrasound machine (echocardiogram), and blood cultures demonstrating the growth of the bacteria in the bloodstream.

Endocarditis requires prolonged treatment with one or more antibiotics, typically for six to eight weeks. These antibiotics are usually given in high concentrations to get deep down into the valve tissue and must therefore be given by intravenous infusion directly into the bloodstream. The duration and intensity of treatment depends on the severity of the infection and the type of bacterial organism that is responsible for the endocarditis. Because of the long duration of the treatment, a PICC line will usually be inserted to deliver the intravenous treatment. In addition to medical therapy with intravenous antibiotics, surgery may sometimes be required to repair or replace the infected heart valve. In my case, as well as the CT scan, the medical team also arranged an urgent echocardiogram to look for IE.

On the afternoon of Wednesday 19th December, the Vascular Access Team came to see me on the ward to insert a PICC central line into my right upper arm (the cephalic vein). They had been told to remove the Venflon cannula as soon as the PICC had been inserted. However, by now everyone knew that it could be very difficult to obtain vascular access in my case. I was concerned that if I lost access via the Venflon (which was working well) and the PICC line failed, I would be unable to receive the intravenous antibiotics. The cannula had been a real 'life-saver' the day before. The vascular access technician and I had a discussion at the bedside, but I refused to let him remove it. He even tried to reassure me that the PICC line had two access points (lumens), and it was unheard of for both of them to fail!

Half an hour after the team left, the nurse came to administer the intravenous amoxycillin. She tried to flush saline through the first lumen opening without any success. She then tried the second lumen and again it refused to be flushed with the saline. After a little discussion about how 'this should never happen', it was back to my faithful Venflon cannula which of course worked straight away. Although the hospital protocols stated that it should have been taken out, I managed to argue that it should remain in place. It continued working with no problem until it was removed when I was discharged. It was still only 48 hours since I'd had the peak symptoms of sepsis and my treatment had only changed to amoxycillin that morning. With no vascular access to administer the early evening intravenous antibiotics, there would have been a long gap in treating the sepsis. With the junior doctors changing shifts shortly afterwards (and the delays that usually entails), it might have been a long time before a new Venflon was in place.

Over the next few hours, my condition finally stabilised, with fewer temperature spikes, and a normal blood pressure, although I still had a fast pulse. The blood cultures and urine samples failed to reveal any source of infection. This, together with no scan evidence of an abscess, was rather perplexing. It was suggested that the sepsis could have been caused by a urinary tract infection.

However, the sample obtained on the day of my admission was inconclusive, with fewer than 50,000 plaque-forming units/ml (pfu/ml) of bacteria, only a few white cells and negligible epithelial cells. It would also have been the first urinary tract infection I'd had for many decades and even those had been minor and were successfully treated with Septrin.

By Friday 21st December, I still had temperature spikes of around 39 degrees centigrade with a heart rate of 83 beats per minute. It was a great relief for everyone that my creatinine and eGFR had also improved and the CRP was now also dropping fast. The insult to my poor transplanted kidney was hopefully over! There was little change throughout Saturday, with smaller, less frequent temperature spikes, generally staying below 38 degrees centigrade. None of the mid-stream urine samples or blood cultures showed evidence of infection and the debate about whether there was an abscess continued.

With Christmas nearly upon us, on Sunday 23rd December, there were discussions about when I might be discharged. A plan was put in place to switch me from intravenous to oral amoxycillin 1g three-times daily from lunchtime. If my temperature and other observations remained stable, then I could be discharged. If everything went according to plan on Sunday, I would take the amoxycillin for another 14 days. My observations did continue to improve, and I switched to taking oral amoxycillin.

I still resisted any attempt to take out the Venflon cannula, though my non-functioning PICC line had been removed a couple of days before. It obviously caused some consternation among the healthcare team as my resistance to removing the Venflon is mentioned at length in my hospital notes. However, it was also recognised that I had poor vascular access! I see this as another example of an occasion when common sense was needed to overrule the 'tick-box culture' that tends to occur throughout the NHS. While many of these protocols are initially established with good intentions for patient safety, staff must also have the flexibility to allow exceptions, since the protocols are often intended as guidelines rather than rules.

Every patient is an individual – and the processes and systems have generally been derived by evaluating most situations and coming up with a risk analysis. In this case, the risk of developing an infection from a Venflon increases with the time it remains in situ. However, if this rule had been adopted in the 1960s the arterio-venous Scribner shunt would never have been allowed to be used for my access to dialysis. For Scribner shunts, a hole had to be punched in the skin to allow the Teflon tube to come from the vein or artery where it had been placed on the exterior of the body. The punch hole for the tube was considerably larger than a Venflon, with a diameter of up to half an inch (4–6mm). Fortunately, I knew that the NHS should be there for individual patients, not for the creation of excessive tick boxes and red tape. Although I was now taking oral antibiotics, I made sure the Venflon remained in place until I was discharged.

On the Sunday there was a palpable desire on the ward to try to get patients home for Christmas, which was now only a couple of days away. Since my admission, I hadn't really been aware of Christmas looming. I had spent the early part of the week in a daze, due to the temperature spikes and rigors. Early in December, my daughter Lucy had persuaded us to see the new film version of A Star is Born with Bradley Cooper and Lady Gaga. We enjoyed the film so much that we went to see it twice and bought the soundtrack. I had taken it in with me when I was admitted, using a new set of headphones that plugged into my iPad. So it was that I spent a considerable amount of time listening to 'A Star is Born' repeatedly. At times when my temperature was high, I became quite tearful, and the music gave me strength to get through the most serious medical crisis I had faced for many decades. That week, the Hospital League of Friends had brought round Christmas presents for the patients. My present was a small writing pad and Christmas card, and for some reason I was over-whelmed by this kind gesture and became quite emotional.

On Monday, Christmas Eve morning, I was sent for another kidney ultra-sound. By now I had become aware of the Christmas fancy dress that the porters and other hospital workers were wearing. It was great to see this but – again – it brought back deep-seated emotions from decades before, associated with being in hospital. The renal ward had a policy of rotating the consultants, with one doctor in charge of the ward for a week at a time begin-ning on the Monday. There are good reasons for having a system of weekly rotation through the ward, and at outpatient clinics. However, on Christmas Eve it meant there was an awfully long changeover ward round, from one consultant to another.

In the modern NHS, ward rounds are often organised quite differently from those I experienced many years ago. The system of consultants being 'one week on the ward', 'one week in clinic', may have managerial and administra-tive advantages, but it also means that the continuity of care is broken from one week to the next. This may of course be offset by ward rounds, weekly multidisciplinary team meetings and other events. However, the problem is that these events are remote from the patient and rely on hospital notes and recollections from members of staff. On the other hand, they may admittedly be an efficient way of reviewing many patients – for example, those who have attended the weekly outpatient clinic.

Today, there are separate ward rounds for the medical and nursing teams. Reviewing more than half a century of my NHS hospital notes, I see that there have always been separate nursing and medical notes, and the nursing notes still record the patient's condition and observations. However, in the modern NHS there are innumerable care plans for every conceivable eventuality. There are pages and pages of forms that need to be filled in. Examples within the Risk Assessment Booklet include 'Smoking Screening Tool', 'Alcohol Screening Tool', 'Record of Mental Capacity and Best Interest (MCA 2005)', 'MUST Malnutrition Universal Screening Tool', 'Waterlow Assessment and SKIN Bundle Care Plan'.

Others include 'Fall Assessments and Care Interventions', 'Patient Handling' and so on. This list is endless. The NHS is often criticised for its endless red tape and paper reports – and this is a prime example. None of it is digitised. Similar booklets are presented every time I attend for a procedure, and I often have a discussion with the nurse about when it is going to be digitised! Could it not be put on an iPad or similar device? They all agree that it is tedious and laborious and distracts from the main subject, the patients themselves.

In 2019 there was a Cochrane review of the scientific literature of one such assessment tool for pressure ulcers, the Waterlow Assessment Tool. The authors were able to identify only two studies evaluating the effect of this tool on the number of pressure ulcers. They concluded that a risk assessment using the Waterlow Tool, 'may make little or no difference to pressure ulcer incidence, or severity, compared with clinical judgement'. They also stated that the certainty of available evidence was too low and too unreliable to demonstrate that structured and systematic pressure ulcer risk assessment tools reduce the incidence or severity of pressure ulcers.

This example from the literature review was selected at random and suggests that, while the original intentions behind such risk assessment tools may have been good, they do not reflect the real world. Indeed, many other studies have reached similar conclusions. The 'tick box' ethos that has spread across the NHS is of very limited benefit to the patient lying in a hospital bed. In fact, these tools can detract from the expertise of the nursing staff who have an intimate and intricate knowledge of their patients. It seems that an entire 'industry' has been created, based on the vast array of risk assessment and care booklets that need to be completed. In my own case, there are literally hundreds of boxes to be ticked every day. One form alone has 140 boxes to be completed in a 24-hour period. These are all done by hand, and transcription of information by humans is known to have an error rate of 1 in 10. If these forms were part of a laboratory research book, in which results are written down, they would have to be checked for accuracy. It would be interesting to know if these care plans are ever reviewed and, if so, what form of assessment or audit process takes place. A brief review of the scientific literature makes no mention of any such audits and I suspect they hardly ever happen.

In the past, ward rounds were usually carried out jointly with the doctors and staff nurses as well as other healthcare professionals, such as physiotherapists and dieticians, involved in the patients' care. This style of ward round might not appear to be time-efficient or cost-effective; and some of us remember the 'bad old days' when an overbearing consultant in his white coat did a ward round once a week, with an entourage of staff and students. But perhaps it is time for a more modern style of ward round, including both doctors and nursing professionals but carried out in a less hierarchical way. Rather than a junior doctor having to charge around to find the nurse in charge of the patient, to address a query that has already been raised by the consultant, there should be a more efficient system. Yet this is how many modern NHS wards still operate – and I have seen this first-hand in various settings.

After lunch, it was decided that I could be discharged, and I would be required to take a one-week course of amoxycillin, 1g three times daily. I telephoned Ann to tell her the good news, and she made her way over to pick me up. Unfortunately, we had to wait until nearly 7pm, at least five hours after I had first been told that I could leave. It wasn't surprising that there was a huge discharge of patients on Christmas Eve, most of whom would need drugs to take home, dispensed by the hospital, but the issue of patients taking up bed space while awaiting take-home medications has plagued NHS hospitals for many years. Fortunately, there are now new processes in place to make discharge more efficient, including discharge lounges where a patient can be discharged and provided with a chair while awaiting their medications.

It was well into the evening by the time we arrived home on Christmas Eve. It had always been my job to prepare the Christmas dinner, starting with a mustard and demerara sugar-glazed ham with cloves for Christmas Eve with mulled wine. Christmas in our household has always been traditional, based on Delia Smith's Christmas TV series and cookbook, which first aired in 1990. This would be our first family Christmas when I had not taken charge of the kitchen and I had to allow others to take the reins, while keeping a beady eye on them from a distance! The sepsis had taken its toll on my energy levels and just being back at home with the family, together with the hustle and bustle of Christmas, was tiring. My mum and Lucy and Olly were home for Christmas, and it was another joyous occasion. Ann was fully aware of how ill I had been, but we had been able to shield the rest of the family from this knowledge to some extent.

I had some concerns about the shortened course of amoxycillin so on Thursday 27th December I phoned my GP. After some discussion we agreed that I should take an additional week's supply, as first suggested the previous Sunday, finishing the course on 6th January 2019. Over the next few days, my health continued to improve, and I gained in strength. We had been invited for New Year's Eve drinks and nibbles at Lavethan Manor on Bodmin Moor with our small singing group.

Ann had been badgering me to take up singing again, as she knew how much I loved sea shanties, and it was a delightful sociable group of friends, some of whom had also known Tom very well. The owners of the Manor had invited members of the group to come and enjoy some festive fayre. Our friends were pleased to see us knowing how I had succumbed to sepsis, but I found it incredibly hard to stay focused while chatting, as my mind kept drifting off mid-conversation. Many people know the feeling of 'post-bacterial or viral' malaise and, for me, having just recovered from severe sepsis, being immunosuppressed and taking steroids made it drag out even longer. It was very tiring, but we had agreed to go along for a short time, and it was a great tonic to see good friends.

Unfortunately, over the next few days, I started to feel off-colour again. My temperature had remained normal until two days after stopping the antibiotics, the evening of Wednesday 9th January, when the symptoms of sepsis returned. This time there were no delays, and we didn't make the mistake of waiting to see if my condition improved. The medical team had been clear that I should come back in if my temperature spiked again. The next day I was awake early, feeling lethargic and sweaty, and my temperature was 38 degrees centigrade despite taking paracetamol. I had had another rigor during the night, so we contacted the ward who told me to come straight in, where I was seen promptly by the consultant at 10am.

My hospital notes said 'source not identified' for the E. Faecalis sepsis and it was worrying that I had fallen ill again so soon after finishing the amoxycillin. A detailed care plan was put in place, with IE being a possible cause of sepsis. The antibiotics were withdrawn for a short period to see if the bacteria could be grown and identified in the blood cultures. My white cells were again raised, at over 12.9, and my CRP was 49. My condition remained stable until Friday 11th January, the mid-stream urine test was negative and, following a discussion with the microbiologist, it was decided to treat my condition as suspected IE.

The NICE guidelines for treating IE involve taking amoxycillin for six weeks (2g every four hours) along with ceftriaxone (2g daily). With this substantial intake of antibiotics, I would need to have another central line inserted. I had been cannulated with a Venflon on first arriving on the ward the day before and had been given intravenous fluids. My reputation for poor access vasculature had preceded me and valiant attempts were made by the medical staff to organise the central line as quickly as possible. However, the demand for central lines within the hospital was high, with only one person in the Vascular Access Team able to insert them. My medical and nursing notes make continual reference to the numerous attempts that were made to get a functioning Venflon that could be used for the intravenous antibiotics and fluids. Sometimes as many as four attempts were made before a successful vein was found, with lots of apologies from the relevant healthcare personnel.

Over the next few days, my temperature continued to fluctuate with spikes and night sweats. My CRP was still elevated (more than 80 with raised white cell counts) and the working diagnosis remained IE. Arrangements were made for me to have a trans-oesophageal echocardiogram (TOE) that would provide a real-time view of my great blood vessels as well as the four heart valves. The TOE is a special type of echocardiogram which uses high-frequency sound waves (ultrasound) to examine the structures of the heart. A transducer (a unit that directs the sound waves) is placed down the oesophagus (the gullet, connecting the mouth to the stomach). As the oesophagus is close to the heart, images from a TOE can give clear pictures of the heart and its structures.

I had the TOE on Thursday 17th January. A foul-tasting anaesthetic spray was used to numb the back of my throat to enable the cardiologist to insert the ultrasonic probe down my gullet and I received a dose of midazolam as a sedative. The cardiologist worked very hard to get good views of the back of my heart, pushing and probing to complete the scan. It was a great relief when suddenly the probe was out and, even better, she told me that everything looked fine with no evidence of 'vegetative' bacterial growth on my valves. Of the numerous procedures I have undergone, this was one of the most unpleasant, possibly only outdone by the un-clotting of my Scribner shunts or the first attempts at inserting a peritoneal catheter in 1969. However, one major improvement in care in the NHS nearly half a century later, is the use of sedatives and pain relief for the comfort of the patient. Midazolam was first patented by Hoffmann-La Roche in 1975 and is among many benzodiazepines, such as diazepam, now used medically. The latter was available in 1969, while nitrous oxide was first used as long ago as 1844.

The source of the infection was still a mystery. Another CT scan and a PET scan of most of my body were booked for Tuesday 22nd January. The nurses were continually pressing for my central line to be inserted, as the cannulas kept failing and I needed frequent antibiotic infusions. Each dose of either amoxycillin or ceftriaxone took 30 minutes to deliver, as they were in 100ml saline. The ceftriaxone in particular irritates the veins if it is delivered too quickly. Finally, on the morning of Wednesday 23rd, I had the PICC line inserted into my left upper arm. It was inserted right down into the major vein to ensure the antibiotics were quickly dispersed, preventing any irritation.

My condition had by now stabilised and Ann and I were discussing the possibility of delivering the antibiotics ourselves at home. The medical team knew we were more than competent to carry out the antibiotic infusions, but there was the small matter of governance, liability and red tape to overcome. The doctors finally sorted it out with the 'powers that be' and the hospital pharmacy. Meanwhile, Ann received training in how to make up the antibiotics and deliver them safely, something she had first done in 1980! The staff were all a little embarrassed, as Ann had only recently retired as a Consultant Diabetologist, but systems are systems and Ann was not proud. I had spent many years making up antibiotic mixtures in the tissue culture laboratory under sterile conditions, so it was all very familiar for me.

While I was still being treated for the sepsis, the porters took me down in my bed to the Freedom Unit for the Plastic Surgery Team on Friday 25th to remove a nasty, fast-growing squamous cell carcinoma from my left foot and to carry out a skin graft. This was one of the last hurdles to be jumped before I could go home. The surgeons came the following Monday to check the skin graft and then gave us the green light to go home.

Of course, there were still more obstacles to sort out before I could finally be discharged. Firstly, the antibiotics were being delivered by an infusion pump. While the ward staff were happy to lend us one of these pumps, the red tape prevented it from happening. The hospital could not be held responsible for the pump on its return if it had been 'off-base'. How things had changed since we had displayed dialysis machines, blood pumps and mannequins on the grass at the Devon County show ground! In the end, we resolved the issue by using an old-fashioned drip stand and releasing the vacuum in the plastic saline bottle with a needle.

The ward and pharmacy worked extremely hard to ensure that the drugs and plastic supplies were ready for Tuesday 29th January. The six-week course of antibiotics would continue until 21st February. Cornwall's Acute Care Team of nurses would come every Wednesday to re-dress the PICC line and would be available during the day if we had any issues. As usual, the discharge process took longer than expected, but by mid-afternoon we finally left the ward to continue my treatment at home. There was torrential rain, and boxes upon boxes of medical supplies to take with us. I couldn't walk due to the stitches in my foot so two of the nurses managed to find porter's trolleys and a wheelchair and off we went to meet the outside world again.

It was wonderful to be back home after another lengthy stay in hospital. Ann had acquired a wooden baby-changing table via Facebook for use in the bathroom, which she had prepared as my clinical room. The amoxycillin had to be given every four hours, at 2am, 6am, 10am, 2pm, 6pm and 10pm, with the ceftriaxone being given at 2pm. It took 15 to 20 minutes to prepare the antibiotic and another 30 minutes to deliver it, leaving just over three hours' rest in between. It was incredibly tiring, but we soon got into a routine. Unfortunately, I was not able to flush the PICC line and attach the bottle with the antibiotic on my own, although I could prepare the antibiotics and prepare the 'giving sets' for all the slots except for 2am when Ann offered to do the preparation of the amoxycillin as well as attaching to the PICC line. This was invaluable, as it allowed me a small respite during the intense schedule. The ring tone alarm on Ann's iPhone would be impressed on our brains for many months!

The system and processes worked well, and we received superb support from the hospital pharmacy, the staff on Mayflower Ward, our GPs and the Community Acute Care team. There were times, however, when I had flashbacks to the days of dialysis and being tied to a machine for hours on end. Opening these black boxes of memories always brings some heightened emotion and a few tears before they are returned to where they belong. The dialysis machine had kept me alive and, no matter how I felt, I had to make the effort to ensure that I would be ready for the next session. What I was enduring with the antibiotics was minor by comparison, as it merely involved being attached to a drip at intervals. I also had a definitive end date of 21st February when it would be over, assuming the sepsis did not return. The days soon passed and, with my blood results remaining stable, I finally came to the end of the course of antibiotics; and the following week the PICC line was removed.

Despite all the intensive scans carried out while I was in hospital, the source of the infection still remains a mystery. It has been suggested that it might be due to a small, retained gallstone, trapped in the bile duct, and I therefore had a cholangio-pancreatography (MRCP) arranged. This is a medical imaging technique using magnetic resonance imaging to visualise the biliary and pancreatic ducts non-invasively. It was used to determine whether a gall-stone was lodged in any of the ducts.

This needle-in-a-haystack attempt to find the abscess and source of infection is the type of search that plagues medical teams looking after immunosuppressed transplant patients and others who are immunodeficient. The weakened immune response may not result in pus formation so it can be extremely difficult to identify sources of infection. Likewise, a mildly raised temperature might be of no significance to the average person, but in a transplant patient it may be the only sign of several issues, ranging from rejection to infection. My baseline temperature is 35.5 centigrade and a rise of only 1 degree centigrade is associated with feeling 'buggy' or under the weather. This temperature is still below what someone in a clinic would consider to be abnormal, but we are all unique human beings. I suspect the normal temperature of 37 degrees centigrade used throughout the NHS, and what we learn in biology classes, is based on countless normal readings. But it is a statistical 'mean' and there are always outliers; I just happen to be at the low end of the range. No doubt there are also people at the top end.

The AKI that affected my transplanted kidney during the first bout of sepsis means that my renal function, as measured by eGFR, has still not returned to its pre-sepsis levels. Before this episode, my creatinine was often around 80–90 with an eGFR of 75–90. Now it seems that the function has dropped by around 10–15 percent. I fear that some of the nephrons in the kidney were 'killed off' during the sepsis episode.

The possibility that I may have succumbed to IE has itself led to discussion about how to prevent the return of E. Faecalis infection. The various cardiac scans failed to show evidence of active IE, but, like an MOT (full body medical scan), these are only as accurate as the day they are performed. NICE guidelines on the use of prophylactic antibiotics for IE centre around dental procedures. The mouth and dental cavities are well known to be portals of entry for the bacteria that gives rise to IE. However, based on one small study, NICE changed its guidelines in 2015, now stating that prophylactic antibiotics may not be useful in preventing IE.

Unfortunately, as with all national guidelines, these are designed for the general population. There are no guidelines for kidney or other SOT recipients. Yet again, as a transplant recipient, I believe there needs to be a common-sense approach, decided on a patient-by-patient basis, together with discussions with appropriate specialists. Taking all this into account, a generalised protocol can be adapted to the individual. My dentist was in no doubt that my being a transplant patient put me in a special high-risk category and he had no hesitation in adopting the old NICE protocol before carrying out any dental work, even if it was just cleaning my teeth. For this reason, I now take 3g amoxycillin as an oral solution two to three hours before I attend for dental work.

Similarly, for all my skin lesion procedures, colorectal surgery, and any invasive investigation (such as colonoscopy), I make sure I have 3g amoxycillin prescribed to be given intravenously, concurrently with 100mg hydrocortisone. This is my personal guideline and is now a routine system that is documented in my hospital notes. There are no NICE protocols that cover this system. It is tailored to me as an individual patient, having had end-stage kidney disease and one of the longest surviving transplanted kidneys in the UK. There are no statistics, clinical trials or other protocols to refer to. The increasing number of patients like me, considered as long-term survivors with a functional transplanted kidney after more than 25 years, are posing new questions on treatment. Rejection has been successfully overcome but long-term immunosuppression has thrown up other complications, which are themselves associated with reduced quality of life and increased morbidity and mortality.

Chapter 15: Final Thoughts

It is now over half a century since that fateful Monday in July 1969 when, aged only 12, I was first taken ill at my school swimming practice. Over this time, there have been phenomenal scientific advances in understanding transplantation and marked improvements in treatment practices for people with kidney failure.

I started writing this book after leaving academic life. The thought that I might one day write about my experiences had been in the back of my mind for some time and I had been gradually gathering copies of my hospital notes. I was perturbed to find that my notes from Guy's, and to a lesser extent Torbay Hospital, had already been destroyed, with none kept on microfiche and no digitised copies. The destruction of Guy's medical records seemed particularly tragic, at a time when such brilliant technology exists to archive old photographs and documents. These records are a unique source of our country's health and social care data; and they can help answer important questions. For example, the Barker (or thrifty phenotype) hypothesis was possible because of immaculate records kept by midwives between the wars. These records led to the understanding that poor intra-uterine growth, as shown by birth weight, predisposes to the metabolic syndrome and death from cardiovascular disease.

Around 75 years' worth of NHS records could surely lead to further insights into changes in patient management. Their destruction denies current and future generations the opportunity to use new technology to test other hypotheses. Once destroyed, they can never be replaced. A major strength of the NHS is that it is a health service stretching nationwide, making it attractive for public health and epidemiological studies, as well as other health or social care studies. The medical history from GP records gives only dates and a code with a brief description of the event. However, looking at my own GP record, it is riddled with mistakes regarding original diagnoses and dates.

Putting this book together involved reading through medical notes from half a century ago, and this triggered memories that I had kept well and truly hidden in several 'black boxes' in my brain. There were records made by doctors and nurses containing a great deal of information about all the tricky episodes I went through, as well as facts that I had either forgotten or was not aware of at the time, including my many brushes with death. This point is best illustrated by the Addenbrooke's records of my first transplant. For instance, I had no idea that I had developed severe pneumonia a few days after receiving my dad's kidney and that it had started to reject. As far as I remembered, the transplant had worked fine from day one, but apparently this was not the case. Seeing all this written down in black and white took some time to absorb. Perhaps the healthcare team were protecting me, a young teenager on his own, or maybe I had selectively, and successfully, suppressed these painful memories.

This period post-transplant in Douglas House came as a shock to me. I was desperately trying to recall the events and had some flashbacks. These proved to be incredibly difficult to deal with, full of emotion and sometimes tears. Ann could sense when I had come across one of these 'black boxes' as my mood changed and I would become withdrawn and quiet. We would then have a long discussion about the episode, which enabled me to open up about my feelings in a way that I had never done before. I think meeting these episodes head-on, and coping with the aftermath, is akin to dealing with post-traumatic stress. They needed to be brought out of the 'box' where they were deeply hidden, into the fresh air, and discussed openly so that I could deal with the issues as my adult self and move on.

Since retiring and 'coming out' as a transplant recipient, I have been involved in several committees as a patient representative. I felt that I was in a unique position, being able to see the problems from both sides, having worked as a tissue-typist and having spent my career researching the causes of kidney disease and rejection. I hoped that this experience, along with living with kidney failure for over half a century and having seen the phenomenal changes in treatment and care, would mean that I could offer objective opinions about what might be needed from the patient's perspective and also about what might be achievable. Various opportunities to act as a patient representative came along, including becoming a member of the newly established committee of Kidney Care UK, with which I had originally been involved with Mrs Elizabeth Ward back in the 1970s. While at Guy's Hospital, I was involved in forming the inaugural Patients' Association which has gone from strength to strength. We also established a patient group locally at Derriford Hospital. I quickly realised there was always a need for patient representatives – and volunteers were highly sought after in certain sectors of the NHS.

These first openings led to my participation in the NHS England/UK Renal Registry 'Think Kidneys' project called 'Transforming Participation in Chronic Kidney Disease'. This was an ambitious project whose aim was to increase patient activation and empowerment. One of the long-term aims of the NHS was to try to develop systems for people with chronic disease and their carers to become 'activated' or 'empowered' by increasing their involvement in managing their own care. The World Health Organisation defines patient empowerment as 'a process through which people gain greater control over decisions or actions affecting their health'.

The 'Think Kidneys' project planned to use various interventions to help patients increase their skill and confidence in managing their disease, such as being involved in their own care plans, increasing healthcare staff members' and the patient's communication skills, and providing peer support. To help the patient, a simple tool was devised to formulate three written questions to which they needed answers during a consultation. Attending a hospital clinic appointment can be daunting, and patients often leave the consulting room with little recollection of what the doctor has just said. Writing the questions down acts as a prompt to ask about issues that are important to the patient rather than the doctor. Unfortunately, the paternalistic 'doctor knows best' approach is still common, despite extensive training and emphasis on teaching communications skills at medical schools. Yet improving patient activation in the management of chronic disease can help reduce healthcare costs, as activated patients tend to attend hospital less frequently as an emergency and, if admitted, their hospital stays are usually shorter.

I believe this is a crucial issue for anyone living with kidney failure, which is unlike any other chronic disease for which there is no cure and only different treatment options. Looking back over the half-century that I have lived with kidney failure, I have clearly been a highly activated patient, without realising it to begin with. There was no coaching, peer mentoring or counselling available to help me and my peers get through living with the condition.

Today, most people with kidney failure (including the very young, those past retirement age and individuals with comorbidities such as diabetes and heart disease) will be offered some form of renal replacement. Many of these people would previously have been denied access to treatment. Consequently, the pool of people being treated is now very large and includes a wide range of personalities: some are content to have everything 'done for them'; others are fiercely independent.

Is it possible to enable individuals to reduce their dependence on healthcare providers? Plenty of people will understand the benefits of building their resilience, increasing awareness and knowledge of their condition and treatment as well as establishing confidence and control of self-management; for others it will be too challenging. Many individuals will have been informed that they will require some form of renal replacement treatment at some point in the future and are currently managing to stave off the inevitable with all the uncertainties that it involves. There is clearly a major role here for psychologists or counsellors, specialising in understanding kidney failure, to be attached to renal units. Unfortunately, management often see this kind of provision as a luxury and inevitably, when budget cuts have to be made, such services disappear. This is surely short-sighted; and it is often left to patient associations or other charities to help fund such posts.

There are countless studies looking at perceptions of people with kidney failure, utilising questionnaires about quality of life, or models devised to find out how individuals cope with this disease. However, these cross-sectional studies only tend to give 'snapshots'. In other words, they look at average responses in a group of individuals at a particular point in time; whereas longitudinal studies follow patients for a number of years. These longer-term studies are clearly much needed but also cost considerable sums of money. One problem is that a cross-sectional study may lead to false assumptions about cause and effect. For instance, half a century ago, people often talked about 'having the will to live'. This phrase was often used among patients, and I can recall my parents telling me, as a 12-year-old, 'you mustn't give up' and 'you must have the will to live'.

Those living with kidney failure usually know of people who have simply given up, unable to live with their disease, or its difficult treatments, any longer. I would hope that these are now few and far between, and that they can be identified by the healthcare team as needing additional support. Many psychological studies in the field of kidney disease are littered with terms such as 'psychological disorders' and 'stressors'. As a patient, I find these terms inappropriate, as it could be argued that what the psychologist perceives as a disorder is in fact a normal, essential, psychological response to a severe bodily disorder, namely kidney failure. Consequently, these are not 'disorders' but normal coping mechanisms that people use to deal with an abnormal situation. Perhaps it is time for psychologists and behavioural scientists to recognise this point and change their terminology.

World Kidney Day 2021 chose as its theme 'Living Well with Kidney Disease'. This highlights the importance of devising strategies to empower patients, families and carers with skills to reduce the massive burden of kidney failure on their lives. It is now recognised that more focus has to be placed on increasing education and goal-setting to achieve 'patient-centred wellness'. These are noble goals but to date have been difficult to attain without all parties being on board. It is not an easy task – but where there's a will there's a way.

There is also the issue of screening for long-term complications. Skin cancer may now have specific screening guidelines for solid organ transplant recipients, but guidelines are still needed for other cancers. For instance, should everyone (including males) receive a human papilloma virus (HPV) vaccination? What is the correct frequency of colonoscopy for bowel tumours? How should lung cancer be screened for?

The success of modern transplantation of kidneys, as well as other solid organs, is thankfully reflected in longer-term survival of both the recipient and the organ. Personally, I spent the first three decades after my transplant free of any long-term complications such as skin or other cancers and I have a relatively normal cardiovascular system, despite my often-raised cholesterol level. However, the last two decades have been fraught with increasing issues such as cancerous lesions, joint replacements, infections and sepsis. This has meant increasing hospitalisation for non-kidney-related issues.

The number of people living with kidney failure is increasing every year, which means that the demands for non-kidney health provision are also going to increase. Some of these can be alleviated by, for example, screening for common cancers, as we know they occur more frequently in kidney transplant recipients. To make this happen, there needs to be good communication between healthcare specialists and individuals with kidney failure. National guidelines designed for normal healthy individuals cannot be applied to those who have been immunosuppressed for years, or who have a disturbed metabolism due to long-term dialysis. The screening should ideally be individualised for each person, but at least for these patient groups.

I have often spoken to doctors, surgeons and immunologists about my transplanted kidney, and whether my body still sees it as 'foreign'. After being implanted into my left pelvic region for so long, how much of it has been infiltrated or encapsulated by my own tissue? At the time of my transplant, the donor kidney probably had 'resident macrophages' and these can elicit an immune response to the recipient (me). I was fortunate that the kidney I received had antigen-presenting proteins on the surface of its cells (HLA tissue typing molecules) that were identical to my own. However, there are numerous other proteins in my kidney that may differ between me and my donor. These 'minor transplantation antigens' may not have been known and therefore could not have been tested for.

It would be unethical for me to request a biopsy of my kidney for research purposes now, as there would be no direct benefit to me and some risk. Instead, researchers need to devise a non-invasive imaging technique that could determine how 'immunogenic' my kidney is. This result could then be translated into the degree of tolerance. If this could be achieved, and it were possible to measure this characteristic reproducibly and safely, it would open up the possibility of weaning SOT recipients off their immunosuppressants. This would be a game-changer, as it would alleviate many of the long-term complications in people like myself. It is encouraging that immunological markers on T-cells of the immune system are finally being identified. This may give us an insight into why certain patients become tolerant to their transplanted kidneys, while others do not.

The other notable applications of biotechnology to treating and even curing kidney failure would be developing an implantable artificial kidney and 'growing' kidneys in the laboratory. There is already a scientific discipline called 'regenerative medicine' that involves the repair and re-creation of damaged tissues and organs. It is primarily aimed at helping to achieve systems that will allow people to have transplants without any need for immunosuppressants. Scientists working on three-dimensional printing and various types of stem cell technologies are pushing these boundaries, in the hope that one day we will no longer be treating kidney failure but curing it.

I am writing this final chapter just as the United Kingdom has emerged from lockdown, following the second wave of the Covid-19 pandemic. There has been tremendous debate about the reporting of deaths from the virus during the pandemic as well as 'cause of death' on death certificates. The public are more aware than ever of what is happening to their data.

In January 2020, I had already become aware of the dire situation in Wuhan, China, and had forewarned my family of the seriousness of the situation. Consequently, when the first lockdown arrived in March 2020, we were mentally prepared for it, having already been taking various precautions. We spent the first lockdown with my 92-year-old mum, and Olly, who had escaped from London just before the travel restrictions were put in place, all under one roof. He was able to work from home and set up an office in Tom's bedroom. Lucy was by now an Emergency Medicine trainee on the front line in A&E at Derriford. With the nice weather, we even managed a few socially distanced tea parties at the end of the front garden!

When the lockdown came in late March, I was included in the 'clinically extremely vulnerable' (CEV) group who were deemed to be at exceedingly high risk from the virus. I used my experience as a health and safety officer, having worked with radiation and pathogens, to create a 'bio-secure' home-stead. It probably drove my family mad, but Ann understood the seriousness of the situation and created laminated signs for the porches with various handwashing solutions, including the infamous alcohol gel. For the first week or so, there really were concerns about fresh food supplies and the inevitable toilet rolls! Being in a rural area, we were lucky to have a village shop that did an amazing job of delivering supplies, as well as the excellent local butcher, who knows all the fields from which his animals have come. We also had fresh milk delivered to the door. For many people, this must have been a horrendous time, particularly those living on their own and unable to access supplies easily.

Because I was in the CEV group, after a couple of weeks I had access to priority slots for home deliveries from certain supermarkets. I also had a weekly food parcel delivery from the government. It was always fascinating to open the cardboard box that had been left in the porch overnight. It was very impressive that the government organised the delivery of hundreds of thousands of these food parcels in a very short space of time. The country was in effect on a 'war footing' against the virus. The supermarket slots were like golddust and, to begin with, it was extremely difficult to book them, due to the demand.

While we were in lockdown, unable to leave the house except to take our black Labrador Molly for a walk, we were at least able to spend precious time with Olly, who at 23 did an amazing job of being at home with 'the oldies'. The weather was hot and dry, and we were able to spend a great deal of time outside playing table tennis during his lunch breaks.

Once it seemed that the first wave of infection was over and lockdown came to an end, Olly went back to London and my mum went back to her house. As a family, we had done very well, living together for nearly three months with no opportunity to get out and do all the things people normally do. Now I clearly needed to put pen to paper and finish the book. I was keeping up to date with the current research literature on Covid-19 in people with SOTs. By autumn, the seminal data started appearing in the press and it made depressing reading. If kidney transplant recipients became infected with Covid-19, approximately 25 percent died within 28 days of being admitted to hospital. A further 25 percent were still in hospital and the rest recovered.

Individuals with a kidney transplant also tended to do worse than people with other transplanted organs. No doubt the reasons for this will become clearer in the future, but early indications suggest that it may be due to the way the virus entered cells through the angiotensinogen converting enzyme receptor (ACE) which is especially abundant in the kidney. With this in mind, we maintained our strict bio-security rules and I effectively continued shielding. Christmas came and went, and once again we were in another extensive lockdown. Finally, the vaccines were rolled out in record time and people in the CEV group (including me) and the elderly were given priority. As 2021 draws to a close, we hope we will soon see the back of Covid-19.

The pandemic has obviously caused massive changes in the way our society functions, and the impact on the NHS has been particularly striking. For the past year or more, all my outpatient clinics have been done by telephone. This was obviously necessary in the early stages of the pandemic but there seems to be no desire to revert to face-to-face clinics. I am not sure that this is good practice in all cases. While I have a good system in place, whereby my routine bloods are taken before the renal clinic and I can access the results within 24 hours, many may not. The consultation takes place just a few days after that, so there can be a meaningful discussion.

However, the only physical consultation I have had was with a plastic surgeon. This came about after I had discovered new skin lesions which needed to be excised and I sent him photographs of them. My first encounter with the hospital following the outbreak made me realise that our perception of, and attitudes to, each other had changed in a small space of time. On leaving the car, I headed to the Outpatient Department. I was manoeuvring around to avoid people as I was on the pavement, and I crossed the road. I viewed everyone as a person who was potentially infected with the virus. The hospital itself was noticeably quiet; and personal protective equipment (PPE) was used throughout. After the first visit I became used to this new 'norm', even when I was being taken to operating theatres for various procedures. It is just another aspect of life to which we have to adapt.

After I had my first vaccination (Pfizer) in February 2021, research was published showing that only around 16 percent of kidney transplant recipients produced meaningful antibody levels to the virus. Even worse, in those patients such as myself, on azathioprine (or MMF), only 5 percent produced antibodies. It seems that, if a transplant patient becomes infected, we will still need to rely on new improved treatments for dealing with this dangerous virus.

Over the last 50-plus years, many of the family members, friends and work colleagues who were essential to my kidney journey have departed from this life. After moving to Plymouth, we able to see my dad (born on 13th February 1929) every few months, as he lived nearby in Newton Abbot. He eventually needed residential and nursing care in a town near us, where he died peacefully on 22 June 2012, aged 83. John's MS got the better of him and he died of pneumonia in his forties, while my eldest brother Trevor died at the beginning of the new millennium. It is remarkable to think that I am the only survivor of the three boys. It is also a reflection of my mum's resilience that she continues to have a reasonable quality of life, despite being riddled with arthritis and coping with other chronic conditions that one would expect to find in a 93-year-old.

In conclusion, I have had to think long and hard about writing this book. It hasn't been easy, particularly revisiting memories that were sealed in 'black boxes' decades ago. However, I was encouraged by numerous people to undertake this venture as a testament to my half-century of overcoming kidney failure. I have no doubt that luck (or fate) has played a part in this. I have often thought how lucky I was to have been in the right place at the right time, right from the beginning of my kidney journey in Torbay and then the RDE Hospitals, where the doctors were prepared to take on a desperately ill 12-year-old.

Then there was the extraordinary moment when Professor Sir Roy Calne intervened, offering life-saving advice and promising to perform my transplant. Lady Luck also came along to ensure that my dad could donate his kidney, which lasted long enough for medical researchers to make enormous strides in treating kidney failure. Kidney donors sometimes develop problems with their remaining kidney, but my dad lived until he was 83 in good health. Then there was the extraordinary good fortune of my being offered and accepting my current fully matched cadaver kidney in a relatively short space of time after having to return to dialysis. These are just a few of the episodes where luck or fate has helped me along the way. People might say 'you make your own luck' and that may be so, but you also need resilience, determination and courage to overcome the obstacles you encounter on a kidney journey like mine.

Having finally pen to paper, I hope this book will provide useful information, guidance and hope for people who are just beginning their own kidney journeys. I can now look forward to completing my 'bucket list' in a timely fashion. With this in mind following the sale of our previous boat during the COVID19 pandemic we have just acquired another one with a fully enclosed heated wheelhouse. From now on I shall be able to stay warm and dry what ever the weather. Once overseas travel becomes a normal pastime again then those railway trips across the globe may once again be undertaken.

Early book reviews – My Kidney and Me

'A fascinating memoir and insight into a life with kidney failure and transplantation'

Professor Andrew Demaine has given a completely engaging account of his life with kidney failure and kidney transplantation. His problems started with acute glomerular disease and a rapid decline of kidney function to total kidney failure when he was only 12 years of age. This was at a time in the United Kingdom when many patients with kidney failure and especially children of only near adult size were never given the opportunity for dialysis. I started my training in Nephrology (kidney disease) in New Zealand in the same decade. Andrew Domaine's struggles with fluid overload, dietary restrictions, peritoneal dialysis and peritonitis, repeated surgery for Scribner shunts and shunt clotting were all too familiar to me and trying to manage all these problems was a source of constant anxiety for me. How pertinent then, that we can now revisit these problems from the eyes of the patient. Andrew was in enormous emotional turmoil and in part assigned his angst into his so called "black box" in order to cope. In a similar manner, I believe that many kidney doctors including myself, did the same in the face of repeated failures of the available treatments, infections and other fatal complications.

I have always had great admiration for my own patients and their usually stoical acceptance of discomfort, curtailed freedom, partner and job losses and the highs and absolute lows of a kidney transplant. Andrew exhibited a truly remarkable degree of resilience and determination to survive and then pursue an extraordinarily successful academic career centred on research aimed at helping patients in his situation.

In the years when he received his first and second transplants only about 50% of the transplanted kidneys would last one year. Even now, with much more sophisticated treatments, the survival of transplanted kidneys at 5 years is still less than 100% and there is a slow but continued loss in subsequent years. How remarkable then, that Andrew Demaine's kidney still has excellent function after 40 years. There are still problems and Andrew has had to endure the long-term consequences of kidney failure and immunosuppression which has caused infections, skin cancers, joint damage and many other complications and admissions to hospital.

The memoir includes accurate and useful information on several medications as well as historical information on many of the individuals who pioneered the treatment of kidney diseases, kidney failure and transplantation.

Andrew Demaine was and continues to be a strong advocate and voice for kidney patients. In these days of anxiety and depression among the young, Andrew gives a great example of resilience and how to live without self-pity or complaint and to survive in what were difficult times for someone in his situation.

His concerns about the paternalism of some health professionals and their lack of consultation with the patient are completely valid and we must hope that this is improving in a new generation of graduates. It is fortunate that he seems to have had excellent care from most of his doctors and other carers.

This is a very moving and instructive memoir and should be important reading for medical and health professionals in training. A person entering a life of kidney failure, dialysis and transplantation for the first time could find Andrew Demaine's memoir somewhat daunting. More importantly, they will also gain knowledge, understanding and the inspiration to cope with both the physical and emotional aspects of their illness.

Professor Ian Simpson MD Consultant Nephrologist, Head of the Auckland Clinical School and Associate Dean Emeritus Professor of Medicine, University of Auckland.

'This is an extraordinary tale of resilience from a key witness to the 20th century's greatest medical achievement.'

I sit in my clinic room at Addenbrooke's Hospital and call in the next patient. We are running a little late and the new arrival, a harassed-looking young woman, voices her displeasure with a small huff as she sits down. I apologise for keeping her waiting, before remarking brightly that her kidney function is completely normal and she is looking very well. The clipped responses remind me she has somewhere else to be, no she doesn't need any more tablets, clinic in 6 months is fine and then she dashes from clinic to collect the children born, I note, 5 years after her kidney transplant. This pattern is repeated through the morning as patients hurry away back to work, to collect extended prescriptions to cover their 3-month tours of the Far East or simply to return to their cars before tickets expire and mortgages are required to release them. Kidney transplantation is a routine part of medicine, like a hip replacement or hernia repair, and patients expect to return to their normal lives. But my colleagues nearing retirement tell different stories, of the days before transplantation became 'respectable'; the days when anti-transplant protests were common and Roy Calne held annual parties for all the surviving transplant recipients.

My Kidney & Me tells the story of these days from a vivid first-person perspective. Andrew Demaine was just 12 years old when he developed kidney failure in 1969 – 11 years before the first use of ciclosporin, and when children with kidney failure were most commonly palliated. His is a story of the early days of dialysis, of Shribner shunts, of sepsis and cardiac arrests due to circuit clots in primitive dialysis machines. The author describes, in harrowing detail, the challenges of survival on dialysis when sessions would take 10-12 hours, circuits that had to be tipped vertically to squeeze the last drops of blood from the machine and constant extreme anaemia as EPO was still 20 years away from development.

The story speeds through the major developments in medicine of the 20th century – taking in trauma, vascular access and the discovery of blood-borne viruses on the way. There are tales of racing from Devon to Cambridge in a storm with a police escort (arranged by the local constabulary) to arrive before a donor kidney in the days before major motorways. All of this is set amongst a deeply personal story of chronic, life-threatening illness, the impact of this on education and family relationships. The realities of dealing with adolescence and a vast array of medical professionals and the systems they worked in lead to a remarkable story of survival. That the author not only survived, but went on to become a major figure in transplant science lends the book particular authority.

This is an extraordinary tale of resilience from a key witness to the 20th century's greatest medical achievement. This book should be read by anyone with an taste for a thrilling story, an interest in medical history and professionals and students in nephrology, transplantation, or chronic illness.

Mr Dominic Summers, PhD, FRCS, Consultant Transplant and Vascular Access Surgeon, Cambridge University Hospitals NHS Foundation Trust and University of Cambridge.

'Andrew Demaine's autobiographical book, My Kidney & Me, is highly readable, dramatic, instructive and inspiring.'

It chronicles the author's 52-year life-and-death struggle to achieve and main-tain a normal and productive life, despite having an incurable .... kidney disease. Besides illuminating Demaine's indomitable grit and courage, *My Kidney & Me* also constitutes a stirring tribute to his supportive family, teachers, health care teams, professional colleagues and community members who encouraged and empowered him to overcome "boulder after boulder" during his journey.

The book is written in an informal and refreshingly frank style sprinkled with touches of humor. The narrative is subtly gripping as it describes pivotal emotional and medical ups and downs" of Demaine's early upbringing in a struggling working-class English family. From his calamitous twelfth year on, the author experiences repeated hospitalizations that are dramatically detailed against a backdrop of evolving breakthroughs in kidney hemodialysis, organ transplantation and emergency trauma treatments. At every step, Demaine leads the reader candidly through his various personal struggles and triumphs, ranging from being comatose in the hospital to being bullied at school, to encountering internal politics and work-life imbalances within renowned British medical research institutions, as well as to his joy at attending and co-organizing prestigious international research conferences. Along the way, the reader shares in Demaine's inner thoughts, those of an "activated patient" – one who is well informed, determined to flourish, and who does not hesitate to push back against abuses like school bullying or reflexive institutional "box-ticking". Throughout the book, the author's firsthand experiences bring to light the pros and cons of the life-saving medical devices that made renal hemodialysis possible and the immunosuppressive drugs that enabled successful organ transplantation. Demaine rightly gives particular emphasis to the emerging consequences of chronic immunosuppression and their important implications for the future.

In sum, *My Kidney & Me* is a unique and compelling story of one person's courageous struggle to overcome major medical and attendant psychological adversities resulting from incurable kidney disease. This reviewer found it to be a gripping, inspiring and enlightening read. *My Kidney & Me* should be required reading for patients with chronic medical conditions, health care professionals, medical students and medical historians, as well as for those concerned with present and future health care policies in the UK and elsewhere.

Dr Peter J Oates BSc PhD, Research Fellow, Diabetes Translational Pharmacology, Pfizer Inc (Retd), CEO and Chief Scientific Officer, Oates Biomedical Consulting, LLC

A real page turner. The book will be of interest to the general population, kidney patients and healthcare professionals, including those working in kidney medicine and transplantation.

Prof Andy Demaine's autobiography is a fascinating, engaging and well written description of an incredible personal story of a young man's (initially a child) struggle with kidney failure, presenting when he was just 12 years old in 1969. A real page turner. He must have been one of very few children offered dialysis in the 1960s. Dialysis today is tough but in the 1960s and 70s it was unbelievably tough, especially for a child. Andy received a kidney transplant from his father, which unfortunately failed after just a few years, and he had to return to dialysis before receiving a deceased donor kidney that continues to function.

The book will be of interest to the general population, kidney patients and healthcare professionals, including those working in kidney medicine and transplantation. For the latter (and current kidney patients), the description of the early days of dialysis and transplantation and the massive improvements over 5 decades is interesting. He describes how and by whom many of these advances were developed and introduced. For everyone, Andy's personal description of what a patient, especially a young one, faces in coping with dialysis and transplantation and his specific problems, especially the long-term side effects of transplantation and the side-effects of the necessary drugs, is truly engaging. Despite almost overwhelming odds and missing huge chunks of schooling, he describes how he had a university education, became a clinical scientist, helping to determine which patients received kidney transplants. He went on to become a highly respected academic, making a great contribution to transplant science.

His narrative is interspersed with miscellaneous facts and descriptions, for instance, relating to some of his interests and hobbies, including trains and boats and many other incidentals, including vignettes about pioneers of dialysis and transplantation, as well as the many amazing individuals who helped him though his life.

Dr Phil Mason PhD FRCP, Consultant Nephrologist and Lead for Transplant Medicine & Honorary Senior Lecturer Oxford University, Oxford Kidney and Transplant Unit, The Churchill Hospital, Oxford

Acknowledgements

The idea for this book first came about just before I retired from academic life. Many people had asked if I was going to write a memoir, particularly as my life spans the early days of dialysis and transplantation as well as my own academic and personal achievements. With this in mind, I realised I needed to obtain copies of my medical records before they were destroyed. I was lucky that I was able to obtain copies of all of them, with the exception of those from Torbay Hospital. While Guy's Hospital had very quickly destroyed my notes, they did give me an abbreviated version and the availability of over half a century of medical records makes this book unique.

I first started to put pen to paper around four years ago, but it soon became clear that I also needed to undertake a great deal of research around the history of dialysis and transplantation. Forensically examining my notes at times proved to be an extremely painful emotional experience and one that I had not been prepared for.

So many people have helped me in my journey that it is not possible to name all of them. At the very top of the list is my dad who so selflessly and bravely donated his kidney to me at a time when kidney transplantation carried substantial risks. My mum also gets a special mention for looking after me during those difficult years. The parents of my donor in November 1974 who agreed to donate their son's kidneys made a courageous decision that has benefitted me for nearly 47 years and hopefully for much longer still. They did this at a time when there was still substantial opposition to kidney donation.

There are many members of healthcare teams over the half-century whose dedication, care, empathy and professionalism ensured that I survived the many medical procedures and treatments they provided. There are obviously some notable people, including Dr Imrie, the GP who first came out to see me on the evening of 7th July 1969 and realised how sick I was. Dr Harry Hall, my Consultant Physician at the Royal Devon and Exeter Hospital, gave me the lifeline of a place on dialysis when most – if not all – hospitals in the UK would have refused me treatment. Mr Shaldon – the Consultant Surgeon who removed my kidneys – I will never know why he made the decision to go ahead but he did, and I am obviously eternally grateful. Drs Peter and Peggy Bisson provided unstinting care and dedication, particularly in the early stages of my kidney failure. There were countless times when Dr Peter Bisson left his home in the middle of the night to deal with one of my emergencies. Later, they also made me welcome in their home and dealt with my emotional needs. There were numerous nurses who went over and above the call of duty, including Fay Pugsley on Bowring Ward and Sister Trott at Whipton for her work in the dialysis unit.

Professor Sir Roy Calne at Cambridge was instrumental in offering the right advice at the right time to my doctors in Exeter. This undoubtedly saved my life, as well as the first transplant that he subsequently performed on me in October 1970. Also at Cambridge were Dr David Evans, my Consultant Nephrologist, who always provided superb care and took an interest in my welfare during the many days and weeks I was alone on the ward. Mr David Dunn, who I nicknamed 'Man from Uncle', expertly created a Scribner shunt and Cimino fistula in the days before imaging techniques were available, using just his fingertips. Mr Maurice 'Taffy' Slapak, the Consultant Surgeon who performed my present transplant, obviously did a great job.

Sister Mary Nugent helped in those early days of dialysis at Douglas House. Sister Sally Taber, as well as providing excellent professional nursing skills, was always in the background, ensuring my emotional needs were also met. Her interest in my welfare continues to the present day. The nursing teams at Douglas House in 1970 as well as C9 in 1974 were exceptional, particularly those I have referred to in the book. There were several patients and their families who I remember fondly for providing practical and emotional support: in particular, in 1974, Brian Pearmain who later founded the National Kidney Patients' Federation, as well as Douglas Mann and Leslie Gardiner. Sadly, all these individuals lost their fight against kidney failure many years ago but I still remember their friendship and support.

Torquay Boys Grammar School supported me through the whole of my illness from 1969 to 1976. They continued to believe in me and in 1973 could easily have decided 'enough was enough'. Instead, they allowed me to continue my sixth form education. Mr Don Roberts stands out among my teachers, having taught me swimming and chemistry during most of my time at the school and he still does so today. It was Mr Smith the Headmaster who ultimately enabled me to complete my schooling there.

While I was at Guy's Hospital, my line manager and PhD supervisor Dr Ken Welsh played a major part during my first employment and the start of my research career. Lesley Kennedy will always be remembered as the person who ensured I settled into my new life and gave me the confidence to play contact rugby, while my first wife Brenda supported and accepted me as a normal person and partner. Professor Stewart Cameron offered superb academic guidance on my PhD as well as the research. He, Drs Gwynn Williams and David Taube, and Mr Mick Bewick, all provided exceptional medical care while I was at Guy's. Professor Alan McGregor gave me an opportunity and the support I needed to create an independent research group. Research cannot be achieved in isolation and, while at Guy's and King's, I was able to collaborate with some outstanding clinical scientists who nurtured my enthusiasm for scientific discovery. These included Professor John Newsom-Davis and Professor Nick Willcox who did a great job of reading my PhD thesis, while Professor Eberhard Ritz in Heidelberg also provided superb input on renal disorders.

My academic career at Plymouth was enriched by several people, first and foremost Professor Ken Rogers who reignited my passion for research by being an invaluable mentor. Professor Les Ebdon (Deputy Vice Chancellor Academic) always made himself available, offering wise counsel and academic support. Professor John Bull (Vice-Chancellor) was supportive of my endeavours and similarly Professor John Tooke, the first Dean of the Peninsula Medical and Dental School. I will always be grateful to Professor Roland Levinsky for seeing things that others were blind to and enabling me to get my Chair.

I have been able to collaborate with many superb people in Derriford Hospital, Plymouth, some of whom have also been involved in my on-going care, including Dr Peter Rowe and Professor Wai Tse. Dr Ed Kaminski proved to be a great collaborator and sounding board, along with Professors Andrew Kingsnorth and Matthew Cramp and Mr John Hammond. There are numerous other clinicians who would have enjoyed the thrill of research, but clinical work and other commitments proved too big a barrier.

I am indebted to many clinicians at the hospital, including renal physicians Drs Richard McGonigle, Imran Saif, Kris Houlberg, Andrew Connor, 'Oz' Hunt, Hilary Cramp and Becky Herbert as well as Dr Simon Fullalove at my GP surgery, for the outstanding care I have received and my dentist Mr Tony Coelho. Mr Andy Murphy has managed to ensure that my skeleton has remained in good shape (with some artificial additions) while Mr Walter Douie has been efficient and superb at dealing with colorectal issues. Mr Antony Fitton and more recently Professor Rory Rickard have together probably had more dealings with me clinically over the past years with my twice-yearly visit to their operating table for the inevitable excision of skin cancers. The conversations while in their hands have been a highlight of these visits. None of these procedures happen without support from many healthcare professionals – and there are numerous anaesthetists and theatre staff who have always provided great care. Some of them now joke that I am a 'regular customer'.

During my career I have supervised scores of research students, from BSc to PhD level, from all backgrounds and walks of life. They have certainly been a rich source of fulfilment and I have enjoyed watching their progress from a distance, many of them becoming highly successful in their own right.

The final stages of writing this book have involved several colleagues and friends who have proof-read various versions of the manuscript and their input has been invaluable. These include my former secretary Julie Austen, Professor Ian Simpson (Auckland) and Dr Phil Mason (Oxford) as well as Mr Dominic Summers (Cambridge). Dr Oscar Serrano (Hartford, Connecticut) and Dr Anna Francis (Sydney, Australia) provided copies of their research publications on cancer risk in paediatric kidney transplant recipients. Dr Peter Oates has been a long-standing friend and scientific collaborator and passed his eagle eye over the manuscript at breath-taking speed. My thanks also go to Kelly Davis for her tremendously effective copy-editing of the final version, Jon Puckey at A2Z Sign & Print for the artwork and David Siddall for the final typesetting and help with publication. I would like to thank Fiona Loud at Kidney Care UK and Professor Wai Tse at the Derriford Hospital for financial support.

Last of all, my thanks go to my long-suffering children Lucy and Olly who have listened to me saying for the past few years 'I must finish my book' as well as providing invaluable feedback. My biggest thanks of all go to my wife Ann who has been an immovable rock of support, always there to ensure that many little issues are dealt with and resolved. She has witnessed me hurtling along the emotional rollercoaster when I was opening the many 'black boxes' and has shared in all the experiences I have relived. I simply wouldn't have got to the end without her.

Printed in Great Britain
by Amazon

70210446R10159